Volume 13

PAPER

POLAROID CAMERA

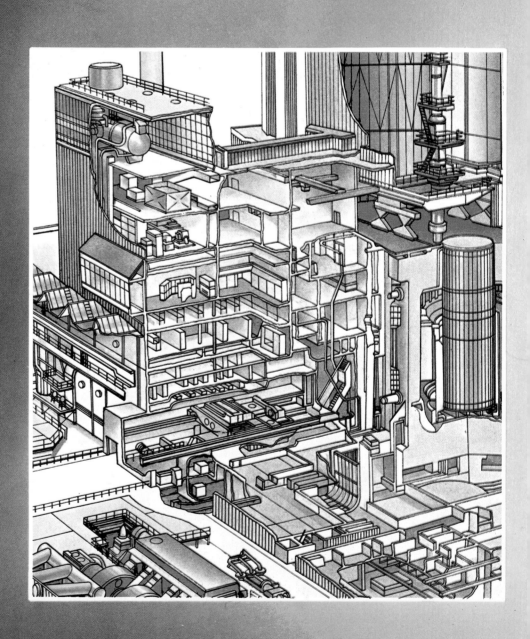

The ILLUSTRATED

SCIENCE *and*
INVENTION

ENCYCLOPEDIA

International Edition

H. S. STUTTMAN CO., INC. *publishers*   New York, N.Y. 10016

how it works

Published by H. S. STUTTMAN CO., Inc.
New York, N.Y. 10016
© Marshall Cavendish Limited 1974, 1976, 1977

Above: papermaking in Thailand the traditional way. The screen has just been dipped into the solution.

Below: trimmed, peeled logs in the grinding machine. Gravity causes the logs to fall on to grinding wheels which are flushed with water. Most paper made in Britain is made from wood.

Below right: the ground logs transferred to the digester.

PAPER manufacture

Papyrus, a water reed, was used as a writing material more than 5000 years ago by the Egyptians, and later by Greek and Roman writers. Animal parchment has been known since Egyptian times and was much favoured by the Romans for permanent records. To make papyrus, layers of reeds are set across each other and pressed and dried; PARCHMENT manufacture is similar to LEATHER manufacture, involving the scraping and treatment of animal skins (except that nowadays certain grades of paper are called *vegetable parchment*). Neither of the ancient processes changed the structure of the basic materials.

The word 'paper' comes from the word papyrus, but true paper was invented in China less than 2000 years ago. The Chinese collected old fishing nets, rags and bits of plants, boiled the materials well, and beat them and stirred them with large amounts of water to make a *pulp*. A sieve dipped in the pulp and removed horizontally would have a layer of pulp on it with the water draining away through the mesh. The layer of pulp was then dried and pressed. The difference between papyrus and paper is that in papermaking the materials are reduced to their fibre structure, and the fibres are re-aligned.

The technique spread to the West when some Chinese papermakers were captured by the Arabs. It reached Europe in the late mediaeval period, and the first English paper factory was established in Hertfordshire in 1490. Paper made possible more literacy, and as literacy spread there was increased demand for paper. In the 20th century the latest advances in papermaking have been exported from America to Japan, so that the technology has made a complete circuit of the globe, but the basic principles have not changed.

OSBORNE/MARKS

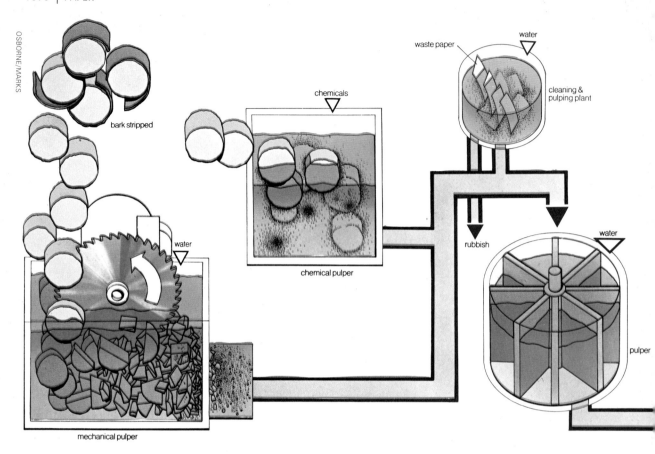

bark stripped

chemicals

water

mechanical pulper

chemical pulper

waste paper

water

cleaning & pulping plant

rubbish

water

pulper

Materials

Materials Rags are used for the highest quality paper, especially the handmade. At the other end of the scale, seed fibres, jute, flax, grasses and other plants may be the source of raw material for papermaking; straw was used extensively in Great Britain during World War 2. The largest amount of paper today, however, is made from wood pulp.

Synthetic and animal fibres have also been tried, but these techniques have remained experimental or too expensive for wide application; papermaking means almost exclusively the use of cellulose vegetable fibres. The fibres vary in size and shape, but are hollow tubes closed at the ends and often tapering. They are held together in their natural state by substances, principally *lignin*, which must usually be dissolved and removed; this is accomplished by chemical treatment and washing of the pulp. The wide variety of methods found in papermaking can be seen in a comparison of *blotting* and *greaseproof wrapping* papers: the one is soft and absorbent, while the other is hard, smooth and dense. The difference is in the choice of fibres, the way they are prepared, and the way they are processed on the papermaking machine.

Pulp manufacture There are basically two methods: *mechanical* and *chemical* (cooking).

Mechanical pulping is used chiefly for coniferous woods. It aims at a high yield rather than a pure pulp; the result is a cheap paper, of which newsprint is a good example, which is not expected to last. The logs are trimmed, de-barked and then ground, usually by rotating grindstones, the fibres being flushed away from the stone with water. If the water supply is lowered, more heat is generated and longer fibres are obtained; in general, shorter fibres (up to a point) result in better paper. The pulp is *screened* several times, and the larger lumps are re-treated or

Above: logs are peeled and mechanically pulped or cooked with chemicals. Waste paper is also widely used. The mixture is further treated mechanically so that the fibres are the right length; the necessary additives are mixed in, and the pulp is poured on to a moving wire belt which is shaken to align the fibres. The sheet of pulp is pressed and dried by a series of rollers.

burned. Depending on whether the pulp is to be processed on the spot or shipped, the excess water is removed in a *concentrator* or on a machine resembling a simple papermaking machine (see below). The result is either *air-dry* (10% moisture) or *wet* or *moist* (45% moisture). 100 tons of dry cut logs can yield more than 90 tons of air-dry pulp, but the strength of the fibres is not high and mechanical pulp is mixed with 15% to 50% chemical pulp before it is used.

Chemical or cooking methods remove more of the unwanted materials, resulting in a lower yield but a higher quality pulp. They are divided generally into two categories: *acid liquor* and *alkaline liquor*.

The acid liquor process is used mostly for spruce, which is the largest commercially profitable tree crop in North America. The liquor is essentially an acid bisulphite with some free sulphur dioxide gas. It can be made by letting water trickle down through a tower containing limestone and blowing in sulphur dioxide gas at the bottom. It is highly corrosive, which means that the works must be made of acid-resistant materials. The logs are sliced and the slices broken up into chips which are then screened. Chips from $\frac{1}{4}$ to $\frac{3}{4}$ inch (0.6 to 1.9 cm) are pressure-cooked in a steam-heated *digester*. The quality is controlled by regulating chip size, liquor-strength, pressure (520 to 760 kN/m², 75 to 110 psi) and cooking time (usually 7 to 12 hours).

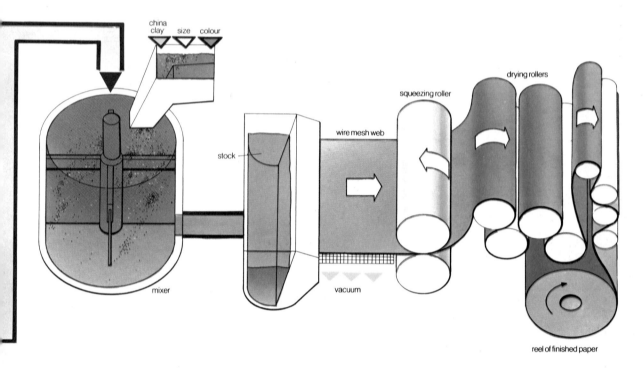

The unused sulphur dioxide and some of the heat can be recovered when cooking is over, but the spent liquor is highly polluting. It can be used in *leather manufacture* as a tanning agent, to lay the dust on roads and in several other ways, but so much of it is produced that it is still a serious pollution problem.

Alkaline liquor processes are similar but the cooking agents are naturally not acidic and therefore less polluting. They are for non-woody fibres such as grasses and rags, for deciduous woods (hardwoods) and for coniferous woods which have a high resin content, such as pine, because the alkali dissolves the resin. The wood is prepared in the same manner as for acidic cooking; other materials are prepared according to their properties. For example, rags must be sorted and straw must be chopped and the dust removed in a cyclone extractor.

The *soda process* uses caustic soda (sodium hydroxide). The amount of soda, cooking time and pressure all vary according to the materials being cooked. With wood, up to 85% of the soda can be recovered from the waste liquor; with other materials less is recovered because of the difficulty of washing it out of the fibres and because the amount of soda used is smaller to begin with. The *kraft* or *sulphate* process results in a stronger fibre; 'Kraft' is the German word for strength. Sodium sulphate is added to the digester; it has no effect on digestion, but is converted to sodium sulphide during the burning of the recovery process. When this in turn is added to the digester it is automatically converted in controlled amounts to sodium hydroxide, so that it aids in digestion but conserves strength. The process generates objectionable smells and is not used near towns; it results in a scum on the waste liquor, which is called *tall oil* and can be used to make soap and lubricants. *Sodium monosulphite*, also called the *neutral sulphite*

process, is one of the newer cooking methods. It depends on sulphur dioxide and caustic soda and results in a high yield, and can be used to treat hardwoods which were not previously suitable for papermaking. The recovery process is still under development.

Continuous digesting is also under development, and there are combined mechanical and chemical methods in use which do not need pressure but lend themselves to continuous operation. For example, straw can be treated in a suitable vessel with an impeller and a solution of hot soda, resulting in a high yield of straw pulp for making packaging grades.

Pulp preparation   After digestion the pulp must be washed, and often bleached. Washing is necessary to get rid of impurities; some pulps can be washed while still in the digester, and this is part of the waste recovery. The first wash results in a strong liquor which can in some cases be recovered; the next wash will result in a weaker liquor which can be used for the first wash of the next batch, and so forth.

With wood pulps and in high capacity operations the digester is emptied immediately so it can be used again. Screens in series, both flat metal tray types and rotating devices, are used to remove impurities, but centrifugal or vortex cleaners are now so efficient that they can replace screens altogether. In a vortex cleaner, as the pulp is rapidly rotated heavier impurities fall to the bottom while pure pulp passes through outlets near the top. One widely used centrifugal machine is called a *rotary vacuum filter* (see FILTRATION); this comprises a wire drum revolving in a vat. Suction from inside the drum draws a layer of pulp on to the wire, sucking the liquor out. The pulp is then washed with hot water sprays and scraped off the wire by a *doctor blade*.

Next follows, if required, some type of bleaching process, depending on the type of pulp and its intended use. Methods vary from the simple addition of bleaching liquor to a series of chemical steps which must be carefully monitored to avoid damaging the fibres. Increasingly nowadays the bleaching is an extension of the digestion process, the exact process being a combination of methods chosen to accomplish maximum yield, strength of fibres and whiteness.

Beating In most cases the pulp arrives at the paper mill in sheet form and must be broken up again. For this purpose a machine called a *hydrapulper* may be used, a tun-shaped vessel with an impeller which disintegrates the pulp in water. Similar treatment is applied to waste paper, an increasingly important raw material, particularly in view of recent increases in the price of pulp.

Next comes the *beating*. Prolonged beating with the traditional machinery is still practised, especially for the handmade papers, but highly developed quality control followed by treatment in machines called *refiners* increasingly fulfils the beating function. In any case, the quality of the finished product is determined more at this point than at any other. The physical action of beating affects the length of the fibres, their plasticity and their capacity for bonding together in the paper machine; therefore beating also determines such characteristics in the paper as bulk, opacity and strength.

The most common type of beating machine is the *hollander*, developed in Holland in the 18th century. It is an oval-shaped tube which has a low wall called a *mid-feather* running across the centre, but stopping short on each side so that the pulp can circulate around it. On one side of the mid-feather the *beater roll* is mounted on a shaft; the beater roll may weigh as much as ten tons and the capacity of the tub may vary from about 90 kg (200 lb) of rags to about $1\frac{1}{2}$ tons of wood pulp, with perhaps five parts pulp to 95 parts water. The roll has bars on its circumference parallel with the shaft; the pulp, now called the *stock* or the *stuff*, is ground against stationary bars on the floor of the tub beneath the roll. The clearance between the roll and the stationary bars is small but adjustable.

The refiner, which has completely superseded the beater in the making of newsprint, for example, is a cone-shaped beater roll in a similarly shaped housing, also equipped with bars and adjustable clearance; the bars in the refiner run at a speed of 3000 feet (over 900 m) per minute. The stock goes through the refiner only once, and the refiners are connected in series if further beating capacity is needed. There are also *disc* refiners, with one rotating disc and one stationary, and combination cone and disc models.

Loading or *fillers*, pigments or dyes if required, and most *sizing* agents may be added to the stuff during beating. Loading materials are added to give improved opacity, and they also help to make the paper stable dimensionally and assist in obtaining a good finish. They are white materials, of which the most common are china clay, titanium oxide and precipitated chalk. Chalk, for example, is added to cigarette paper to make it burn more evenly. Sizing agents, of which resin is the most common, render the paper resistant to penetration by water (but do not make it waterproof) so that it can be written upon with water-based writing ink. Printing inks are oil or spirit based, and so papers for printing do not need to be sized, but completely unsized paper, called *waterleaf*, is not common. Wrapping papers may have to be written upon, for example, and certainly papers used in LITHOGRAPHY should have some water resistance. (See also INK MANUFACTURE.)

Papermaking machines The actual papermaking process is a continuous one. The most common type of machine is the *Fourdrinier*, named after the two brothers, stationers, who built the first one in Hertfordshire in 1803. Their machine deposited the paper on to pieces of felt, after which it was finished by hand; the modern machine starts with the dilute stock at the *wet end* and finishes with reels of paper at the *dry end*. The additives (loadings and so forth) can be mixed into the stock in the wet end of the machine, instead of in the beating, if desired.

The stock is continuously delivered on to an endless belt called the *cloth* which is made of a wire or plastic mesh. A short sideways *shake* is applied to the cloth where the stock first meets it, to improve the way the fibres mesh together. Drainage of water begins immediately through the mesh of the cloth, bring-

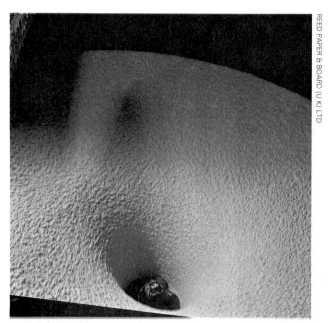

Left: wood pulp being prepared for the papermaking machine.

Bottom left: the dry end of the continuous process papermaking machine. The paper has just gone through the drying train and the calender rolls; the moisture and static electricity content has also been adjusted. The reel of paper can be slit to size on the machine as it is reeled up; alternatively it is taken to a cutting machine which can slit, cross-cut and inspect the paper as well as count the sheets.

Bottom: the wet end of the machine. The pulp is poured on to a moving belt of plastic or wire mesh, which is given a shake to cause the fibres to align themselves; water is sucked out from below with vacuum assistance. Then it goes around rollers on a belt of felt and more water is squeezed out.

ing the fibres closer together until the stock becomes a cohesive *web*. Then suction is introduced by means of vacuum boxes underneath the web; at this point also, a light wire-covered roll called the *dandy roll* rides on the upper surface of the web, usually turned by the travelling web (but sometimes turning under power) and gently pressing it. A wire design can be wired or soldered to the dandy roll to impress the *watermark* of the manufacturer on to the web.

The web is now separated from the cloth by a pair of rollers, or, on the latest model machines, by a single suction roller. These are called *couch* rolls. The volume of water removed up to this point is rich in fibre, chemicals and so forth, much of which is recovered. The web is deposited on a felt and carried between pairs of pressure rolls which remove more of the water; the felt frequently becomes clogged and must be cleaned.

The water content of the web has now been reduced to about 65%, and the web passes to the dry end of the machine, where it passes around a series of pairs of steam-heated iron cylinders. At the end of the *drying train*, the paper is without a finish and has been over-dried to about 3 to 4% moisture content. The paper passes through several *calender stacks*, which are pairs of highly polished chilled iron pressure rolls. The stacks smooth the surface, sometimes using a little water to do so. Finally the paper passes over cooled *sweat* rolls, which adjust the moisture content and reduce the static electricity, and is wound on to large reels. To avoid problems with dimensional stability, many printing papers are conditioned on the reel by passage through a hot wet atmosphere which adjusts the moisture content to 6 or 8%, which is normal for this type of paper when mature.

The paper is slit to the width and reel diameter required, if it is to be used from the reel, and paper to be used in sheet form is taken to a cutting machine where it is slit and cross-cut in the same operation. For greater accuracy and clean edges, some papers are afterwards guillotine trimmed. Sheet papers are generally inspected, torn or faulty sheets removed, and counted for packing; nowadays this can be done electronically at the cutting stage.

Other machines The *MG* machine (for Machine Glazed) produces paper which is highly glazed on one side and rough on the other. The paper is used for posters, general wrapping and carrier bags; the glaze is imparted by a large, highly polished drying cylinder. The paper is stuck to the face of the cylinder by a pressure roll and the surface in contact takes on the polish of the metal.

Boards for cartons, packaging and so forth are made by a different method of sheet formation on a *cylinder mould* machine. A wire covered roll rotates in a vat of dilute stock. Water filters through to the inside of the roll and a layer of fibres is left on the surface which is transferred to a felt. The process makes only a thin layer; to make up the greater thickness of board, several such moulds are placed in series so that a multi-layer structure is built up on the underside of a *making felt*, which is then reversed and carried through the rest of the machine. The greater advantage of this type of machine is that the centre layers of board can be made entirely of cheaper materials, such as waste paper.

Nowadays suction devices are becoming more common to assist the couch and other rollers on papermaking machinery. Some machines have the dry end entirely covered by a hood, within which fans and pipes remove moisture-laden air, enabling the machine to run faster. A modern fast newsprint machine will run at around 1000 m/min (3280 feet per minute).

PAPIN, Denis (1647–c1712)

In the early history of the steam engine, Denis Papin, a French physicist, was first to propose that the condensation of steam in a cylinder would produce a vacuum into which a piston would be driven by the pressure of the air above. In this way he linked the experimental science of artificial vacuums with the needs of technology. All the ATMOSPHERIC ENGINES, including NEWCOMEN's eighteenth century design, are based on this principle.

Denis Papin is always described as doctor of medicine, but cannot have practised long, for at the age of 26 he was taken on by Christiaan HUYGENS as a research worker for the Académie Royale des Sciences in Paris, where he worked on Huygens' idea of evacuating a cylinder by the explosion of a charge of gunpowder, which was much more rapid than evacuation by means of a pump.

Two years later Papin decided to move to London, perhaps because as a Protestant he feared religious discrimination. Recommended by Huygens, he held a comparable position with BOYLE and may have been responsible for improvements to Boyle's later air pumps. In 1681, he published his first major invention, the 'digester', a crude progenitor of the pressure cooker and the AUTOCLAVE. As the boiling point of water is related to the pressure on it, water under great pressure will not boil until it reaches a proportionately high temperature. Water can thus be used to dissolve hard bones, and reduce them to an edible jelly. Members of the Royal Society were invited to a 'Philosophic Dinner' to taste the results. Papin then devised a scheme to use atmospheric pressure to drive an engine, but it came to nothing. Papin went to Venice for a while, returned to England in 1684, and in 1687 at last obtained a regular position as professor of mathematics at Marburg in Germany. He knew he was expected to show the mechanical applications of his knowledge. Within a year he had invented the earliest form of centrifugal pump, which was used in local drainage work; he applied the same principle to the ventilation of a coal mine. Neither version was widely adopted. Papin resumed the gunpowder experiments of his Paris days, but soon realized this was unsatisfactory. But, as he pointed out, 'since it is a property of water that a small quantity of it turned into vapour by heat has an elastic force like that of air, but on cold supervening is again resolved into water, so that no trace of the said elastic force remains' the expansion of steam would serve to raise the piston, and the subsequent condensation would provide the vacuum. This principle was duly tested and the results published in 1690. Papin hoped that he could use this to drive a ship, transmitting the motion of a row of pistons through racks and pinions to paddle wheels; there was a thought of land transport too, which may have reached the stage of a small model. But the centrifugal pump was the only invention which he developed so as to earn even a modest success. At Marburg he found few pupils and many trials, and in 1696 he moved to Cassel.

When Savery's steam engine was first presented before the Royal Society he was invited to give an opinion. But not until 1705 did he take up steam engine research again, abandoning his own idea for Savery's which he modified considerably. One prototype was built; it caused a stir locally, but was not exploited and eventually dismantled. Papin then revived his notion of a steamboat, to be driven by his new engine, and he decided to return to London as there would be more call for such a ship in a great port. A small manually operated paddle-boat had been tried out on the river Fulda, in Germany, but was smashed up by local bargees, afraid of competition.

In London, Papin, now over 60, tried to persuade the Royal Society to sponsor his boat, asking for no more than £15 to cover the cost of the boiler; trials would show his version's superiority to the original Savery engine. But Savery now held the whiphand; Papin was turned down, and he died in London in poverty and obscurity. He had enjoyed the support of some of the greatest physicists in Europe, yet his life is a tale of wandering and frustration.

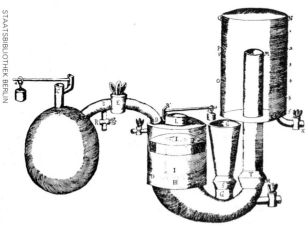

STAATSBIBLIOTHEK BERLIN

Above: this is Papin's modification of the steam engine built by Thomas Savery (c 1650–1715), which was mostly used for supplying water to the gardens of country houses. Papin recognized the superiority of Savery's machine to his own and made improvements to it, while Savery had abandoned development; nevertheless, Papin died in poverty while Savery's patents remained in force.

Right: Denis Papin in 1689. The great physicist died in poverty.

RADIO TIMES HULTON PICTURE LIBRARY

PARACHUTE

A parachute is an umbrella-shaped device for producing drag when it is pulled through a fluid. When a parachute is strongly constructed and is to be used under water or at high speed in the air, it is usually called a *drogue*. As its name implies, the parachute was intended to prevent an object from falling too rapidly; many experiments were made using animals dropped from high buildings, but it was not until the advent of the free BALLOON which gave sufficient altitude that a man could make a descent by himself.

In 1797, Garnerin made the first attempt with a linen parachute; it was 23 ft (7 m) across when laid out as a flat disc, and in spite of a violent descent, he courageously demonstrated his parachute in Europe for several years. Many other experiments were tried but the parachute did not achieve more than entertainment value until World War 1, when British Army balloonists and German airmen were saved from their crashing aircraft. In 1926, parachutes were produced for airmen with the flat disc design, but with the panels cut on the bias (diagonally across the fabric) to give greater flexibility and strength. This basic design is still in use today.

The parachute comprises a *pack* into which it is folded and a *harness*. The harness is designed to fit the parachutist in such a way that his violent de-acceleration when the parachute opens will not injure him, and so that it can be quickly released in case the parachutist comes down in water or in a high wind which might drag him across the ground. The *ripcord* is pulled by the parachutist a few seconds after leaving the aircraft so that the opening chute will be clear of the superstructure. Pulling the ripcord removes a pin which holds shut the flaps on the pack; a small *pilot* chute, folded between the flaps, is ejected by a spring and, entering the slipstream, pulls the main parachute out of the pack. For paratroopers, the ripcord is attached to a *static line* in the aircraft so that it opens automatically. In high speed aircraft, the crew member is ejected from the aircraft, seat and all, and the descent is entirely automatic (see EJECTION SEAT).

A safe rate of descent is considered to be 20 ft (6.6 m) per second. A larger parachute is provided for a paratrooper to maintain this rate because he is more heavily laden than an ejecting pilot or a sport parachutist. *Sky divers* will *free fall* for thousands of feet, altering rate of descent and direction by spreading or arching their bodies. Parachuting for sport is carefully controlled for safety, and sky divers are required to open their parachutes at not less than 2200 ft (670 m). The force with which a parachutist strikes the ground is about the same as that of jumping from a height of eight feet (2.6 m).

Design A parachute inflates when the air entering the mouth is arrested by the fabric at the crown so that the pressure created there spreads to the outer panels. If the permeability (also called porosity) of the fabric is excessive, the pressure will be insufficient to spread the outer panels and the parachute will 'squid' in a partly inflated state. When the porosity of the fabric is small, the parachute will inflate rapidly but the spillage of air around the edge of the advancing periphery forces it to swing sideways. A man descending on a parachute experiences the swing himself because his resistance to the sideways motion is less than that of the parachute.

A parachute made from concentric ribbon rings must have other narrow ribbons running from the crown outwards across the rings as well as the main load-carrying webbings. During inflation, all the ribbons flutter until the air pressure spreading outwards from the crown tensions the radial ribbons and restrains the fluttering of each successive ring. The quickness of inflation is dependent on the number of these radial ribbons.

Below left: a parachute with open gores, which allow it to be steered by pulling on the nylon cords, distorting the gores.

Below right: a parachutist wearing an Irvin 'Hitefinder' which opens the parachute. A barometric capsule contracts as pressure increases, operating a trigger at a pre-determined height.

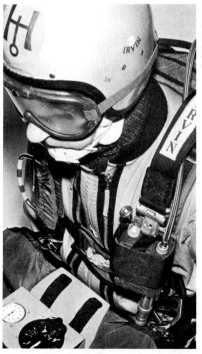

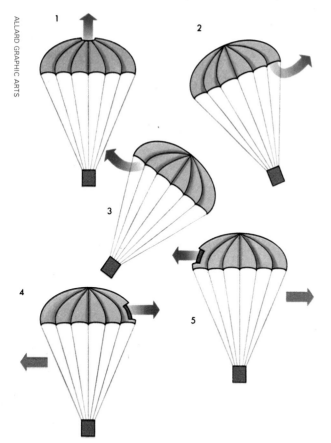

1

2

3

4

5

C 01

Above: parachute construction. They are made in different ways according to how they will be used: for dropping cargo, heavy parachutes up to 100 feet (30 m) in diameter, or clusters of parachutes, are used; for supersonic parachutes, formation of shock waves and mass flux of air must be considered. Since before World War 2 parachute design has become highly specialized.

Right: a parachute on the ground after a successful descent.

Left: an apex vent in the top of the chute allows compressed air to escape and permits a steady descent, as in number one. Without the vent the air would spill from the periphery of the chute, causing violent sideways oscillations, as in two and three. A vent in the side of the chute will cause a jet effect, and the chute will drift horizontally with respect to the ground, as in four and five. The chutist can steer the parachute by pulling on the cords.

In 1942, it was noticed that if a complete fabric parachute suffered a split in one *gore* (radial ribbon) during the inflation, it did not swing but maintained a steady glide in a direction away from the split. A parachute with an open gore was fitted with two handles connected to the bottom corners of this gore and it was found that a light pull would distort either side of the gore and a reasonable degree of control was achieved. After this design had been entered for the Second World Parachuting Championships in 1953, the principle was developed by parachutists in many countries until today a man can so control his parachute that he can touch a target a few centimetres across. Important features in these advanced designs are the centre cord, which holds the crown down to force the rapid opening of the canopy; the set of control slots to give a quick change of direction or speed; and the extension panels which spread the canopy and counter any swing induced when making a rapid turn.

The principle of inducing lift over the front surface of a gliding parachute led inevitably to the construction of fabric wings. One successful design has a nearly triangular shape, with internal rigging to maintain its form and slots to extend the lift over the upper surface. Inflation of this type is rapid and has to be carefully controlled to avoid injury to the parachutist. The rectangular shape of parachute with its ram air inflatable front section and rear edge 'flaps' has to be flown as a winged glider. It cannot be turned about an axis like a circular parachute but must be aimed at the target and stalled to reduce the speed; the action is similar to that of a bird when it is landing. These wing designs are effective but complicated to make, and this has led to the development of basic umbrella shapes which have good gliding qualities. A virtually imporous fabric is used to make a conical shape whose half section is the upper surface of an AEROFOIL at a declination of about 45 degrees to the axis of the cone. Two large open panels, covered with fine netting, are positioned apart at the back of the cone to give control in glide and turn. Many other ingenious designs have been produced but their success has depended upon whether they could be inflated consistently and manufactured economically. (see also PARAGLIDER.)

Manufacture Most parachutes are made up from triangular gores which are constructed by sewing together panels cut from *lays* of fabric, which may be as many as two hundred thicknesses. The panel patterns which determine the shape of the parachute are marked out on the lay and cut through with an electrically powered knife. Each panel has to be calculated to give the parachute its correct size and shape, and because cost is important the simplest design to meet the performance specification has to be chosen, ranging between the specially shaped parachute with a great variety of panels and the flat disc with a few bias cut panels. The construction must also permit a steady flow of work through the sewing machines with the minimum of handling of a large bulk of fabric. Automatic pattern machines are used wherever possible.

When supply dropping parachutes became very large (as much as 66 ft—20 m—inflated size) it was decided that they should be made in five pieces: a strong crown to withstand the initial air forces of the inflation and four lighter-weight side segments to spread and give the full drag. This method allowed the workshop facilities for making man-carrying parachutes to be used, and the pieces could be stored separately

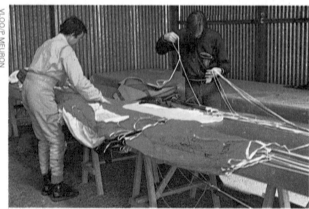

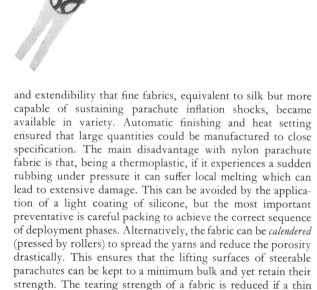

Above: parachute inspection and packing. Parachutes not used regularly must be unpacked, dried out and inspected; air conditioned towers are used.

Right: a fully opened parachute in descent. The pilot chute at the top is the one that opens first to pull the main chute out of the pack. The harness has quick-release hooks on it so that the chutist can release himself in a hurry if he lands in a high wind.

until required for rigging into a complete assembly. An extension of this manufacturing method was the production of squares of fabric which could be assembled into three different parachute sizes. Each square measured 13 ft (4 m) across and they were tied together in regular cross shaped patterns; five to carry 500 lb (230 kg), twelve for 1500 lb (690 kg) and twenty squares to carry 2500 lb (1150 kg); the rigging lines and webbing strops were all made separately ready for assembly as required.

When German engineers designed ribbon parachutes they made a ribbon foundation from which the gore shapes were cut after the main load bearing webbings had been stitched into place. This required the use of specially designed travelling sewing machines. Without such machines, the ribbons have to be laid out on a jig and tacked, usually with a hot needle, before being stitched together. To avoid this complexity, the ring slot parachute was devised in which fabric rings much wider than the ribbons were used. These rings were reinforced along their edges and then assembled with the techniques normally used for making the man-carrying parachutes. Ribbon designs are still essential where great strength is required; parachutes of this type have been flown at speeds of more than twice the speed of sound.

Materials Until World War 2, parachutes were made from either natural fibres such as flax, cotton and silk, or later from modified cellulose fibres (see FIBRE, synthetic) such as viscose and acetate rayon. Designs were limited by the bulkiness of the cotton and flax or the cost of the silk and fine rayons until the discovery of nylon in 1939 in both America and Germany. This continuous manmade fibre was so superior in strength

and extendibility that fine fabrics, equivalent to silk but more capable of sustaining parachute inflation shocks, became available in variety. Automatic finishing and heat setting ensured that large quantities could be manufactured to close specification. The main disadvantage with nylon parachute fabric is that, being a thermoplastic, if it experiences a sudden rubbing under pressure it can suffer local melting which can lead to extensive damage. This can be avoided by the application of a light coating of silicone, but the most important preventative is careful packing to achieve the correct sequence of deployment phases. Alternatively, the fabric can be *calendered* (pressed by rollers) to spread the yarns and reduce the porosity drastically. This ensures that the lifting surfaces of steerable parachutes can be kept to a minimum bulk and yet retain their strength. The tearing strength of a fabric is reduced if a thin coating is applied to reduce the porosity.

Cross-shaped supply dropping parachutes are made from squares of woven polypropylene ribbon yarn. This material is not only low in cost, but it has shown that a stiff fabric will cause the parachute to inflate quickly. Experiments have been made with crêpe papers and polyethylene; although these parachutes worked successfully, the materials and the method of construction were not suitable for modern usage or mass production.

Nylon harness webbing and cordages are only half as bulky as their earlier equivalents made in flax, and they are capable of being dyed and treated with finishes which reduce the degradation due to the action of sunlight. This feature is important when a harness has to be exposed under the cockpit canopy of an aircraft for periods of months at a time.

PARAGLIDER

With the appearance of paragliders, also called *hang gliders*, the age-old dream of strapping on a pair of wings and emulating the birds has come true. Countless pioneers down the ages have fixed feathers or fanciful wings to their bodies in attempts to fly, but their lack of technical expertise has been reflected in the toll of deaths and injuries. Lilienthal in Germany and Pilcher in England in the late 19th century showed that this method of aviation was at least feasible, though both men eventually lost their lives during experiments.

The technical basis for what is probably the fastest-growing sport in the world was put on a sound footing by Francis M Rogallo, a scientist at America's National Aeronautics and Space Administration, who investigated the possible uses of kites as recovery devices for manned spacecraft. The idea was not taken up, but the data provided the foundation for the new sport which has been developing in California since 1970.

The basic hang glider, and the most commonly used at the present time, is a direct descendent of the design tested by NASA, and is known as a *rogallo* after its designer. It is the simplest possible flying machine, comprising a keel about 18 ft long ($5\frac{1}{2}$ m) with a cross-member of about the same length mounted horizontally halfway along it. Two sharply raked leading-edge members are attached by their forward ends to the keel and are each braced by the cross-member to form an A-shaped structure. The frame is covered by a lightweight material such as nylon. The pilot hangs vertically below the intersection of the keel and the cross-member in a harness which supports the seat and shoulders so that he cannot fall out. Hanging just in front of him is a control bar, called the trapeze, which is attached to the keel and braced to the corners of the craft by means of cables.

Above: the paraglider pilot in this photo has managed to catch an updraught and is steering the craft by means of the control bar, called the trapeze, which is connected to the corners of the craft by means of cables.

Below: in this picture, the pilot has just run down a slope into the wind. The airspeed is a combination of the pilot's running speed and the speed of the wind; if this exceeds 14 to 16 mph (23 to 26 km/h) as it has here, the craft is lifted into the air.

Below right: the experimental parawing recovery device invented by Rogallo for NASA which inspired the sport of paragliding.

The pilot controls the glider by pulling or pushing the bar or moving it to one side or the other. He contributes by far the greatest proportion of the total airborne weight—the glider weighs about 40 lb (18 kg)—and so, acting as a pendulum, he is able to move the trapeze to make the craft take up the desired attitude. By pushing on the trapeze the pilot causes the nose to rise, so reducing the speed, for example.

To fly, the pilot straps himself into the harness, raises the craft to his shoulders, and runs down a slope. If the angle of the slope is greater than the gliding angle, the craft lifts itself into the air when the airspeed has risen to 14 to 16 mph (23 to 26 km/h). On a calm day the pilot steers his machine to a landing at the bottom of the hill, pulling up and losing speed so that he lands on his feet. But if a wind is blowing up the hill, its strength may be sufficient to sustain the glider, and the pilot is able to turn parallel to the hill as soon as he has taken off, and fly along in an area of rising air. This is known as slope soaring, and can be continued as long as the wind blows.

Rogallos are simple and cheap to build and fly, and they can be folded up into a small bundle for carrying under the arm. However, owing to their shape they are inefficient. The criterion for efficiency for any GLIDER, whether of conventional design or for hang gliding, is the gliding angle—the greater the efficiency the greater the distance travelled for every foot of height lost. A conventional glider can now achieve glides of 50:1, while the figure for most hang gliders is about 4:1. In an effort to improve the performance, enthusiasts have been experimenting with hang gliders having wings more like those of conventional aircraft and glide angles of about 10:1. So rapidly is the sport developing that these newer craft may supplant the rogallos, despite their increased cost and greater difficulty of transport and assembly.

PARAVANE

A paravane is a device which is towed underwater by ships to cut the mooring ropes of buoyant naval MINES.

A moored mine is held just below the surface of the sea by a length of wire attached to a *sinker* (anchor) on the sea bed. As the moored mine is buoyant, it will bob to the surface and remain floating if its mooring wire to the sinker is cut. Once floating on the surface it can be seen and therefore avoided or detonated harmlessly by rifle fire.

Construction The paravane is a kind of underwater kite and it consists of a torpedo-like body having *planes,* looking rather like aircraft wings, projecting on each side. It is buoyant, and depends on a downward force on the planes when it is towed along to keep it underwater. A rudder situated at the tail of the paravane is controlled by a preset hydrostatic device within the paravane body and automatically keeps the paravane at the correct predetermined depth. The paravane is towed, or *streamed,* from the forefoot of a ship (directly below the bow), and rides well away from the side at about the same depth as the ship's keel. The mooring wire of a mine which lies in the path of a paravane wire will be snagged and forced to slide away from the ship towards the paravane. The paravane towing wire is so constructed that it saws through the mine mooring wire while it slides along, but if the sawing action fails to cut the mine's wire completely, a cutting device secured to the paravane completes the task.

During the minesweeping operations, two paravanes are streamed, one on each side of the ship. They are attached to the

Below : a device similar to a paravane is used to control the opening and depth of trawl nets. Metal weights are attached to one of the planes to ensure the correct attitude underwater.

FISHING NEWS INTERNATIONAL

ship by means of a V-shaped *towing shoe*, which can be hauled up or down the stem (the front part of the bow). A wire for hauling up the towing shoe runs directly on to the foredeck through the *bullring*, while a downhaul wire leads through a vertical pipe built into the ship's stem. To begin streaming, the towing shoe is hauled right up to deck level in order to shackle on the paravane wires. The shoe is then hauled down to its deep towing position and the paravanes are launched overboard from the sides of the ship.

Paravanés were used by most classes of warship, including destroyers, cruisers, battleships and aircraft carriers, in both World Wars. They were also used by a few merchant ships whose voyages took them unescorted near or through mined waters. Paravanes are not normally fitted to warships today, but can be quickly added if required.

In the FISHING INDUSTRY devices called *otter boards,* which work on a similar principle to paravanes, are used to hold open the mouth of a trawl net as it is towed along underwater.

Left: an otter board of the type commonly used with trawl nets. The flow of water over the surface of the otter board gives rise to a sideways force which holds the trawl net open.

Below: a paravane consists of a torpedo shaped body having two wing-like planes extending one from each side. During minesweeping operations it is towed from the forefoot of a ship by means of a towing wire attached to a point just above the paravane cutter. The mooring wires of naval mines are cut either by the paravane towing wire or by the cutter, and the mines, which are buoyant, then float to the surface where they can be detonated harmlessly by rifle fire. Paravanes are towed in pairs, one on each side of the ship.

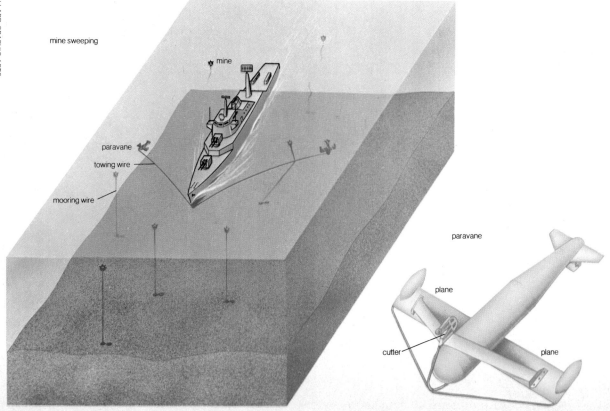

mine sweeping

mine

paravane

towing wire

mooring wire

paravane

plane

cutter

plane

PARCHMENT MAKING

While papyrus, made from vegetable parts hammered and pressed into sheets, was the earliest paper, invented about 3000 BC, leather and parchment were also used in early times for documents which would receive more handling, because these materials were more sturdy. The British Museum has a parchment scroll dating from about 1280 BC. Parchment was also used for drumheads.

The word parchment is believed to come from Pergamum, a Greek city in Asia Minor. After about 100 AD scrolls began to be replaced by the *codex,* a method of folding and binding sheets into what we would call a book. Parchment was used for the codex until not long before the invention of the printing press; from about 1100 AD papermaking techniques were imported from the Orient, but the durability of the ancient books which survive is due to parchment.

Parchment is made from the skins of young animals, preferably calves and goats. The best parchment is made from calfskin and is called *vellum,* from the Latin for calf (vitulus). It is washed, soaked in clean water for 24 hours, and then soaked in a thin liquor containing about one third lime. Liming loosens the hair and the bundles of fibres, called *collagen.* The lime bath takes several days depending on the temperature.

The hair is then scraped off the hide with a dull knife blade. This is followed by another lime bath in a fresh mixture, after which the hide is washed and stretched on a frame.

The hide is dried at about 68°F (20°C), washed with fresh water, partly dried and washed again. At the same time it is scraped and shaved thin with a traditional knife having a semi-circular blade. Then it is rubbed smooth with pumice or a similar mild abrasive and allowed to dry, stretched in a frame.

It will be seen that this technique is a development of LEATHER MANUFACTURE as it had already been practised since pre-historic times. It is interesting to note that while leather is comprised of bundles of fibres, the technique of making parchment results in the collagen forming into layers, which lend themselves to the scraping treatment. The scraping itself is a delicate, skilled operation; the quality of the scraping and drying determines the quality of the parchment. In modern times machinery has been invented which can slice a hide into several thinner sheets, eliminating some waste as well as much painstaking work.

In ancient times, the sheets of parchment were sewn together at the edge to make a scroll; when the codex was invented, the sheets began to be folded to be bound into a *volumen* (volume). (The scroll had been called the *volvulus.*) One fold was called a *folio,* two folds a *quarto,* and so forth, terms which are still used in modern bookmaking.

Below left: parchment making is an old industry in south-east London. In this picture the skins are being scalded with boiling water to make the cleaning easier. The skins become soft and the hard lumps of flesh will soon come off.

Below right top: the skin being scraped with the planing knife, smoothing the skin into vellum. The knife is very sharp and the semi-circular shape is the traditional one used in parchment making for hundreds of years. It is also quite heavy and needs great skill to use it properly.

Below right: adjusting tension on the frame.

THE SCIENCE MUSEUM

RADIO TIMES HULTON PICTURE LIBRARY

PARSONS, Charles (1854–1931)

Charles Algernon Parsons, who became famous for his invention of the steam TURBINE, was the son of the third Earl of Rosse, a distinguished engineer and astronomer. He was born in London, but spent most of his boyhood at the family home of Birr Castle in Ireland, where his father had built the world's largest telescope. Charles Parsons never went to school, but received private tuition from the eminent scientists who visited his father. He was a bright scholar, enjoyed outdoor sports—especially rowing—and spent many happy hours making things in his father's workshop. In 1866 Charles and his brothers constructed a 4 hp steam carriage which reputedly travelled at 10 mph.

At the age of 17 Charles Parsons entered Trinity College, Dublin, then two years later he moved to St John's College, Cambridge, where he obtained a degree in mathematics. At university his practical experiments included an unusual high-speed steam engine. This was an epicycloidal engine in which the cylinders actually rotated around the crankshaft, but at half its speed.

In 1877 Parsons joined W G Armstrong & Co at Elswick as an apprentice, and here he was allowed to build his engine. Kitson's of Leeds took over the manufacture of this engine and Charles Parsons joined them at the end of his four-year apprenticeship. He set up an experimental shop and turned his attention to TORPEDOES. In Leeds he met Katherine Bethell, and they were married in January 1883. Part of their honeymoon was spent watching torpedo trials at Roundhay Lake in Leeds. His wife unfortunately caught rheumatic fever, but recovered in the spring and their honeymoon was resumed with an extended visit to America.

When they returned, Parsons now aged 29 joined Clarke, Chapman & Co at Gateshead and his most important work began. The firm wanted a high-speed steam engine to drive a dynamo and Parsons decided to forget the reciprocating engine and turned to the idea of a steam turbine. The principle of a turbine is rather like a windmill, but with steam turning tiny enclosed blades instead of the wind turning sails. There are no reciprocating parts, so the turbine is very smooth running, but extremely high speeds are necessary to achieve sufficient power. Parsons' first turbine was built in 1884; five years later over 350 had been supplied, including the first for a public power station. In 1889 Parsons set up his own company in Newcastle, which manufactured, besides steam turbines, dynamos and various electrical apparatus. Probably the most spectacular demonstration of the steam turbine was the unofficial appearance of his little vessel *Turbinia* at the 1897 naval review held at Spithead, in the south of England. The first vessel to be powered by turbine, she had a top speed of $34\frac{1}{2}$ knots and was much faster than any other ship afloat. The steam turbine replaced the old steam engines in many fields and even today most power stations are powered by steam turbines.

Parsons continued experimenting with gearing, optical instruments and attempts to crystallize carbon. He was knighted in 1911. He died 20 years later, while on a cruise in the West Indies.

Top left: axial flow turbo blower designed and built in 1901 by Charles Parsons' Company in Newcastle. He had begun building steam turbines as early as 1884, and they soon began to replace steam engines in many applications. This model ran at 3000 ft³/min and 196 psi. Left: Sir Charles Parsons in 1921.

PARTICLE ACCELERATORS

Particle accelerators are machines used to give energy to beams of electrically charged sub-atomic particles. They make it possible to have high energies concentrated in a tiny volume at predetermined positions and in a controlled fashion. This ability has been used for a variety of experimental and practical purposes in the field of nuclear physics.

Accelerators of many types have been developed in an effort to achieve higher and higher energies. Yet in all the different types there are some basic features in common. The essential ingredients are a source of charged particles and electric and magnetic fields which are used to accelerate and guide them. Many kinds of particles can be accelerated—not only the basic PROTONS, NEUTRONS and ELECTRONS but also composite ones such as *alpha particles,* which consist of two protons and two neutrons and are therefore helium IONS.

Basic features of accelerators

A familiar object which uses all the principles of a particle accelerator is the CATHODE RAY TUBE of a TELEVISION set.

In this a narrow beam of electrons is fired at a fluorescent screen and made to travel rapidly across it. Where the beam strikes the screen it makes the fluorescent material glow to produce a picture. The electrons are produced by heating a filament so that they gain enough energy to break away from the atoms in the filament wire and 'boil off'. Each electron carries with it a single negative charge. When they boil off they find themselves in an electric field which is set up by applying a voltage between the filament (which becomes the electrically negative *cathode*) and another electrode (the *anode*) nearer to the screen.

The electrons fly away from the cathode towards the anode gaining energy as they do so. Just as with the attractions and repulsions between North and South poles of magnets, so a negative electron is repelled by a negative electrode and attracted by a positive electrode. Exactly the opposite would happen with a particle carrying a positive charge, such as a proton. It is accelerated away from the positive electrode towards the negative.

Magnetic fields have the property of curving the paths of charged particles. Therefore, magnets can be used in a television set to bend the electron paths so that they finish up in a narrow beam in spite of emerging from the filament as a spray of electrons moving in all directions. The bending power of the magnet focuses the electron beam in a way comparable to the effect of a lens on a beam of light.

These principles underlie even the most advanced accelerator techniques. What is needed is a source of charged particles where electrons, protons or other ions are broken away from atoms. The particles are then exposed in one way or another to an electric field which accelerates them (this is known more correctly as an *electric field gradient*—the electrons in the television tube 'roll down an electrical hill'). They move in a magnetic field which bends their path to focus them or to control their direction.

One more feature is usually necessary: a good vacuum in the region where the particles are accelerated prevents them being scattered on air molecules which would make it more difficult to hold them in a beam.

The expression 'electron volt' is used to describe the energy a particle receives, since this gives a simple relationship to the accelerating voltage. For example, the television set will have its anode at something like 10,000 volts (usually expressed as 10 kV) positive compared to the cathode. Each electron reaching the television screen has been accelerated to an energy of 10,000 electron volts (written 10 keV).

The other common energy units are MeV for million electron volts and GeV for *giga* electron volts (thousand million electron volts, also called BeV in the USA since the American 'thousand million' is a billion). Accelerators are described as a 10 GeV machine and so on.

Uses of accelerators

The most powerful particle accelerators are used in research to discover the fundamental components of matter and to study their behaviour. As accelerators have been developed to give higher and higher energies they have uncovered an incredibly complex world on a smaller scale than the atomic nucleus involving hundreds of previously unknown particles (see PARTICLE PHYSICS). Studying these particles has revealed phenomena which overthrow many 'commonsense' ideas about how Nature works.

This research has become possible because as accelerators give particles higher and higher energy so they can probe other particles more penetratingly. For example, a particle

Beam outlets on the Nimrod 7GeV proton synchrotron, which is used to investigate the properties of elementary particles and the forces between them. A pulse of protons, initially accelerated in a linear accelerator, is injected into the synchrotron. After about a million revolutions the accelerated protons reach their maximum energy and are made to collide with a 'target' by means of a magnetic field to guide the beam. Those which are travelling at a favourable angle then come out of the synchrotron down a beam pipe to be focused on various types of particle detectors such as spark or multiwire chambers.

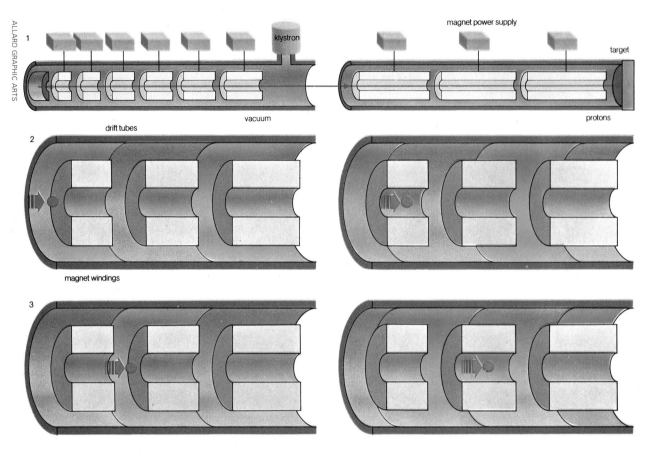

accelerated to an energy of several MeV can penetrate the nucleus of an atom and either break it up or transform it in some way. Probing the nucleus was one of the first uses of accelerators and, mistakenly, led to their popular name of 'atom-smashers'. Such accelerators are really 'nucleus-smashers'; the atom is smashed much more easily. Striking a match gives the low energies (in the eV range) which can tear electrons from an atom.

At GeV energies, accelerated particles can penetrate not just the cluster of particles in a nucleus but other individual particles leading to spectacular transformations. At the instant the collision takes place, the energy can be sufficiently high to create completely new particles (in accordance with EINSTEIN's famous $E=mc^2$ relationship which specifies that mass and energy are interchangeable). It is accelerators of GeV energies which are used in the most advanced research into the nature of matter.

But only a very small proportion of particle accelerators, and these the most powerful ones, are used in research of this type. The vast majority are used in industry and medicine. Quite apart from television tubes, there are X-ray machines used in hospitals and for non-destructive testing in industry (see QUALITY CONTROL). Other accelerators produce radio-ISOTOPES (forms of ELEMENTS with unstable nuclei which throw off particles after a time and can thus be traced in medical, industrial or agricultural systems by using PARTICLE DETECTORS). There are also radiation therapy machines for the treatment of cancer, and a long list of other practical applications.

Types of accelerator The simple types of accelerator are *linear*—they move particles in straight lines. A television tube is a linear accelerator in this sense (except for the deflec-

tions in the beam needed to produce the picture). So is the VAN DE GRAAFF GENERATOR, a high-voltage generator often used to accelerate particles in the laboratory.

There are also more specialized linear accelerators. A common type was invented by Alvarez. It has a long cylindrical tank along which hollow tubes are set up in a straight line with gaps in between them. The tank is fed with electrical power at high frequency which has the effect of swinging the electric field backwards and forwards in the tank. Charged particles are fed in at one end in a beam directed through the hollow tubes. The timing of the swing of the electric field and the length of the tubes is arranged so that when the field is in the right direction to accelerate the particles, they emerge into the gaps between the tubes. In effect, if they are positively charged particles (protons), when the tube behind them becomes positive, the tube in front becomes negative, and they are accelerated across the gap. The electric field then swings in the opposite direction. This would decelerate the protons but they are safely hidden inside the next tube and the decelerating field does not reach them.

This process is repeated many times along the tank and the protons emerge with an accumulated energy of perhaps 20 MeV. They will be travelling faster as they approach the end of the tank and the tubes have to be made longer than at the input end so that they hide the faster protons for sufficient time while the field swings round. Magnetic fields play an important role in keeping the beam focused as it travels along the axis of the tank; a magnet is usually built into each tube.

The most powerful linear accelerators are an 800 MeV proton machine at Los Alamos, USA, which partly uses the Alvarez technique, and a 20 GeV electron machine at Stanford, USA.

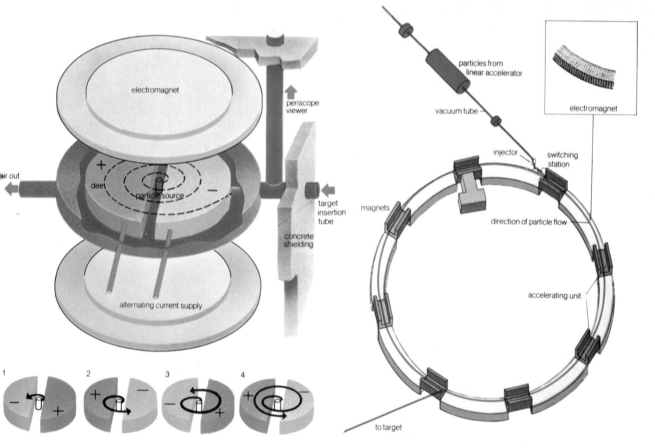

Above left: a linear accelerator. The particles are accelerated by waves of electric field set up by a klystron along the copper walls of the vacuum cylinder. When the polarity of the field is such that it would retard the particle it is shielded by one of the drift tubes which increase in length along the cylinder to compensate for the increased speed of the particle.

Above: a cyclotron. This consists of two hollow 'dees' mounted inside a vacuum chamber which is situated between the poles of an electromagnet. The dees are alternately charged positive and negative, and a particle created or introduced at the centre will be accelerated between them, moving in a widening spiral under the influence of the magnet until it reaches the outer edge.

Above right: a synchrotron. Particles are injected into the vacuum tube of the synchrotron and are guided in a wide circle by powerful electromagnets. They are sped up on each orbit by the accelerating units until the required energy is reached and they can be extracted into the experimental halls for study or use.

Cyclotrons

A limitation of the linear accelerator is that each of its components is used just once in the acceleration process. To reach very high energies, linear accelerators become prohibitively long—the Stanford machine, two miles (3.2 km) long, is close to the reasonable limit. This is where circular machines hold the advantage. If particles can be made to come round again to pass through the same acceleration station many times there are obvious gains.

The first accelerator of this type was invented by E O Lawrence and is known as the *cyclotron*. The charged particles are fed into the centre of a vacuum chamber shaped like a large shoe polish tin containing a slightly smaller one divided into two D-shaped halves called 'dees'. The halves have a small

gap between them and the accelerating electric field is applied across the gap. A circular magnet covers the chamber and gives a constant field throughout the whole chamber volume where the particles travel. This has the effect of curving the paths of the particles as they shoot from one 'dee' to another. The radius of the curve that a particular particle follows depends on its speed—the higher the speed the shallower the curve.

Particles are fed in at the centre. They cross the gap and the field accelerates them. They then swing round a small semicircle inside one of the dees because of the magnetic field. Meanwhile, the electric field across the gap is reversed and when they emerge into it again they are accelerated a second time. In the other dee, they swing round a slightly larger semicircle (since they are moving faster) and when they come out again into the gap the electric field has again been reversed to give them a further 'kick'. This process continues, and the particles follow a spiral path increasing in energy all the time until they fly out at the circumference of the vacuum chamber.

Synchro-cyclotrons

The cyclotrons are excellent and comparatively simple machines to provide particles up to energies of about 20 MeV. Above that energy, however, they run into a phenomenon explained in Einstein's RELATIVITY theory and they no longer work. In the cyclotron the electric field across the gap is swung from one direction to another at a fixed frequency. It is therefore important that the particles spend the same amount of time describing the semicircles no matter what their energy so that they always emerge into the gap at the right time to receive their next kick. But when they have been accelerated to speeds close to the speed of light, the particles begin to increase in mass rather than increasing steadily in speed (they can never exceed the speed of light).

At 20 MeV a proton has increased in mass by about 2%
and it then takes 2% longer to get around its semicircle in the
cyclotron than when it has low energy at the centre of the
machine. It begins to get out of step with the accelerating field
in the gap.

The solution, which has made higher energies possible, is
gradually to reduce the frequency at which the field across the
gap is swung around so as to keep in step with the orbiting
speed of the particles as their increasing mass slows this down.
This varient of the cyclotron is called the *synchro-cyclotron* since
its electric field is synchronized with the orbiting speed of the
particles. The largest machine of this type is at the Joffe
Physico-technical Institute at Gatchina near Leningrad, USSR.
It accelerates protons to a peak energy of 1 GeV.

Synchrotrons For energies beyond 1 GeV, cyclotron-
type accelerators become technically unwieldy monsters. The
magnet for example, weighs many thousands of tons and is
about 30 ft (10 m) in diameter. Above this size the most advanced type of accelerator to date—the *synchrotron*—comes into
action. It uses the same idea of accelerating particles back round
a circle so that the same accelerating stations can be used to
increase their energy further.

The difference is that, instead of using a constant magnetic
field which allows the particles to spiral outwards while their
speed grows, the synchrotron increases its magnetic field in
step so as to hold the particles on exactly the same circle no
matter what their speed. This allows a hollow central ring of
smaller magnets to be used instead of one huge one, and a
narrow circular tube instead of a wide chamber.

Charged particles are usually fed into the circular vacuum

*Top left: the Aldermaston six million
volt Van de Graaff high voltage
electrostatic generator. The constant
energy particle beams produced are
used to bombard different targets,
initiating nuclear reactions which
are studied in particle physics.*

*Left: a linear accelerator which
is designed to accelerate heavy particles.
The outer tube is 90 × 10 ft (27 × 3 m),
dwarfing the man at the far end.*

*Top right: the intersection of an ISR
(intersecting storage ring). These devices
make it possible to observe almost head-on
collisions between protons at an energy
equivalent to 2000 GeV protons striking
a fixed target. Because of the high
energy in the mass of the proton-
proton interaction, heavy particle
experiments are possible.*

*Near right: a Cockcroft-Walton
proton accelerator which in the 1930s
was the first important particle
accelerator. It consists of an ion
source, an accelerating tube and
a high voltage generator.*

*Far right: a section of the world's
largest (1½ km) ring accelerator, USSR.*

tube of the synchrotron from a linear accelerator so that they are already at an energy of several tens of MeV. They then move around the synchrotron ring with the magnets powered to give a low field. On moving round the ring they encounter several accelerating stations where electric fields give them an energy kick. The particles would then tend to move on to a wider circle but the magnet field is nudged higher to hold them in the ring. Again the frequency at which the accelerating stations give their kicks has to be progressively adjusted to take account of the orbiting speed and the effect of the growing mass of the particles (a proton travelling along with an energy of 30 GeV is about thirty times heavier than when it is 'at rest'). When the particles have been taken up to the desired energy they are thrown out of the ring by altering their path with magnets. A new burst of particles is fed in, with the magnetic field again low, and the process starts again.

There is no theoretical limit to the energy which can be achieved in this way and the world's most powerful accelerators are all of this type.

The highest energy proton machine is the 400 GeV synchrotron at Batavia near Chicago, USA. Its ring is 1¼ miles in diameter. A European equivalent is scheduled to come into action in 1977. It is being built in an underground tunnel under the Franco-Swiss frontier near Geneva.

If there is demand for still higher energies in the future, it is likely that the more powerful magnetic fields available by the newly developed SUPERCONDUCTING magnets will be brought into play. With similar machine dimensions to the biggest accelerators of today, the synchrotron could then provide particles with energies of 1000 GeV.

PARTICLE DETECTORS

Particle detectors are devices which enable the smallest components of matter, such as electrons or protons, to be observed. Since these particles are extremely small, less than a million millionth of a centimetre across, they cannot be seen directly by eye even using the most powerful microscopes and they have to be observed indirectly. This is possible through observing effects that they produce when passing through a detector, which they can activate in various ways.

The majority of particle detectors use the effect of ionization. When a particle which has an electric charge travels with high energy through a solid, liquid or gas, it can knock electrons out of the atoms that are in its path. This is known as ionization (see ION AND IONIZATION) and it is the liberated electrons or ionized atom which can then be picked out in some way to 'see' where the particle travelled.

The scientists who study the behaviour of the basic particles of matter like to know several things. For each particle involved, they like to know where it is and when, how fast it is travelling and what type of particle it is. The particle detectors are therefore designed to give this sort of information as precisely as possible. As an example of the accuracies which can be achieved, different detectors can indicate where particles have passed to within a few thousandths of a millimetre and indicate when they passed to within a few thousand millionths of a second.

Traditionally, most detectors have given their information in visual form—such as the particles producing tracks in emulsions, and BUBBLE CHAMBERS. This has particular advantages in that the particular interactions can be seen and the information is available as a permanent record on film. It involves, however, the rather tedious process of developing the film, looking to see if anything of interest has happened and, if so, measuring the track positions before sending the information to a computer for calculations on some aspect of particle behaviour. Nowadays the tendency is towards detectors which give their information as electrical pulses. These pulses can be passed directly to the computer without any intervening stage (a situation known as having a detector 'on-line'). Information can then be collected much more quickly and easily.

There are various types of detector, the earlier ones depending on photographic analysis.

Nuclear emulsions   One of the first detection techniques was the use of special photographic emulsions, known as *nuclear emulsions* because they were used in studies of nuclear particles. Thick layers of emulsion, with a silver bromide content about ten times higher than in normal film, record the passage of individual charged particles which damage the silver bromide molecules in their path. Tracks appear when the emulsion is developed.

The technique can pinpoint with very high accuracy (a few thousandths of a millimetre) where particles pass but it does not give useful information about when the particle travelled

Below: the diagrammatic representation of a visual spark chamber. Sparks are formed along the path of the charged particle when a high voltage pulse is applied very quickly after it has passed. A TV camera converts the light from the spark into electrical signals.

A simple scintillation counter. When particles pass from the sample in the cover (right) to a surrounding crystal it flashes. These scintillations are amplified by a photomultiplier (centre) and passed electrically to a computer for analysis.

ALLARD GRAPHIC ARTS

high voltage pulser

charged particle

mirror

spark

spark

spark

camera

into the emulsion. Also the emulsion contains a variety of atoms and it can often be difficult to decipher which particles are now involved in producing the tracks. Nuclear emulsions are now used less but in the late 1940s they were the most popular particle detectors. They were, for example, flown in balloons or stacked on mountain tops to detect the particles, called *cosmic rays*, which hurtle into the Earth's atmosphere from outer space. This led to the discovery of *pions*, particles which play a crucial role in the nucleus (see PARTICLE PHYSICS).

Cloud and bubble chambers

These particle detectors also record tracks of particles visually by taking photographs either of the trail of liquid droplets in a CLOUD CHAMBER, or the trail of vapour bubbles in a bubble chamber. They are used in experiments at PARTICLE ACCELERATORS, where they make it possible to take pictures of all the charged particles emerging from a collision between an accelerated particle and a particle in the chamber. They give good accuracy in measuring positions but again demand the tedious process of developing, scanning and measuring film.

Large bubble chambers are still prominent in experiments at accelerators and the technique has been used in discovering most of the 200 particles which are now known.

Spark chamber

The spark chamber collects information, on the whereabouts of charged particles, in the form of electrical pulses.

A typical spark chamber consists of two planes of thin paral-lel stretched wires with a gap of about a centimetre between them which is filled with a gas such as argon (see INERT GAS). A pulse of about fifteen thousand volts is applied across the gap when other detectors indicate that a particle is on its way. This pulse is almost enough for electrical breakdown to occur so that a spark passes between the planes.

When a charged particle passes through the gap it causes ionization in the gas and disturbs the electrical condition enough for a spark to cross between the gap at the position of the ionization. The spark produces an electrical pulse on the wire where it hits and thus the particle position is known to be somewhere along a particular wire. Normally, several such chambers are set up back to back with the parallel wires aligned in different directions in each plane. The particle path is then known to be where the wires 'that fire' cross one another.

The accuracy to which the particle position can be determined is not very high since wires are usually about a millimetre apart. Better accuracy can be obtained by photographing the sparks between planes of aluminium foil, used instead of wires. These are called *optical spark chambers*. A recent development avoids the intermediary of film by using a television camera to look at the sparks. The camera converts the position of the light produced by the spark directly into electrical pulses, operating in much the same way as it does when communicating normal television pictures.

Spark chamber detectors being used for the study of the very weak currents produced by the interaction of leptons. The body of the detector is 7 m long and consists of 150 spark chambers. Two mirrors, each over 15 m², reflect the track images to a camera.

Below: a scintillation counter, which is extremely fast at detecting particles. A charged particle passing through the scintillating material causes a tiny flash which is amplified by a photomultiplier tube and an electrical pulse is relayed to a computer.

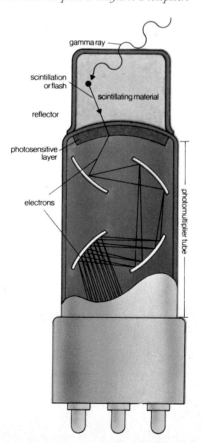

Geiger, proportional and drift The GEIGER COUN-TER is another detector which was very useful in the early days of nuclear physics but which has now been replaced almost entirely by more advanced detectors. It uses the ionization produced in a gas by the passage of a charged particle to give an electrical pulse on a wire. The voltages that are applied are high and the liberated electrons and ions are accelerated enough to cause ionization themselves. Thus the particle initiates an avalanche of electrons, giving a large pulse on the wire.

If the voltage is not set so high the full avalanche does not occur. Instead, the number of electrons reaching the wire depends only on the number liberated by the particle. The pulse on the wire is proportional to the initial ionization and the detector is called a *proportional counter*.

The two latest forms of particle detector use this phenomenon. The first is called a *multiwire proportional chamber* (MPC). It consists of planes of parallel wires which collect electrical signals when they are closest to the path of the particle, like the spark chamber. Lower voltages are applied, however, and the wires do not receive a full spark but the more moderate number of electrons proportional to the ionization that has been caused. Amplifiers attached to each wire increase the signal before passing it to the computer.

The MPC is continuously receptive to the passage of a particle, since it does not need a high voltage pulse like the spark chamber. When a spark chamber fires, its voltage drops and it takes a hundredth of a second before it has recovered enough to give another spark—this is a long 'dead time' if a spray of particles is arriving from an accelerator. The MPC can also record several particles at once with signals arriving on different wires and can say when a particle arrives to an accuracy of much better than a tenth of a millionth of a second (over ten times better than the spark chamber).

The most recent detector is the *drift chamber*, a further development of the MPC. The gap between the wire planes is made larger and, instead of determining the particle position simply by detecting a signal on the wire nearest to it, signals are picked up on several wires and the time taken by electrons to drift to wires under the influence of the electric field is measured. This says where the particle has passed with great accuracy in position (some hundredths of a millimetre) and in timing (a few thousand millionths of a second).

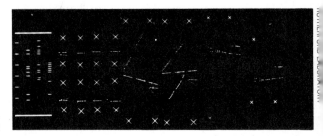

RUTHERFORD LABORATORY

Scintillation counters Even faster timing, but without good information about position, can be obtained from scintillation counters which use the property of some materials, for example, types of plastic, to give a flash of light when crossed by a high energy charged particle. In a scintillation counter, a block of plastic is wrapped up light-tight and the light flash due to the passage of a particle is conveyed via light-pipes to a PHOTOMULTIPLIER TUBE. The light falls on an electrode, releasing electrons, and thus gives an electrical pulse which can be passed to a computer or can alert other detectors that a particle is on its way. The timing accuracy can be a thousandth of a millionth of a second.

Cerenkov counter This detector is often used to distinguish between particles. It is based on the principle that a high energy particle can exceed the local speed of light, for example, in a block of Lucite (similar to 'Perspex'). When this occurs the atoms in the path of the particle are so disturbed that they emit light which comes off at an angle in the wake of the particle like the bow wave of a ship (or like the sonic wave when a plane has exceeded the speed of sound). By measuring this angle with photomultiplier tubes the velocity of the particle may be found.

If the particle passes through a magnetic field before it reaches the counter, its path will be curved to an extent depending on its mass multiplied by its velocity. The Cerenkov counter then measures the velocity and the particle is identified because of its mass.

Top left: typical photo from an optical spark chamber experiment. Two views of each of 12 spark chambers and a set of fiducial (reference) crosses can be seen.

Bottom left: gamma ray scintillation detectors fixed to the skids on each side of the helicopter are used to detect uranium ore. In the cabin is a 3 channel gamma recorder with separate chart outputs for uranium, thorium and potassium. The torpedo-like object is a magnetometer.

Top: in this multiwire proportional chamber a constant potential, usually about 3 kV, is maintained across the planes of wires. The current of electrons produced by each ionizing particle is amplified by an avalanche effect in the high field region near each wire, but no actual spark is formed.

Bottom right: a 1.5 m cryogenic hydrogen bubble chamber. The target contains liquid hydrogen, while the rest of the chamber is filled with a mixture of liquid neon and hydrogen.

RUTHERFORD LABORATORY

PARTICLE PHYSICS

Particle physics is the study of the behaviour of the fundamental components of matter. It is the continuation of the research which uncovered the mechanism of the ATOM and of the NUCLEUS at the heart of the atom. Present research is concerned with investigating the nature of the individual particles which make up the atom and of the many other related particles, recently discovered in experiments at PARTICLE ACCELERATORS.

The number of different particles which have been identified is about 200. The list includes 'antiparticles', identical in mass but opposite in many of their properties to their particle equivalents. For example, an electron is pushed away by an electrode which has a negative voltage while an *antielectron* (or *positron*) is pulled towards it. This is because the electron carries a negative electric charge, while the positron carries a positive electric charge.

The particles range in mass from the *photon* (the particle of light—see QUANTUM THEORY), which conveys ENERGY but itself has no mass, to those such as the particles known by the letters N and Z which have a mass three times that of the PROTON and NEUTRON (these form the nucleus which accounts for most of the mass of any atom). Particles have many other measurable properties such as electrical charge (positive, negative or neutral) and spin. When they interact with one another it has been found that some 'conservation laws' apply dictating what can emerge from the interaction. For example, the particles which emerge from an interaction must carry the same total electric charge as those which went in, they must emerge with the same mass energy, and so on.

Big differences have been found in the types of particle interaction and they have led to the description of particle behaviour as being controlled by four forces: strong, electromagnetic, weak and gravitational. They are easily distinguished because their relative strengths are very different. The electromagnetic force is a hundred times, the weak force a thousand million times and the gravitational force over a million, million, million, million, million million times less powerful than the strong force.

Following the categories of force, the particles themselves are grouped into categories. Those that feel the strong force are called *hadrons* and those that are sensitive to the weak force, but not to the strong force are called *leptons*. Those that are electrically charged feel the electromagnetic force and all particles that have mass feel the gravitational force.

Gravitational force The gravitational force acts between all particles which have mass. It was responsible for the falling apple that prompted Newton's gravitational law (the apple fell because of the gravitational attraction of the Earth), and it controls the motions of the Earth and planets in orbit around the Sun because of the mutual gravitational attractions. It is always an 'attractive' force,—two masses are pulled towards one another and are never pushed apart. The effect is proportional to the product of the masses involved and it stretches out from a mass to infinity, decreasing as the inverse square of the distance from the mass (for example, twice as far away the effect is four times weaker).

Despite the might of gravitational effects when large masses are involved, on the scale of individual particles it is extremely feeble and can generally be ignored since it is overshadowed by the other forces involved.

Electromagnetic force The electromagnetic force acts between all particles carrying an electric charge. It is seen in action in all the phenomena of ELECTRICITY and MAGNETISM,

The particles shown here were detected on film through the ionization effects produced (seen as tracks) when passing through a particle detector. Below left: discovery of the positron (1932). The radius of curvature and the ionization density of the thin track enabled the mass to be deduced, which was found to be equal to that of an electron. Bottom left: first observation (1947) of the decay of a π⁺ meson, or pion, which is the track in the emulsion at the bottom, into a μ⁺ meson or muon (vertical track). Below right: a cloud chamber photo (1947) showing the decay of a heavy neutral particle (kaon) into two charged particles, seen as an inverted 'V' in the bottom right hand corner. Bottom right: the decay of a π meson (top track) into a μ meson which decays into a positron. Slower moving particles produce more ionization, which is shown by the track intensities.

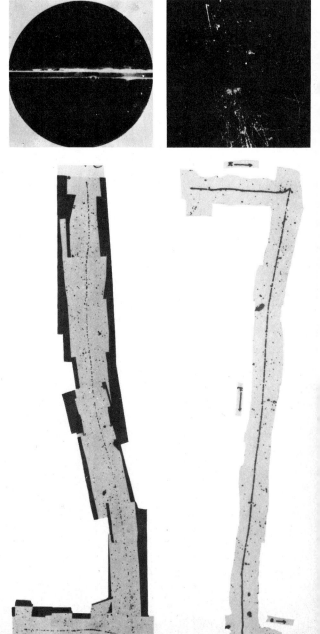

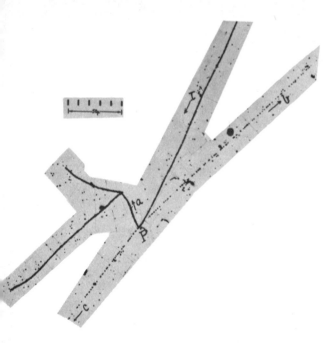

Left: the first observation (1949) of the decay of a K meson (kaon) into three π mesons (pions). Track 'a' is made by a slow moving π⁻ meson which is captured by a nucleus and disintegrates. Tracks 'b' and 'c' are made by fast moving π mesons.

Centre: this event was recorded in 1958. An antiproton is annihilated by a nucleus and produces a 'star' consisting of a slow recoil nucleus (track 1), a π⁻ meson (track 2) which in turn produces a star, three π mesons (tracks 3, 4 and 6), a π⁻ meson (track 7), and a π⁺ meson (track 5) which shows a pion to muon to electron decay chain.

Bottom: a hydrogen bubble chamber photo taken in 1965 shows the decay of an omega particle, which has a mass of 1672 MeV and a lifetime of 1.1 × 10⁻¹⁰ seconds. The event as recorded and its interpretation are shown side by side.

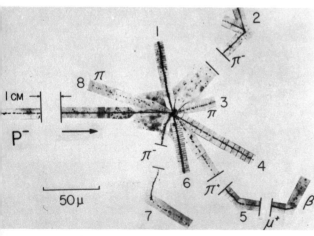

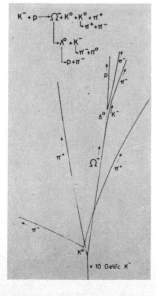

in LIGHT and in radio waves (see ELECTROMAGNETIC RADIATION). It controls the motions of the negative electrons around the positive nucleus of the atom and is thus the source of all atomic behaviour. It is attractive between oppositely charged particles, pulling them together, and repulsive between similarly charged particles, pushing them apart. The effect is proportional to the product of the two charges involved and it stretches out from a charge to infinity decreasing as the inverse square of the distance from the charge in a similar way to the gravitational force.

The way in which the electromagnetic force acts is described in a theory known as *quantum electrodynamics*, QED, which says that each particle is surrounded by a cloud of photons—the packets of energy without mass such as are present in light. The particle is seen as constantly lobbing out these photons and then catching them again. If a photon meets another particle an interaction takes place (such as a pulling together if the particles are oppositely charged); via the photon a particle has passed a message to the other particle. The photon cloud is densest near the particle and thins when moving out from the particle to infinity. This explains how the strength of the electromagnetic interaction falls off with distance.

QED has proved to be a highly successful theory. It can be tested because, if charged particles have a photon cloud, this will slightly modify their properties. These slight changes have been measured and found to agree with the predictions of QED theory to an accuracy of a few parts in a million. The theory was developed to explain a comparatively small range of phenomena but it has worked perfectly in predicting the effect of the electromagnetic force, whether at distances as small as a thousandth of a millionth of a millionth of a centimetre (deep inside a charged particle) or out to distances as large as a million miles.

Strong force The strong force acts between hadrons. It can be seen in action in the nucleus of the atom, where it holds clusters of protons and neutrons close together despite the electromagnetic force between the positively charged protons trying to push them apart. Its effect is felt only at short distances of about the dimensions of the nucleus (a millionth of a millionth of a centimetre) which explains why the nucleus does not pull in other hadrons unless they actually enter the nuclear volume.

The way in which the strong force acts is interpreted as being through the exchange of particles known as *mesons* of which the pi meson (or pion) is the most common example. A hadron communicates its presence to another hadron by exchanging a pion like charged particles exchanging photons. The pion, however, has mass (about a quarter of that of the proton) and the pion cloud sticks very close to the hadron, so the strong force does not spread out far from the particle.

This comparatively simple picture was thrown into confusion by the discovery at accelerators of a multitude of hadrons and mesons. When particles were hit with other particles which had been accelerated to high energies many previously unknown particles emerged, all acting under the influence of the strong force: in the early 1960s particle physicists collected new particles rather like botanists collecting new flowers, with no understanding of why they should exist or of what role they play in Nature. As the properties of the particles were determined it was realized that there are orderly relationships between them, rather like those between groups of chemical ELEMENTS.

Just as the structure of the atom underlies the relationship of the Periodic Table, so it is believed that there is structure in the hadrons leading to their relationships. The hadrons group together in sets of eight and ten particles of related properties and it was deduced that these sets could result from the existence of three, more basic, objects, given the name *quarks*, coming together in different ways to build up the hadrons.

Recently, there has been a series of experiments where high energy particles of different kinds have been bounced off protons and neutrons. The aim is similar to the famous experiment of *Rutherford* at the beginning of this century. He bounced particles off an atom and from the way that they scattered, he was able to deduce the presence of the tiny nucleus at its centre. The scattering of particles on protons and neutrons indicates the presence within these hadrons of three tiny grains —possibly the quarks. It appears, therefore, as if the particles that we had regarded as the fundamental components of matter are themselves composed of more basic objects.

It has, however, proved impossible to liberate a quark from inside a hadron, no matter how hard it has been hit, and the idea of quarks, despite its success in explaining and predicting the existence and behaviour of particles under the influence of the strong force, is still not supported by completely convincing experimental evidence.

Weak force The weak force can be seen in action in the break up, or decay, of particles into other particles. The time involved in particle decay can be about a thousand millionth of a second. This is very long on the scale of particle interactions (the strong force acts a million million times faster) and reflects the weakness of the force. As far as is known, the force operates within a particle and does not extend beyond its boundary.

Until the high energy accelerators came into action, most of the knowledge of the weak force came from observation of the radioactive decay (see RADIOACTIVITY) of the nucleus—in particular, the so-called *beta decay* due to the break-up of a neutron into a proton and electron. It became clear that since the electron emerges with a variety of energies some other particle must be carrying away the remainder of the energy from the break-up. This invisible particle is called a *neutrino* ('little neutral one'). It has no charge and is a lepton, feeling only the weak force. W Pauli felt safe, therefore, in betting a case of champagne that such a particle would never be observed. Unfortunately for Pauli, it has been observed interacting with other particles around nuclear reactors, from which millions of neutrinos pour out every second, and at high energy accelerators, where beams of neutrinos are used to study the weak force.

Such experiments have revealed that the behaviour of particles under the influence of the weak force overthrows many 'commonsense' ideas about the laws of Nature. The first overthrow came in the 1950s from measurements on the electrons emerging from the beta decay of the nucleus. They

Above: a beam of high speed deuterons from the Berkeley cyclotron. A deuteron is a stable but lightly bound combination of one proton and one neutron.

Below: schematic representation of the families and relative masses of some elementary particles. They are shown in an

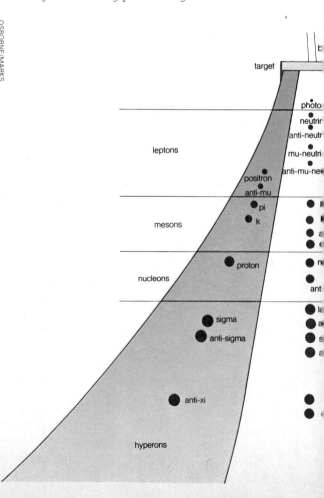

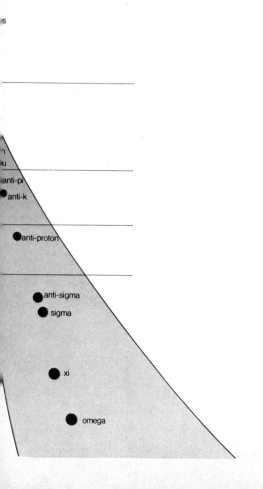

are all observed to be spinning in a clockwise direction, implying that the unseen neutrinos coming out with them are spinning in an anticlockwise direction. This means that when the weak force is in action Nature is concerned about directions. Previously it has always been believed that 'right' and 'left' were human conventions, to help us, for example, drive on the safe side of the road, but that Nature did not distinguish between right and left—that Nature did not insist on things happening in a particular direction. Following these experiments on the weak force, it became possible to communicate our 'right' and 'left' to an inhabitant of a remote planet by asking him to observe the spin direction of the electrons coming from beta decay.

Ten years later, observing the weak force in action in the decay of one of a type of meson known as the neutral *kaon* produced a more drastic overthrow of a commonsense idea. It showed that not only was Nature concerned about direction in space, it is also concerned about direction in time. The belief that going backwards in time would see events exactly reversed, like a film running backwards, is no longer valid.

No satisfactory theory exists to explain all the manifestations of the weak force which have been observed. One theory has taken over the idea of the exchange of a particle in a similar way to the photon in the electromagnetic and the pion in the strong force. It is called the intermediate *boson* or W particle but it has never been discovered. The weak force is the most mysterious of those in action in particle physics.

imaginary accelerator beam with the positively charged particles in the red part, negatively charged in the blue and those with no net charge in the centre. To the right an atom of hydrogen consisting of a proton and an electron is compared with one of anti-hydrogen in which the particles, an anti-proton and a positron, each has the same mass as those in hydrogen but the opposite charge.

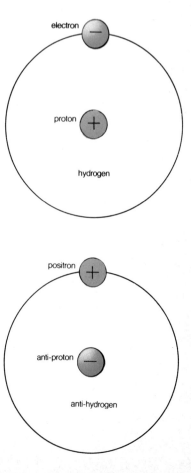

PASCAL, Blaise (1623–1662)

Skill at mechanical engineering and experimental physics is not often combined in the same personality with intense religious feeling and a brilliant, nervous prose style: Blaise Pascal must be very rare in excelling at all four. The first to construct a workable CALCULATING MACHINE, he demonstrated atmospheric pressure, established theoretical principles for the hydraulic transmission of power, and contributed extensively to mathematics, from conic sections to probability theory.

His mother died when he was three, and his father then devoted himself to the upbringing of Blaise and his two sisters. Keenly interested in mathematics and in new ideas in science, as well as fervently devout, he passed these attitudes on to his son, who spent an enclosed and withdrawn childhood, suffering often from ill health. It is said his father would not teach Blaise geometry for fear it would overtax his delicate system—so he worked out the basic theorems for himself, chalking on the tiles of his nursery floor.

When Blaise was 16 the family moved to Rouen, where his father was to be commissioner for upper Normandy. To help with the accounts Blaise developed an adding machine; a set of dials activated gears with ten teeth (or other numbers appropriate to non-decimal currency), which turned drums marked with the numerals. Each gear shaft bore a catch to move the next gear one tooth for each of its own revolutions. The figures to be added were dialled in turn, and the sum appeared in a window in the outer plate. The device could also be used for subtraction, but multiplication was a slow and awkward process. Over the years he did what he could to popularize his invention, and a few dozen models were built. But they were very expensive, so although their ingenuity was admired, few were bought.

In 1646, Pascal learned of Torricelli's experiments on the artificial creation of a vacuum, and he began to recreate these experiments for himself, devising fresh apparatus, such as the 'vacuum within a vacuum', so as to observe what happens in the absence of any external force to keep the mercury column in its place. But what held the mercury in place in the single tube? Torricelli had suggested it was the weight of the air; Pascal argued this could best be proved by comparing mercury levels at the foot and the peak of a mountain. Tests were carried out on the Puy de Dôme, according to his instructions, in September 1648. His predictions were confirmed; he hoped this could now be used to measure the heights of mountains and changes in the weather, interpreted as changes in the weight of the atmosphere. Nevertheless he was involved in a long controversy about whether he really had created an artificial vacuum, for many then still held the belief in 'horror vacui'—a true vacuum is impossible in nature. The argument led him to treat air as a compressible fluid in his *Treatise of the Weight of the Mass of the Air*; he then proceeded to discuss the behaviour of the incompressible fluid, water, in his *Treatise of the Equilibrium of Fluids*. Here he demonstrated what became known as Pascal's Principle, that in a fluid at rest the pressure is transmitted equally in all directions. He was able to relate the state of equilibrium between two connected columns of water of different diameter to the law of the lever, and so link hydrostatics to general mechanics. He saw this principle could be used in machinery. Much later the hydraulic press and similar devices were derived from it.

All this research was done before Pascal was thirty—in 1654 he had an intense religious experience, and gave up science,

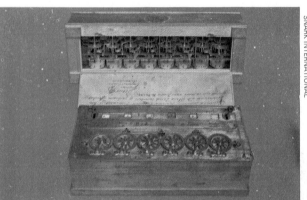

Top: Pascal, physicist, mathematician and religious thinker, crammed a lot into a relatively short life in spite of bad health.
Bottom: Pascal's calculating machine, reputedly invented when he was 19. A set of dials worked gears which turned drums bearing numerals. Each figure was dialled in turn, the sum appearing in the window.

mathematics and technology, except for some work on the solution of the cycloid (undertaken to distract his mind from toothache) and the promotion of a scheme for urban public transport. He was drawn into religious controversy; notes for a defence of Christianity were published as his *Pensées* (thoughts) after his death. More conscious than his contemporaries of the implications of the new physics for his religion, these thoughts were as incisive and original as his scientific work. But these last years of his life were dominated by illness and pain; he died before he was forty, having packed three careers into such a short working life.

PASTA MAKING

The word 'pasta' comes from the Italian term *pasta alimentare* which means alimentary or food paste, and is a generic name for various food products such as spaghetti, macaroni, vermicelli, tagliatelle, lasagna and so on. The basic pasta ingredients are *durum semolina* and water, but sometimes other foods are included, such as eggs or spinach. Durum semolina, so called because it comes from a variety of wheat which is noted for its hardness, is that part of the grain which is not reduced during milling to the fineness of particle size of flour.

Contrary to popular belief, pasta itself is not particularly fattening in comparison with some other foods. In nutritional terms, it contains 11 to 12% protein (in the dry state), the vitamins B_1, B_2 and nicotinic acid (niacin), and the minerals calcium and iron. The calorific value of pasta before cooking is 103 kcal/oz (1 kilocalorie = 1 food Calorie = 1000 heat calories), which is equivalent to 34 kcal/oz after cooking, since the pasta gains considerably in weight by absorbing water.

Manufacture

In early commercial production, replacing what was once a 'home' industry, batch processes were used to mix, knead and extrude the dough. The pasta was cut by a rotating knife as it was extruded, or by hand in the case of long shapes such as spaghetti. Batch manufacturing, however, is obsolete and the modern industry uses continuous processes.

Production begins with the raw materials being fed into the mixer at a predetermined rate and in proportion to the desired composition of the product. Different grades of semolina may be blended together. This involves the use of two or more silos, the rate of delivery of each semolina to the mixing area being controlled by a computerized system in most modern factories. The semolina, or blend, is fed to the mixer by a vibrator, the flow rate being controlled by the frequency of vibration. Water is fed to the mixer either volumetrically or by forced flow through an orifice of fixed diameter. Fail-safe devices are fitted to stop the flow should one ingredient fail to arrive correctly.

The type of mixer generally used consists of a horizontal trough along which is a centrally positioned shaft bearing arms or paddles which rotate continually. The ingredients are fed in at one end of the trough and by the action of the shaft gradually move to the other end, the mixing being effected by the rotating paddles. The mix then passes to another trough mixer, which is held under vacuum to prevent the inclusion of air bubbles in the final product, and here the water and semolina mixture is converted to a dough. It is claimed that the vacuum condition also improves the colour and general appearance of the product.

The shaft at the discharge end of the second mixer is formed into a 'worm' (ARCHIMEDEAN SCREW) which has the action of further kneading the dough as it passes along it and of building up a considerable pressure within the enclosed space, (about 100 kg/cm² or 1420 psi). Finally the dough is extruded through a die which consists of a large number of holes whose size and shape determine the type of pasta being produced.

The materials used in the construction of the mixing and

Below: modern spaghetti production. The spaghetti is extruded through a die as continuous strands which are cut and draped over a bar for conveying to the drying section. Loose strands and other cut remnants are collected below and recycled.

Bottom left: the blender for the dry semolina, water and any other ingredients such as egg or spinach which gradually form a dough.

Bottom right: macaroni drying in Naples early this century.

BASSANO/BUITONI

RASSANO/BUITONI

STAATSBIBLIOTHEK BERLIN

extrusion equipment are normally stainless steel or bronze. Occasionally the internal surfaces are coated with PTFE ('Teflon'), which is considered to result in a smoother surface on the pasta.

On extrusion small pieces of pasta such as shells and short macaroni (known as *short cut*) are produced by a rotating knife which passes over the surface of the die. The speed at which the knife rotates determines the size of the pasta.

Drying   After cutting, the pasta, which is still wet and flexible, must be dried and careful handling is necessary to maintain the shape. Spaghetti is dried by dropping the strands over bars, fitted to an endless chain system which moves very slowly through a drying tunnel. Short cut pasta is dried either on trays which are mechanically loaded on to a continually moving system or by tumbling.

It is not a simple drying operation, since cracking will occur if the pasta is dried too quickly. To avoid this the outer surface of the pasta is allowed to dry followed by a period of 'relaxation' to ensure that the moisture content throughout the pasta comes to equilibrium. So first the pasta surface is rapidly pre-dried to prevent the pieces from sticking together and to reduce the moisture content from about 30% to 21%. Then the pasta enters the drying tunnel and is subjected to alternate periods of drying and relaxation, until the moisture content is reduced to 12%. This results in a product with a shelf-life of at least a year, providing the packaging is adequate. The time taken to dry pasta depends on its shape and the type of machinery used. Spaghetti, for example, normally takes 24 hours.

PATERNOSTER LIFT (see lift)
PELTON WHEEL (see turbine)

Above: this is a pasta die which is attached to the extruder. The dough is extruded through the apertures which, in this die, produce macaroni—hence the centrally positioned pins.

Below: semolina is fed to the mixer at a rate regulated by a vibrator, while the correct amount of water is added simultaneously. Paddles blend the ingredients to a smooth dough which is extruded through a die, shaped for a particular type of pasta. Finally the pasta is dried under carefully controlled conditions.

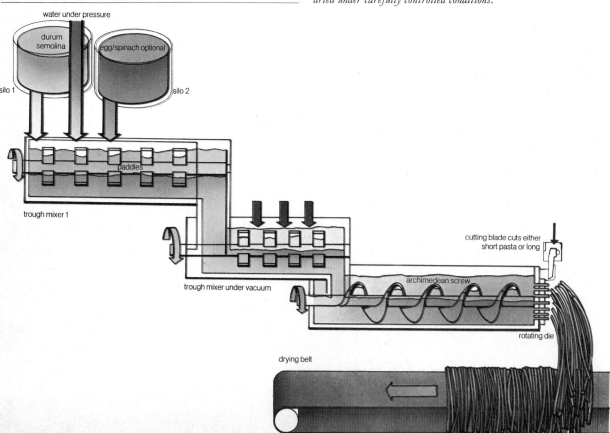

PENDULUM

A pendulum is basically any suspended object that is free to swing. The term may also be applied to an object suspended on a spring and free to oscillate vertically, and to one suspended on a wire and free to twist to and fro. Pendulums are applied in many devices, usually for their time-keeping properties: a pendulum's swings all take the same time, provided they are small.

The physicist speaks of a *simple pendulum*. An ideal simple pendulum would be a weight of negligible volume, the *bob*, suspended on a cord of negligible weight. It is contrasted with a *compound pendulum*, one whose weight cannot be regarded as concentrated at a single point. An example of the latter would be a rod free to swing about one end.

The *period* of a pendulum is its time of swing from, say, its extreme left-hand position back to the same point. The period of a simple pendulum that was completely free of frictional resistance would be independent of the weight of the bob. But the longer the pendulum the longer its period: the period is proportional to the square root of the length. Thus, a doubling of the period is brought about by lengthening the pendulum by a factor of four. Clock pendulums are finely regulated by raising or lowering the bob by tiny amounts.

The pendulum's period also depends on the effective strength of gravity. A pendulum at the equator beats very slightly more slowly than it would at the poles. Gravity is weaker at the equator, because the radius of the Earth is greater there. In addition, points on the equator travel at a thousand miles per hour (1600 km/h), because of the daily rotation of the Earth. This gives rise to a CENTRIFUGAL FORCE that effectively reduces the pull of gravity.

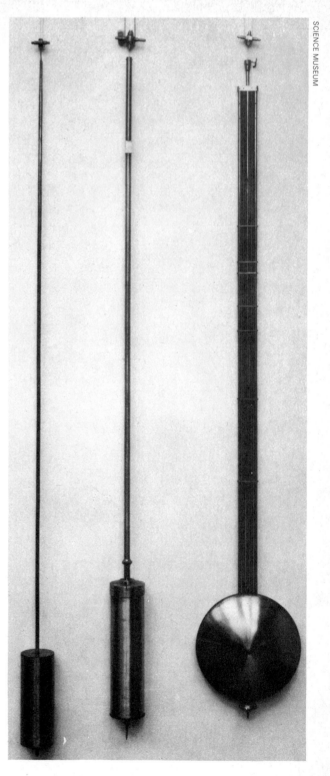

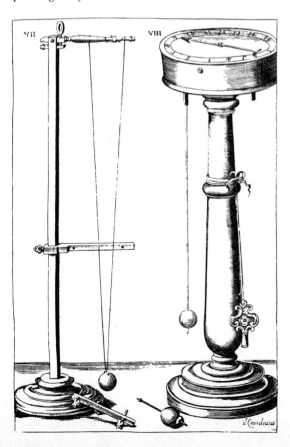

Left: a bifilar (two wire) pendulum described by the Florence Academy of Experiments in 1691. The two wires restricted the direction of movement and the movable bar enabled the length to be varied. The other device probably counted swings.

Above: three types of pendulum: the uncompensated bob; Graham's mercury compensated bob; and Harrison's gridiron pendulum.

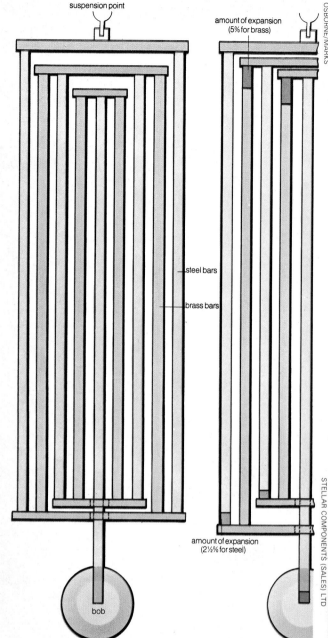

suspension point

amount of expansion
(5% for brass)

steel bars

brass bars

amount of expansion
(2½% for steel)

bob

OSBORNE/MARKS

A 'seconds' pendulum is one that takes a second to make a left-to-right swing, and an equal time to make the return, thus having a period of two seconds. At any place, the seconds pendulum has a length close to a metre (about 39 inches).

On other planetary bodies, the period of a pendulum would be very different from its terrestrial value. On the Moon, whose gravity is one-sixth that of the Earth's, a one-metre pendulum would take $2\frac{1}{2}$ seconds to make a left-to-right swing.

The best-known application of the pendulum is in regulating CLOCKS. This use was suggested by Leonardo da VINCI and by GALILEO, but the first practical pendulum clock was made by Christiaan HUYGENS in 1656. In a pendulum clock a slowly descending weight drives the hands, and the pendulum controls the rate at which the hands advance. Some of the energy released by the weight is used to give the pendulum an impulse on each swing and so keep it moving.

The metal rod of a clock pendulum will expand when the temperature rises, and contract when it falls. Some kinds of pendulum have been constructed to overcome this, such as the

Below: a pair of pendulums is used on this car thief protection device. If the car is tampered with, the movement will cause the inner pendulum to touch the outer, thus completing an alarm circuit.

Far right: this elegant clock movement, made by Visbagh of the Hague in 1700, uses the cycloidal cheeks at the pendulum's point of suspension to correct for large angles of swing.

Left: the principle of the gridiron pendulum is shown here in a much exaggerated form for clarity. Brass expands about twice as much as steel: here the expansions are given as 5% and 2½% respectively, impossible in practice as the metals would melt. The amount of expansion of each is shown shaded in the right-hand diagram, at the higher temperature. The pendulum stays the same overall length.

STELLAR COMPONENTS (SALES) LTD

Subsequent positions of a swinging pendulum. At either end of its swing, the restoring force of gravity just equals the energy which makes it swing and it hangs briefly before it swings back again. The period of the pendulum varies with the square root of its length.

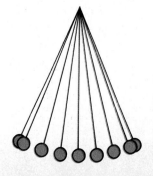

'gridiron' pendulum, made of alternating rods of brass and steel. Brass changes its length proportionately more than does steel for a given temperature change. Upward expansion of the brass rods in the grid compensates for downward expansion of the steel.

Another kind of temperature-compensating pendulum uses mercury in a jar as a bob. The upward expansion of the mercury compensates for the downward expansion of the pendulum rod. Nowadays pendulum rods are likely to be made of the nickel-steel alloy Invar, which shows little length-change with temperature.

Another timekeeping use of the pendulum is in the musician's METRONOME. This uses a compound pendulum, having a weight mounted below the centre of gravity and another mounted above. The centre of gravity, and hence effective length of the pendulum, can be altered by moving the top weight up and down. Hence the metronome can be made to tick with a varying beat.

A heavy weight hanging from a pivot about which it is free to swing will tend to remain stationary if the support is abruptly moved. This principle is used in many kinds of *seismograph*, or earthquake recorder. Two suspended weights, free to swing north–south and east–west respectively, record ground tremors in those directions. Vertical tremors are recorded by a weight hanging on a spring. The tiny relative movements of the pendulums and the ground are amplified mechanically, optically or electronically.

A moving pendulum tends to keep swinging in the same direction even if its support is turned. FOUCAULT exploited this fact in his demonstration of the Earth's rotation. A pendulum 60 metres long, suspended from the roof of the Pantheon in Paris slowly changed its apparent direction of swing during the 24 hours. In reality the pendulum was keeping the same orientation in space while the Earth turned beneath it.

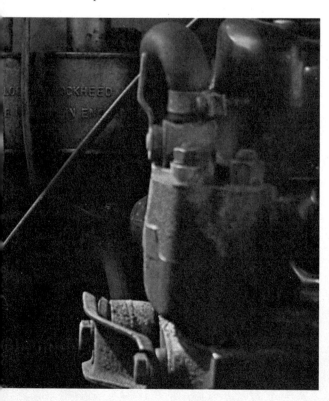

PEN RECORDER

It is frequently necessary to measure an electrical quantity that is being used as an analogue of some other varying quantity, such as temperature, pressure or strain. When a continuous and permanent record of such a varying quantity is required, a pen recorder is often used. In addition, pen recorders are frequently used to record electrical measurements such as voltage, current, power and frequency.

The purpose of a pen recorder is therefore twofold: to record instantaneous data which can also be presented by a conventional indicating instrument, and also to present data that could not readily be obtained from such an instrument. Examples of the latter use are the recording of voltage and current waveforms and of transient events during a process. Most pen recorders in use today are the electrical type, but there are some which are purely mechanical in operation, such as the aneroid barograph (see BAROMETER).

Continuous recorders A pen recorder is basically a moving coil instrument (like an AMMETER) which has a pen (in place of the normal pointer) that draws a trace on a moving chart. A common arrangement has the pen tip in contact with the moving chart, which is driven at a low and uniform speed in a direction at right angles to the pen. The path traced by the

Below: in this pen recorder, used for meteorological work, two instruments are combined into one unit. The left hand chart records wind direction and the right hand one records wind speed.

pen on to the moving chart gives a continuous record of the deflections of the recorder's moving coil, the chart being appropriately calibrated to give a measure of the variations of the physical quantity being measured.

Pen recorders can be broadly grouped into two classes; those with a vertical pen arm and those with a horizontal pen arm. The former type has the advantage that the calibrations on the chart are straight, whereas in the latter type they are segments of circles. The pen, however, is generally heavier in the instruments with a vertical pen, since the ink must be carried in the pen at the end of the arm (some instruments carry the ink in a small trough into which the pen nib dips periodically).

Instruments with a horizontal pen generally carry the ink in a well at the pen's axis, and the ink flows by capillary action along the arm to the writing point.

Pen recorders are often classified according to their speed of response, that is, the speed at which they respond to changes in the value of the physical quantity being measured. Instruments intended to record information normally shown by conventional instruments have a typical response time, from zero to full scale deflection, of several seconds. For the purpose for which this type of instrument is used the response time is relatively unimportant and so it is not generally quoted in the maker's specifications.

A pen recorder with a moving coil movement can, however, be made to have a response time of about one tenth of a second. Here the moving parts must be as light as possible and the driv-

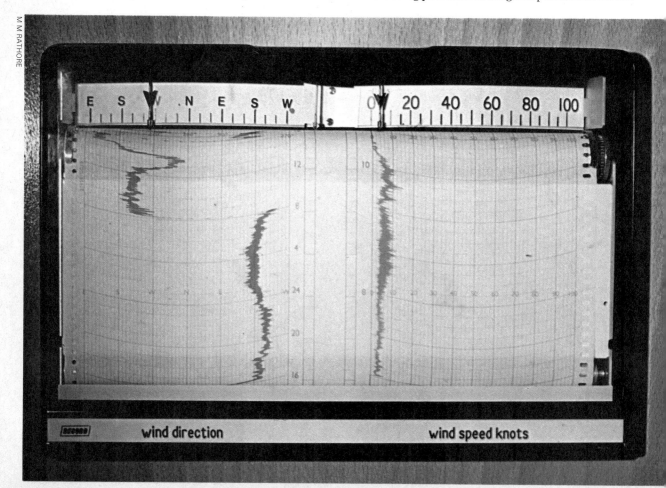

ing power must be increased. The power needed to drive a recorder with a fast response is often greater than that available from the source providing the input data. In such cases the signal from the data source may be fed to an AMPLIFIER whose output is then used to drive the recorder movement, often in conjunction with a SERVOMECHANISM.

Intermittent recorders A variation of the normal pen recorder is the intermittent type where the pen is not kept in continuous contact with the chart, but pressed against it at intervals by a 'chopper bar' mechanism. The trace appears as a series of dots as opposed to a line or graph, and is satisfactory for recording comparatively slow changes of the recorded quantity. This type of recorder is not, of course, suitable for fast response phenomena such as electrical transients.

Intermittent recorders often use a typewriter ribbon in place of liquid ink since a much longer unattended operating period is possible and a greater range of ambient working temperature is permissable.

Uses There are countless applications for electrical pen recorders, or chart recorders as they are sometimes called, in process industries, laboratories, in fact anywhere a recording of a physical variable needs to be retained for further examination.

The ways in which the chart can be marked vary considerably;

for example, some recorders use a stylus to mark sensitized paper instead of using liquid ink, and others use ball point pens on ordinary paper.

A very sensitive form of chart recorder used in such applications as ECG and EEG machines (see ELECTRONICS IN MEDICINE) deflects a spot of light on to a light-sensitive chart. In the case of an ECG machine, the movement is based on a silver-plated quartz filament suspended in a magnetic field. The minute electric currents produced by the contractions of the heart muscles are picked up by electrodes attached to the patient's body, and passed through the filament, which undergoes a deflection whose direction and magnitude will depend on the direction and strength of the current.

The movement of the filament is projected, by means of an optical system, as a spot of light on to a moving strip of paper which is coated with a light-sensitive compound. When no current is flowing through the filament the trace is a straight line, but currents associated with the muscular action of the heart cause the spot of light to oscillate and thus trace a typical curve on the light-sensitive chart. Any irregularities of the heart function appear as corresponding irregularities in the curve, enabling the heart specialist to diagnose the disease or other cause of these deviations from the normal pattern.

Below: a typical pen recorder, showing the chart drive arrangement, the scale and pen, and the pen drive servo motor, which is the horizontal cylinder at the centre of the instrument.

Below: an end view of a similar instrument to the one on the left. This one has two pens and so two pen drive servo motors are used. Hollow tubes carry the ink to the pen tips.

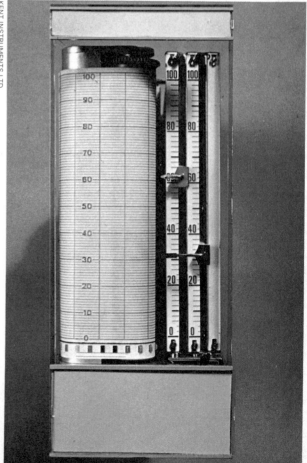

KENT INSTRUMENTS LTD

PERCUSSION INSTRUMENTS

Percussion instruments fall into two groups: the *membrano-phones*, those with skins which are struck, and the *idiophones*, those made of materials so dense and hard that they vibrate sonorously when struck. Instruments in both groups are struck, either directly or through a mechanism, or they sound as the result of some other motion, for example when a movement of the player or his garments, or of an animal or its harness, shakes the instrument so that pellets within or without rattle against it. Such rattles, originally made of seed pods, are among the earliest instruments known to man. Also of great antiquity are *slit drums*, made of fallen trees or hollow logs, and some of the *concussion* instruments, such as pairs of stones or bars of wood which are clashed together. All these instruments are represented in our orchestras and are continually developing and altering in response to changes in musical style.

Idiophones While our concussion sticks, the *claves*, are much the same as those used by Neolithic man, the metal con-cusion instruments, the *cymbals*, have altered greatly over the centuries. Mediaeval cymbals were small, thick, high-domed instruments producing a bell-like sound; those of the 18th and early 19th centuries were larger and thinner, yet different from those in use today. The modern instrument is forged from a BRASS, the exact constituents of which are a well-kept secret, being spun and hammered under so exact a control that cymbals can be produced with long or short vibration periods, accord-ing to whether they are required as *crash*, *ride*, *high-hat* or *orchestral* cymbals. The high-hat cymbal, for example, is the dance-band drummer's top cymbal on which he sets the beat, and will have a shorter vibration period than orchestral cymbals.

Sets of wooden bars of differing musical pitches have been

Above: orchestral kettledrums, developed from the drums of the 15th century Turkish cavalry. The picture shows the tensioning devices used for tuning the drums.

Below: a Guatemalan marimba. The modern xylophone is an excellent example of how musical instruments evolve: African slaves in America copied European instruments, which were then developed by Guatemalans and Mexicans and reintroduced to Europe.

used in South East Asia and in Africa since prehistoric times and have diffused from there to the rest of the world. The pitch of a bar depends upon the density and thickness; the tone can be improved and the pitch lowered by thinning the bar under its centre, as has long been known in Africa but realized in the West only within this century. A simple form of *xylophone* was used in Europe from the 15th to the early 20th centuries, until the modern instrument, with its broad bars and metal resonating tubes, was imported from America, where it had been developed from the Mexican and Guatemalan *marimbas* which were copies of instruments built in the New World by African slaves. Instruments of similar shape but with metal bars are also used: the *glockenspiel* [orchestral bells] with small steel bars and the *vibraphone*, which has wider and thinner bars of alloy with, in the tops of each of the resonating tubes which hang below the bars, revolving fans which open and close the resonators, so producing the throbbing vibration characteristic of the instrument.

Other metal instruments in common use include the *triangle*, a steel bar bent into triangular shape; the *gong* and the bells. The gong is a great dish of forged bronze which originated in western Asia. Orchestral instruments were imported from China, where the best were made, until, within the last thirty years, a European firm discovered the necessary technology. Large bells have been cast in Europe since mediaeval times (see BELLS), often by itinerant bell-founders working in the churchyard, but so great a mass of bronze is impracticable in the orchestra; steel plates or brass tubes are used instead.

Membranophones The earliest of the membranophones was probably the *kettledrum*, originally, as the name implies, a cooking vessel covered with a skin. The orchestral kettledrums, the *timpani*, were adopted from the cavalry of the invading Turkish armies in the 15th century. Timpani are tuned to definite pitches, their pitch varying according to the diameter, thickness and tension of the skin or drum-head. The heads of the Turkish drums were tensioned with a network of thongs, but in Europe tensioning by screwing metal rods into brackets soon became general and is still used today.

During the 19th century various methods of quicker tuning were invented, ranging from a single handle, the tension of

Below: a Balinese Gamelan orchestra. Bamboo flutes, bowed string instruments and the human voice are used to carry the melody; the music is complex rhythmically and highly developed polyphonically.

which was transmitted by cables equally round the head, to a foot pedal which controlled a set of tensioning rods. The *pedal timpani*, on which the drummer can play and tune simultaneously, are now in almost universal use and are played in sets of from two to four drums, occasionally more. Soft-headed beaters are normally used; their manipulation requires considerable skill, for the longer the beater remains in contact with the head, the less sound is produced. Total relaxation of the wrists and very fast reactions are necessary.

The *side drum*, or *snare drum*, was also introduced in the 15th century, but differs from the timpani in that it has a cylindrical body or shell with a head at each end and is not intended to produce a note of definite pitch. It is played with wooden sticks and has a set of snares, strands of wire or gut, running below the lower head which give it a dry, rattling sound. The sound is so short that it is impossible to produce a continuous roll with single strokes, and the player must double his striking speed by forcing each stroke to rebound.

Other sizes of drum are also used: the *tenor* drum, a larger version of the side drum but without snares, and the *bass* drum, which is larger still, from three to six feet (about 1 to 2 m) in diameter. In popular and dance music a smaller bass drum, struck by a foot pedal, is employed and is accompanied by several sizes of *tom-tom*, smaller two-headed drums also without snares. A single headed drum with a cylindrical frame is the *tambourine*, which has small metal cymbals let into the frame to provide an added jingle.

Other instruments of recent importation from folk musics of different parts of the world include the rattles such as the *maracas*, the *castanets*, *wood blocks*, *bongos*, *conga drums* and the most recently invented percussion instruments, the West Indian *steel drums*, which are made from the tops and bottoms of oil drums.

Below: a Caribbean steel band drummer. The drums are made from the tops and bottoms of oil drums; music and instruments continue to evolve out of whatever materials are available.

PERIODIC TABLE

The modern definition of an ELEMENT as a material which can neither be created nor destroyed was first proposed by Robert BOYLE in 1661. The direct relationship between elements and atoms however was not understood until the start of the 19th century, when DALTON proposed his atomic theory. Dalton's assertion that 'all the atoms of the same element are identical in all respects, especially in weight' led naturally to the experimental determination of the relative masses, or *atomic weights*, of different types of atom.

In 1863 Newlands observed that on arranging elements in order of increasing atomic weight: 'the eighth element, starting from a given one, is a kind of repetition of the first, like the eight notes in an octave of music'. Newlands had discovered the essence of the *periodic law* of the elements, and it is ironic that the London Chemical Society refused to publish his work. Six years later MENDELEEV proposed his periodic law; he demonstrated convincingly that a periodic relationship existed between the properties of an element and its atomic weight. However, on arranging the elements in the form of a table so as to display this relationship, he found he had to leave gaps to preserve strict periodicity. He correctly identified these gaps with elements as yet undiscovered and went on to make some remarkable predictions. For example, there was a gap between gallium and arsenic in the fourth row of his periodic table immediately below silicon, and on the basis of this information he was able to provide a startlingly detailed description of many of the physical and chemical properties of the missing element which, when it was actually discovered 15 years later, was named germanium.

Periodic nature of atomic properties The vast majority of an atom's mass is accounted for by the PROTONS and NEUTRONS which form the NUCLEUS. On moving along the periodic table, each successively heavier atom has one more positively charged proton in its nucleus and one more negatively charged electron surrounding it. The number of neutrons also increases, there usually being a few more neutrons than protons in any nucleus. Every atom of a particular element will have the same number of protons in its nucleus; this number is called the *atomic number* and characterizes the element. The number of neutrons in the nucleus may vary slightly, and this accounts for the various ISOTOPES of an element, which have almost identical physical and chemical properties and occupy the same position in the periodic table. Elements normally consist of several isotopes in fairly constant proportions, and this accounts for the fact that atomic weights are not usually whole numbers, and also for the anomaly that argon, A, has an atomic weight slightly greater than potassium, K, which immediately succeeds it in the periodic table.

The chemical properties of an atom depend on the organization of the ELECTRONS surrounding the nucleus (see BOND, chemical). The number of electrons in a neutral atom will equal the number of protons and therefore the atomic number of the element. The electrons of a free atom occupy very well defined QUANTUM *states*, each with a unique energy. The states are broadly grouped into divisions each designated by a *principal quantum number*. The states within each division are further classified into s, p, d and f types. For the first principal quantum number only s type states are possible, for the second s and p types, for the third s, p and d types, and so on. The various types can accept only a certain number of electrons; s states have a maximum capacity of two electrons, p states have a maximum capacity of six electrons, d states have a maximum

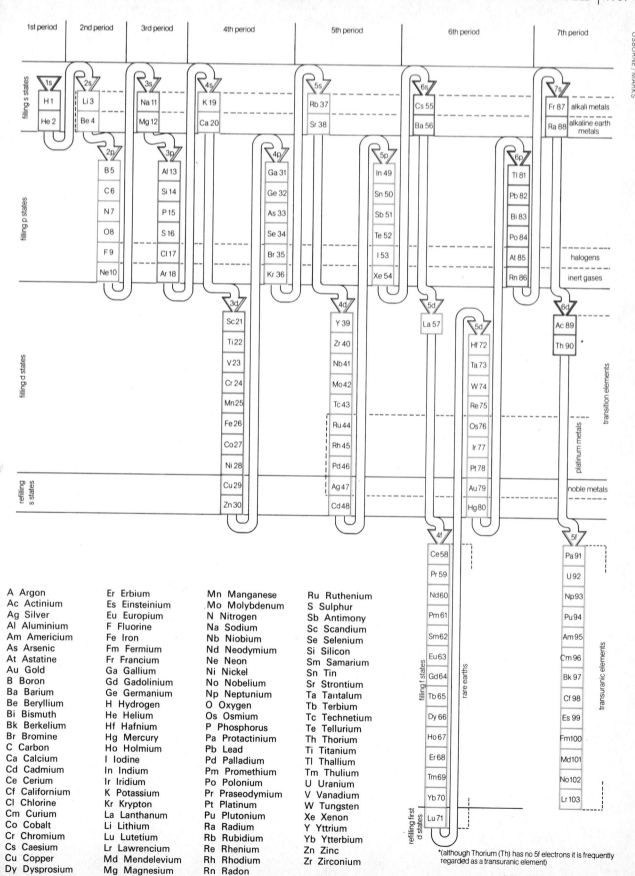

OSBORNE / MARKS

1st period	2nd period	3rd period	4th period	5th period	6th period	7th period

filling s states

1s H 1 — 2s Li 3 — 3s Na 11 — 4s K 19 — 5s Rb 37 — 6s Cs 55 — 7s Fr 87 — alkali metals

He 2 — Be 4 — Mg 12 — Ca 20 — Sr 38 — Ba 56 — Ra 88 — alkaline earth metals

filling p states

2p: B 5, C 6, N 7, O 8, F 9, Ne 10

3p: Al 13, Si 14, P 15, S 16, Cl 17, Ar 18

4p: Ga 31, Ge 32, As 33, Se 34, Br 35, Kr 36

5p: In 49, Sn 50, Sb 51, Te 52, I 53, Xe 54

6p: Tl 81, Pb 82, Bi 83, Po 84, At 85 (halogens), Rn 86 (inert gases)

filling d states

3d: Sc 21, Ti 22, V 23, Cr 24, Mn 25, Fe 26, Co 27, Ni 28

4d: Y 39, Zr 40, Nb 41, Mo 42, Tc 43, Ru 44, Rh 45, Pd 46

5d: La 57; Hf 72, Ta 73, W 74, Re 75, Os 76, Ir 77, Pt 78

6d: Ac 89, Th 90 *

transition elements

platinum metals

refilling s states

Cu 29, Zn 30

Ag 47, Cd 48

Au 79, Hg 80

noble metals

filling f states

4f: Ce 58, Pr 59, Nd 60, Pm 61, Sm 62, Eu 63, Gd 64, Tb 65, Dy 66, Ho 67, Er 68, Tm 69, Yb 70

refilling first d states: Lu 71

5f: Pa 91, U 92, Np 93, Pu 94, Am 95, Cm 96, Bk 97, Cf 98, Es 99, Fm 100, Md 101, No 102, Lr 103

rare earths

transuranic elements

A Argon	Er Erbium	Mn Manganese	Ru Ruthenium
Ac Actinium	Es Einsteinium	Mo Molybdenum	S Sulphur
Ag Silver	Eu Europium	N Nitrogen	Sb Antimony
Al Aluminium	F Fluorine	Na Sodium	Sc Scandium
Am Americium	Fe Iron	Nb Niobium	Se Selenium
As Arsenic	Fm Fermium	Nd Neodymium	Si Silicon
At Astatine	Fr Francium	Ne Neon	Sm Samarium
Au Gold	Ga Gallium	Ni Nickel	Sn Tin
B Boron	Gd Gadolinium	No Nobelium	Sr Strontium
Ba Barium	Ge Germanium	Np Neptunium	Ta Tantalum
Be Beryllium	H Hydrogen	O Oxygen	Tb Terbium
Bi Bismuth	He Helium	Os Osmium	Tc Technetium
Bk Berkelium	Hf Hafnium	P Phosphorus	Te Tellurium
Br Bromine	Hg Mercury	Pa Protactinium	Th Thorium
C Carbon	Ho Holmium	Pb Lead	Ti Titanium
Ca Calcium	I Iodine	Pd Palladium	Tl Thallium
Cd Cadmium	In Indium	Pm Promethium	Tm Thulium
Ce Cerium	Ir Iridium	Po Polonium	U Uranium
Cf Californium	K Potassium	Pr Praseodymium	V Vanadium
Cl Chlorine	Kr Krypton	Pt Platinum	W Tungsten
Cm Curium	La Lanthanum	Pu Plutonium	Xe Xenon
Co Cobalt	Li Lithium	Ra Radium	Y Yttrium
Cr Chromium	Lu Lutetium	Rb Rubidium	Yb Ytterbium
Cs Caesium	Lr Lawrencium	Re Rhenium	Zn Zinc
Cu Copper	Md Mendelevium	Rh Rhodium	Zr Zirconium
Dy Dysprosium	Mg Magnesium	Rn Radon	

*(although Thorium (Th) has no 5f electrons it is frequently regarded as a transuranic element)

capacity of ten electrons, and f states have a maximum capacity of 14. A given state (or electron occupying that state) is described by writing first the principal quantum number followed by the state type, for example '3s'. One can think of an atom as being surrounded by a large number of available electron states, which are filled by the electrons roughly in order of increasing quantum number. For example the helium atom, He, has an atomic number of two and hence two electrons which occupy the states of lowest energy, in other words both the 1s states. Argon, A, on the other hand, has 18 electrons and the 1s, 2s, 2p, 3s and 3p states are filled. The electronic configuration of argon can be written $1s^2 2s^2 p^6 3s^2 p^6$, the superscript numbers denoting the number of electrons in each energy state, that is to say two in the 1s state, two in the 2s state, six in the 2p state, two in the 3s state and six in the 3p state, making 18 in all.

In terms of electrons, the periodic table represents the progressive filling of electron shells, and the similarity in properties between two elements which lie one above the other in the table can be seen as a similarity in their electron configuration. For example, fluorine (see HALOGEN) has the electron configuration $1s^2 2s^2 p^5$ and CHLORINE, which is very similar in many of its physical and chemical properties, has the configuration $1s^2 2s^2 p^6 3s^2 p^5$; in both cases the outer electron structure is $s^2 p^5$ and this is what counts in determining the properties of an element. The similarity in the properties of elements which have the same number of p states occupied by outer electrons is most marked. Compare for example, lithium, sodium and potassium (see ALKALI METAL); beryllium, magnesium and calcium (see ALKALINE EARTH METAL); CARBON, SILICON and germanium; the halogens; and the INERT GASES. In inert gas atoms, the outer electrons exactly fill a p state and are strongly bound to the nucleus. It is therefore difficult for any to be removed for the purpose of chemical bonding, and also the atom is not predisposed to accept any electrons from an adjacent atom, no matter how readily available.

Periodic arrangement of the elements One proton with one 1s electron surrounding it forms a HYDROGEN atom. The addition of a further electron, proton and two neutrons gives a helium atom which has a complete electron shell (the 1s shell) and is an inert gas. Hydrogen and helium together form the first *period* of the periodic table. The next atom, lithium, Li, has (in addition to the two 1s electrons) one 2s electron and beryllium, Be, has two. The six elements from boron, B, to neon, Ne, correspond to the progressive filling of the six 2p states. The third period is similar to the second in that it involves the filling of s and p states; the two 3s states corresponding to sodium, Na, and magnesium, Mg, and the six 2p states corresponding to the series from aluminium, Al,

Crookes' spiral form of the periodic table, which expressed his ideas of the generation and relation of the elements. 19th century chemists speculated a lot about the possible connections between elements. Some suggested that matter was continuously created from energy in outer space.

to argon, A. The next atom after argon is potassium, K, which starts the fourth period. At first sight one might expect potassium to start the filling of the 3d states, but instead its outer electron joins one of the 4s states and as a result the element is a typical alkali metal. Calcium, Ca, has two 4s electrons and it is with the next element, scandium, Sc, that the filling of the 3d states commences. At nickel, Ni, eight out of ten available 3d states are occupied in addition to the two 4s ones. The next element, COPPER, Cu, however, has all of its ten 3d states occupied, the extra electron having come from one of the 4s states, which is itself filled again on moving to ZINC, Zn. Elements which have incomplete d states are called TRANSITION ELEMENTS. The next six electrons fill the 4p states to give the series from gallium, Ga, to krypton, Kr. The fifth period is very similar to the fourth with the 5s states being filled first, followed by the 4d and 5p. The fourteen 4f states are not filled until after the two 6s and one of the 5d states in the next period. The elements corresponding to the filling of the 4f states are known as the *rare earths*. After the rare earth series the remainder of the 5d states are occupied, and finally the sixth period is completed with the filling of the 6p states in the series thallium, Tl, to radon, Rn. The seventh period is only partially complete, but new elements are added to it from time to time as they are discovered, or rather made artificially for a few milliseconds in a PARTICLE ACCELERATOR (see SYNTHETIC ELEMENT). The quest for new elements is spurred on by the theoretical prediction of an 'island of stability' in the region of atomic number 110, which means that if physicists succeed in actually making element 110 then it may be stable enough to form a solid material.

The marked similarity in the properties of elements occurring at similar positions in the various periods is emphasized by ordering the table vertically into *groups*. Traditionally the groups were numbered I_A to VIII_A and I_B to VIII_B, but in the light of detailed knowledge of electronic arrangement which we now have, this labelling is a little arbitrary in some places. The alkali metals and alkaline earth metals constitute groups I_A and II_A, the first five of the transition metal groups constitute groups III_A to VII_A and the next three (for example iron, Fe, cobalt, Co, and nickel, Ni, in the fourth period) are all put into group VIII_A. The noble metals form group I_B; and zinc, cadmium, Cd, and MERCURY, Hg, are put into group II_B. The six elements of each period which correspond to the filling of the p states then constitute groups III_B. Rare earths and the corresponding elements in the seventh period (called the *actinons* or *transuranic elements*) are not included in the classification into groups. It is apparent that there is little point in dividing the transition metals into groups as the properties of these elements do not change systematically along the series. The reason for this is that the arrangement of the outer d electrons does not influence the bonding properties as much as in the case of outer s and p electrons.

Today, the group numbers tend to be used only for the elements corresponding to the filling of the s and p states, where the difference in properties of successive elements is most marked, and hence the similarities between elements in equivalent positions in different periods clearly apparent. The group numbers are used in particular to describe the semiconducting materials formed by combining a group III element such as gallium with an element from group V such as arsenic (III–V SEMICONDUCTORS), or an element from group II such as cadium with one from group VI such as SULPHUR (II–VI semiconductors).

PERISCOPE

Periscopes are usually associated with SUBMARINES, but they have many other uses, for example observing the amount of smoke passing through a funnel or chimney, bridge observations in destroyers, remote viewing of test rocket and guided missile motors, viewing aircraft models in wind tunnels, observations in atomic reactors, looking out of army tanks, looking over trees for forest fires, and examining bores of small diameter tubes. There is even one in the House of Commons in London enabling the heating engineer to adjust conditions to suit the number of people present.

The simplest type of periscope, which was used in the trenches in World War I, has a tube with a mirror at the top and a viewing mirror at the bottom. To have a reasonable field of view, the mirrors have to be close together.

Submarine periscopes In a submarine periscope the top window is sometimes 50 ft (15 m) above the eye lens and the tube only up to 10 in (25 cm) in diameter, so a number of TELESCOPE lens systems are fitted to maintain the field of view. Two types of periscope are fitted in submarines, a monocular type with a small diameter top tube, and a binocular type with a larger top tube for light gathering. Binocular vision is achieved by fitting two aligned optical systems into the same tube. Because of an optical illusion, objects seen through a tube look smaller than they really are, and it is therefore necessary to introduce some magnification into a periscope system. The normal LENS system gives a magnification of six, but a $\frac{1}{4}$ times diminishing telescope can be introduced to give an overall magnification of $1\frac{1}{2}$. This gives the observer a more accurate impression of object size.

Light enters the periscope through a top window. It is reflected by a PRISM which directs the rays down the periscope tube, through the diminishing telescope (if inserted), and through an *objective lens* which brings the rays to a *focal point*, where a *graticule* is fitted. The graticule is usually a cross etched into a lens to act as a sighting mark. The light then passes through another objective lens. To minimize vibration of the image in the eye lens when the submarine is moving,

Below: a periscope in use in a submarine. Modern periscopes, as used in submarines, are designed to accommodate various items of auxiliary equipment including rangefinders and sextants.

VICKERS LTD

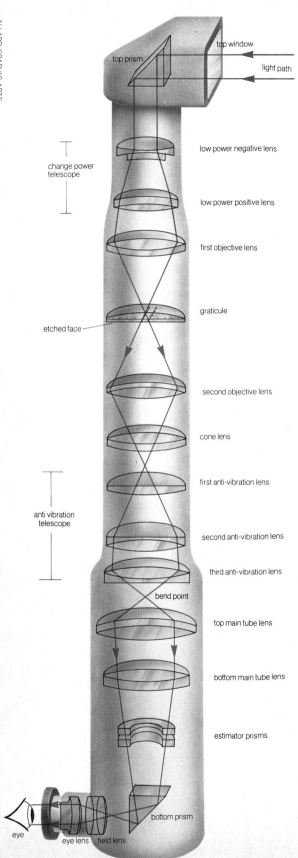

top window

light path

top prism

low power negative lens

change power
telescope

low power positive lens

first objective lens

graticule

etched face

second objective lens

cone lens

first anti-vibration lens

anti vibration
telescope

second anti-vibration lens

third anti-vibration lens

bend point

top main tube lens

bottom main tube lens

estimator prisms

bottom prism

eye

eye lens   field lens

*Above: using a periscope to direct the fire of a gun (1876). Such
devices were of limited use because the field of view narrows as the
two mirrors are moved further apart, but suitable in the trenches.*

Below: periscope undergoing final inspection before installation.

*Left: a diagrammatic representation of a typical submarine
periscope lens system. To save space, the main tube of the
periscope, between the two main tube lenses, has been omitted. The
anti-vibration telescope ensures that the image will remain steady
when the submarine is under way.*

another telescope system is fitted which directs the image formed at the graticule to a point where vibration has the least effect. The light then passes in parallel rays between the two main tube lenses. The bottom main tube lens focuses the rays through a prism, which reflects the rays into the horizontal, and on to a *field lens* where the image is observed through an *eye lens* which can be focused to suit the individual. In binocular periscopes a second pair of prisms is fitted in the eyepiece, enabling the distance between the eye lenses to be adjusted. It is possible to introduce another prism into the system for mounting a camera.

The top prism can be pivoted vertically to scan above and below the horizon by means of a rack and pinion mechanism operated through pulleys and wires from the *left training handle* at the bottom of the periscope. The diminishing, or change power telescope can be inserted or removed from the lens system in the same way, but the control is located on the *right training handle*.

A pair of contra-rotating prisms, called the *estimator*, can be inserted above the bottom prism by means of a handle and gearing. When rotated, these prisms produce a ghost image. If the base of the ghost image is placed at the top of the real image, the angle subtended by this movement can be read on a scale, and if the height of the object is known, its range can be calculated. The periscope is usually equipped with a small calculator for this purpose.

In some periscopes a SEXTANT is fitted. The light for this system enters through a window below the top main window. Normally, a horizon has to be visible for sextant readings to be taken, but in some cases it is possible to take sightings when no horizon is visible by introducing an artificial horizon. This is achieved by a complex system of lenses, calculators and a gyro (see GYROSCOPE) built into the periscope.

The periscope is supported by a bracket, called a *crosshead*, which is attached to twin hydraulic hoists which move the periscope up or down through a gland and bearings so that it protrudes out of the submarine fin. In the crosshead are devices which transmit the bearings of objects to various computers in the submarine. The modern periscope is not purely for observation, it is an integral part of a submarine's weapons and navigation systems.

PERPETUAL MOTION MACHINE

The idea of constructing a machine that would operate continuously without any kind of fuel has fascinated inventors for centuries. The practical applications of such a machine would be almost limitless, as no doubt would be the financial reward to its inventor. A perpetual motion machine has, however, never been constructed, and there are very good theoretical reasons for supposing that one never will be. For obvious reasons, inventors have concentrated on designing perpetual motion machines which can be used to do useful work rather than devices which simply continue in motion without driving anything. The various designs proposed for the first type of perpetual motion machine invariably violate either the first or second law of THERMODYNAMICS.

Overbalancing wheels The first law of thermo-dynamics, sometimes called the principle of conservation of energy, states that although energy can be converted from one form to another, it can never be created or destroyed. The majority of proposals for perpetual motion machines ignore this principle, in other words they are more than 100%

Above: perpetual motion by magnetism, suggested by Athanasius Kircher in 1643. The spherical magnet A attracts the iron ball at D until it reaches E where it drops back to D again—it doesn't work.

efficient, delivering more energy than they consume. Typical of this sort of machine is the *overbalancing wheel*, which has a number of pivoted weights attached to its perimeter. The wheel is mounted vertically with its axis horizontal and the weights are arranged so that, as the wheel revolves, they will pivot so as to lie further from the axis on the descending side of the wheel than on the ascending side. The idea is that the weights on the descending side, being further from the wheel axis, will exert a greater turning force on the wheel than the weights on the ascending side and thus maintain the rotation of the wheel. What the theory ignores is that although the weights on the descending side will exert a greater turning force, there are fewer of them than on the ascending side of the wheel. The result is that the overall turning force on the wheel is zero.

One of the most famous overbalancing wheels was the one constructed by the Marquis of Worcester and demonstrated to Charles I in about 1638. The wheel was 14 ft (4.3 m) in diameter and had 40 pivoted weights each weighing 50 lb (23 kg). Since the wheel was so heavy, its momentum would have kept it going for a considerable period once it had been set in motion, and it is likely that this would have given a fairly convincing illusion of perpetual motion.

Hydraulic devices Another common proposal for a perpetual motion machine was to arrange a watermill so that it would not only grind corn, but also feed its own millstream by means of a pump attached to the water wheel. The problem here is that the amount of energy which can be extracted by allowing water to flow over a water wheel from a higher level to a lower level is precisely the same as the energy needed to raise the water again from the lower level to the higher one.

In 1686 Abbé de la Roque designed a perpetual motion device which consisted of a large bowl of water having an external tube leading from the bottom of the bowl to a point above the surface of the water. He argued that the weight of water in the bowl, being much greater than the weight of water

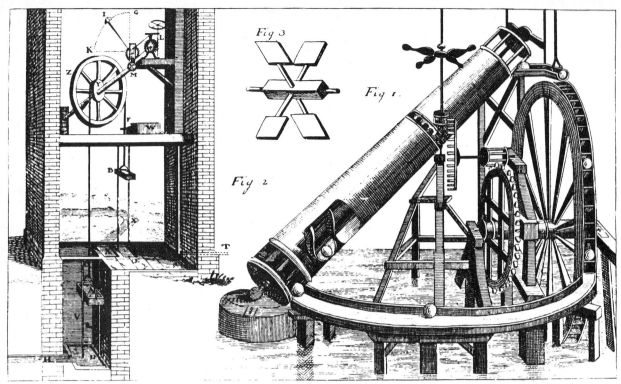

Above: in this perpetual motion machine, iron balls drive the 'water wheel' which, in turn, operates the Archimedean screw, raising the balls back to the top of the wheel. Like all perpetual motion machines, they would, if they worked, break the first law of thermo-dynamics which says that energy cannot be created out of nothing.
Below left: this machine was designed to constantly feed and circulate water through a water fountain by the principle of perpetual motion. Water is raised by the Archimedean screw which is driven by the

wheel and lead ball arrangement. The balls are arranged to be further from the wheel axis as they descend, giving a turning force.
Below: this paddle wheel consists of interconnected tubes with bellows at the extremities. The system is filled with mercury and weights are placed on one side of the bellows. On the ascent side, the weights force the mercury out of these bellows and into the bellows on the descent side which is consequently heavier, thus providing a nett turning force which keeps the wheel moving.

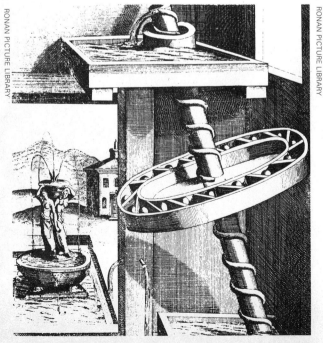

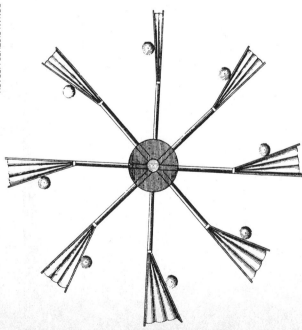

start stop lever

overbalancing wheel

fan

Above: a design of around 1900 for a road vehicle powered by an overbalancing wheel connected to the rear wheels through a mechanical linkage (not shown). An air-driven fan is also coupled to the rear wheels. Needless to say, the arrangement does not work.

in the tube, would push the water through the tube and set up a continuous circulation of water which could then be used to drive a water wheel. This machine was the forerunner of many later, more advanced designs which all failed to operate because the pressure at a given distance beneath a water surface is constant; it does not depend on the area of the water surface.

Other designs There have been many perpetual motion machines designed on electrical or magnetic principles. One such machine had a magnet fixed at the top of an inclined ramp. A ball bearing was pulled up the ramp by magnetic attraction but fell through a hole in the ramp before reaching the magnet; it then ran along a guide back to the bottom of the ramp and the cycle of events was repeated. A machine of this sort could not work because, if the magnet was strong enough to pull the ball up the ramp, it would not let it fall through the hole.

Since heat is a form of energy, it might be thought possible to extract heat from a suitable source and convert it into useful mechanical work. If this were possible, ships could be built which would use the heat energy of the ocean as their sole source of propulsive power. Unfortunately, such a system would violate the second law of thermodynamics which states that it is impossible to convert heat energy at a single temperature into mechanical energy: if the Earth was entirely at a single temperature, none of its heat energy could be utilized.

The only sort of perpetual motion machine which is theoretically possible is the type which simply continues in motion without any energy being extracted. A heavy wheel mounted in a vacuum between almost frictionless bearings would certainly continue to rotate for a long time before coming to a stop. It would not, however, rotate indefinitely because it is impossible to eliminate friction and to create a perfect vacuum. If certain metals, for example lead, are cooled to very low temperatures, their electrical resistance vanishes entirely (see SUPERCONDUCTIVITY), and an electric current will flow indefinitely in a ring of the metal without energy being supplied.

There are some devices which give an appearance of perpetual motion, but they always derive energy from some external source. Self-winding watches, for example, get their energy from movement of the wearer's wrist; a weight inside the watch is displaced each time the watch is moved and this causes it to be wound slightly. The difference between day and night-time air temperature can be used to wind clocks. The winding mechanism is operated by a bellows which expands and contracts as the air temperature changes. In this case the energy comes from the Sun heating the atmosphere in the day.

'PERSPEX' MANUFACTURE (see plastics)

PEST CONTROL

Pests include animals that attack field and plantation crops or produce such as grain, and also those that attack farm animals and man, often transmitting disease organisms to them. About a quarter of the world's food supply is consumed or destroyed by pests, mainly insects, nematodes (for example eelworms) and rodents (rats and mice), while much sickness and disease is spread by pests such as mites, ticks, mosquitos, tsetse flies and snails. Other prevalent pests include birds, millipedes, woodlice and slugs.

In planning control measures, the first essential is an accurate identification of the pest concerned and an assessment of the amount of damage it is doing so that control measures and their benefits can be costed. After that it is desirable to know its life-cycle, periods of activity and quiescence, how it overwinters and whether it originates within the field attacked or migrates in from elsewhere, what other plants it attacks and whether it feeds exposed or in concealment, and if it has natural enemies. Without some of this knowledge, control measures can only be a temporary expedient to stop an attack already under way. With more information, better measures can be planned, and attacks can sometimes be forecast and steps taken to avoid or prevent them.

Indirect control Indirect ways to control pest attack include crop rotation, choice of crop variety to avoid attack, changing the sowing date so that a critical stage of growth does not coincide with the period of activity of a particular pest, and application of fertilizer to encourage rapid early growth. Crop rotation is most effective against immobile or relatively

RENTOKIL LTD

immobile pests such as cyst-nematodes, and insects that over-winter in the soil, or pests that attack only one particular crop. Crop rotation, however, is ineffective against mobile pests, for example, birds, strong-flying insects, greenflies carried by air currents; against pests deriving their numbers from wild or semi-wild alternative food plants (such as frit flies from grassland that lay eggs on oat seedlings); or against pests such as wireworms, leatherjackets, slugs and millipedes able to feed on several crops.

Sometimes crop varieties that resist attack can be bred: oats, clover, and lucerne resistant to stem nematodes; potatoes and cereals resistant to cyst-nematodes; and raspberries and lettuce resistant to greenflies. Often, however, indirect methods are insufficiently effective and pesticides must be used.

Direct control   Poison baits, seed treatments, and sprays, dusts, or granules containing potent pesticides are various means of direct control. For pests in soil, warehouses and buildings, fumigants are normally used. These are usually liquids but sometimes powders, which vaporize and spread themselves throughout the infested area. In glasshouses, smoke canisters and aerosols may be used.

Chemicals were first tried against the Colorado potato beetle about 1850 when it spread from desert plants to potato patches in the USA. From then until the 1940s, almost the only chemicals that could be used were arsenic compounds or insecticidal extracts from plants, such as *rotenone* from Derris roots, *pyrethrum* from flower heads and *nicotine* from tobacco waste. After the discovery of the *organochlorine* insecticide DDT in Switzerland in 1939, things changed rapidly. *Lindane* (gamma BHC—benzene hexachloride) soon followed, as did the powerful soil insecticides *aldrin* and *dieldrin* (now withdrawn in Britain and Australasia). Because of their persistence and killing power, and because they kill by contact, even if an insect walks over a film left by dust or spray applied days or weeks earlier, these organochlorine pesticides lessened costs and revolutionized pest control in buildings, fields and orchards and made possible the control of mosquito-borne malaria.

A parallel advance pioneered in Germany was the *organo-phosphorus* pesticides, many of which are absorbed by plant roots and leaves and permeate all parts. Usually they kill only those animals that feed on plants or suck their sap, that is, not by contact, so sparing beneficial species. A range of these

PHOTOGRAPHIC LIBRARY OF AUSTRALIA

PHOTOGRAPHIC LIBRARY OF AUSTRALIA

Left: fogging a pyrethrum insecticide in a bakery with a Swing-fog machine. Stored food pests such as warehouse moths are controlled in this way.

Bottom: two dramatic pictures showing a field of prickly pear before and after attack by a species of moth called Cactoblastis. At one period the American prickly pear was spreading at the rate of a million acres a year in Queensland, Australia, until this form of biological control was introduced. The moths were brought from Argentina and multiplied in quarantine.

Right: soil injection machinery for safely introducing liquid fumigants into the soil.

compounds is now available, persisting in plants from a few days to several weeks. Unfortunately, unlike DDT which is relatively harmless to man and domestic animals, organo-phosphorus compounds are intensely poisonous. The *carbamates* are another group of pesticides, some of which behave like organochlorine and some like organophosphorus compounds. Recently, a new range of pyrethrum contact insecticides has been synthesized which are as potent as DDT but without some of the disadvantages of organochlorine, organophosphorus and carbamate pesticides. *Warfarin* and similar poisons, which prevent the blood from clotting, are used in poison baits for rats, mice and grey squirrels, while *metaldehyde* has proved effective in bran baits for slugs.

Applying pesticides

With few exceptions the pure pesticide is rarely employed. Most are marketed ready for use except that those intended as sprays must first be diluted with water. Common diluents include inert dust, oils, solvents, water and air, of which the last two are cheapest. Hydrated lime, diatomaceous earth, talc and other clay minerals are common dust diluents. Granules are made from attapulgite clay, corncob grit or coal dust.

In orchards fairly large amounts of spray are applied (100 gallons or more per acre) to secure good coverage of leaves, buds, twigs and fruits. Sometimes the spray is propelled by a blast of air from a powerful fan. Fields are treated with much smaller amounts of more concentrated spray by a method called low-volume spraying. Where pesticides in granule form are considered more appropriate, they are sprayed by machines designed to cover a large area quickly. Poison baits are usually pelleted, but are applied by the same machines.

Spraying, dusting and granule applying machinery cannot pass through tall or mature crops, or through forests or dense plantations. These must be treated from the air. Fixed wing aircraft are cheapest for large areas, but helicopters have several advantages: they are more manoeuvrable, do not require landing strips, and the downdraught they generate helps to force pesticides into crops. They are, however, expensive to maintain. Light aircraft have proved essential to control locusts in remote areas. Ideally they should be attacked in the outbreak areas before vast swarms issue. Bands of wingless juveniles (hoppers) on the ground can be attacked with persistent contact insecticides (dieldrin) sprayed in a lattice pattern from the air over a marked area. Alternatively poison bait can be dropped from the air. Flying swarms can be sprayed thinly and repeatedly from an altitude slightly above them.

Because rats and mice are wary, killing them with poison baits must be a planned operation in which unpoisoned bait is first offered at a number of baiting points inaccessible to livestock and humans. When the rodents are feeding freely, poison bait is substituted. If further baiting is needed, the food material should be changed, as survivors may shun the first bait if it made them sick. Fumigants are applied by soil injection machines or from canisters to areas of land or bulks of produce covered by gas-tight sheets. In glasshouses the soil is often steamed to rid it of pests, principally nematodes.

Natural enemies

The numbers of most pests are limited by naturally occurring enemies, for example, ladybird beetles that feed on greenflies, ichneumon flies that lay eggs in the young of many insects, or predatory beetles and spiders. Unfortunately some pesticides kill many of these beneficial species, which may result in massive outbreaks or in the emergence of new pests. The red spider mites have increased greatly since orchards were sprayed to control other pests and diseases, mainly because spraying kills their principal enemy the red-kneed capsid.

To avoid these problems, growers use pesticides selectively so that they kill only the target species. The particles of pesticide may be coated with *zein* (an amine obtained from maize) or encapsulated so that it ceases to kill by contact, and must be ingested. Alternatively, the pesticide is applied when the beneficial species is absent or quiescent. Sometimes the pesticide can be placed only where it is needed, for example, on seeds or in the seed row. Increasingly, several methods of control are combined or integrated, with the object of decreasing or eliminating pesticides and encouraging natural enemies.

Resistance to pesticides

DDT resistance in house-flies was first observed in Sweden in 1946 and was almost worldwide by 1950. Since then many insects have developed resistance to organochlorine and organophosphorus pesticides, and rats resistant to Warfarin have appeared in Britain. Recently a new rodenticide—Sorexa-CR—has been developed. It works by providing too much vitamin D (responsible for the deposition of calcium in the body) and too little vitamin K, which is vital for blood coagulation. Probably, as their use continues, most current pesticides will cease to be effective against many pests. Hence the importance of discovering new kinds of pesticides such as the pyrethrums, insect moulting and growth hormones and agents that cause sexual sterility.

Hazards to man and wildlife Because pesticides in sprays and dust may be inhaled or penetrate the skin, most developed countries have stringent legislation which insists that operatives must wear protective clothing when dispensing or applying pesticides. In Britain, Government chemists, monitoring home and imported produce, have shown that it contains only minute traces of pesticides far below accepted tolerances and that the amounts ingested in people's diets are trivial. The accumulation of pesticides in the tissues of birds and other animals has caused much concern among those interested in the preservation of rare species. If thoughtlessly applied, pesticides kill bees and wild life and, if allowed to enter waterways, may kill the fish. Those applied to soil greatly change the soil fauna. For these reasons most countries have regulations to ensure only careful and approved usage.

Biological control In biological control, natural enemies such as predators, parasites, fungi, bacteria, or viruses are used to control pest species. It has met with some spectacular successes in warm oceanic or geographic islands, mainly against pests recently introduced without their enemies. As

Spraying an apple orchard with a mixture of fertilizer and insecticide. Insects such as spider mites and aphids can do enormous damage, so spraying must be continued throughout the vegetation period.

long ago as 1892 an Australian ladybird beetle was introduced to control mealy bugs in Californian citrus plantations but it did not survive the winter. About 1917, it was found possible to breed ladybirds on potato sprouts infested with mealy bugs, making possible the release of millions of ladybirds at a cost less than that of spraying. In 1929 two parasites introduced from Australia replaced the release of ladybirds to control one kind of mealy bug, but ladybirds are still used to control the other kind and also to control mealy bugs in glasshouses.

The scale of biological control operations is sometimes very great. In Canada and the USA, many millions of species of parasites and predators have been liberated against some 200 pests but only a few liberations have been entirely successful. In the UK the most spectacular success was the control of rabbits by the *myxoma* virus spread by the rabbit flea, following its spread from France in 1952. Other successes include the liberation of predatory mites to control glasshouse red spider mites on cucumbers and tomatoes, and the liberation of a parasite to control greenhouse whitefly.

Although interest in biological control, in indirect and integrated methods, and in resistant plant varieties has greatly increased because of the difficulties and hazards of applying pesticides, nevertheless we cannot dispense with them entirely if the world food supply is to be maintained or increased.

PETROLEUM REFINING (see oil refining)

Top: in drier climates insects such as spider mites are often a problem, while in damper climates fungus diseases such as apple scab occur. Here damaged fruit is compared with apples sprayed with fungicide.

Bottom: the Pieris caterpillar, which attacks cabbage, is sprayed as soon as possible after hatching with a stomach poison such as DDT. In market gardens it is sprayed from a tractor with a boom.

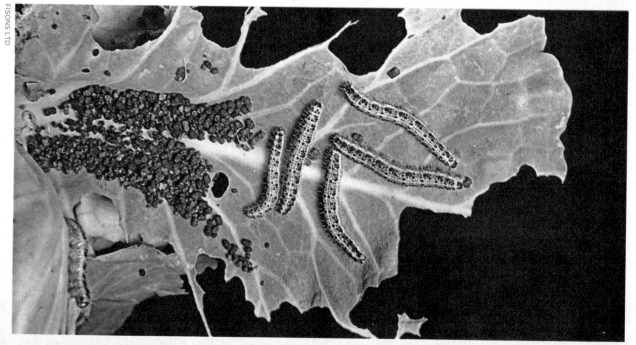

BASF

FISONS LTD

PETROL [GASOLINE] PUMP

A petrol pump is a means of dispensing an accurately measured volume of petrol, and calculating the cost to the customer of this volume. The basic single petrol pump contains a pumping unit to pump the petrol from a storage tank to the dispensing nozzle, a meter unit to measure the volume of petrol, and a 'computer' to calculate the cost.

The motor driven pumping unit creates a partial vacuum at its inlet port, which is connected to an underground storage tank. The atmospheric pressure acting on the surface of the petrol in the tank forces it up to fill this vacuum. Once petrol is drawn into the pumping unit, it is then pumped under pressure through a filter, to remove dirt particles, and an air separation chamber, to remove air bubbles, before entering the meter unit. This is normally a *positive displacement* type meter, which produces a rotational output directly proportional to the volume which passes through it. From the meter the liquid passes through a hose to the dispensing nozzle.

The rotational output from the meter is now used to drive the computer, which continuously calculates the cost of the petrol being dispensed. This computer may be a mechanical unit, directly driven by the meter, or it may be an electronic computer, in which case the drive is via a TRANSDUCER, which is a unit for converting the mechanical rotations into electrical impulses. The computer also displays the volume dispensed, the corresponding cost, and the price per gallon (or litre), the setting of the latter being variable.

Blending or mixing pump The function of the blending or mixing pump is to draw a high octane petrol from one storage tank and a low octane petrol from a separate tank, and mix these in a preset ratio so as to produce one or more 'blended' petrols of intermediate octane ratings.

The pump contains two separate pumping and metering systems, one computer and one dispensing nozzle. The high and low octane fuels are pumped through the two meters, and then pass into a *blend valve* which determines the ratio of high octane petrol to low octane petrol being dispensed. Separate hoses then take the two fuels to the dispensing nozzle, where they are mixed. The rotational outputs produced by the two meters now drive into a common computer, which arithmetically adds these outputs together to give the total volume of petrol being dispensed. It also calculates the corresponding cost, and displays this together with the volume and the price per gallon. An additional function of the blender computer is to control, via the blend valve, the ratio of high octane to low octane petrol being dispensed, to ensure a high degree of accuracy.

Self service pumps There are two types of self service systems: *post-payment*, where the pumps are controlled by a central controller, and the customer pays at the central control point after the petrol has been dispensed; and *pre-payment*, where the pumps are controlled by an integral counting mechanism, and payment must be made into the counting mechanism before fuel is dispensed.

A customer using a post-payment system must signal the central controller that he intends using a particular petrol pump. The controller then switches electrical power to the pump motor, which allows the pump to be used. After the customer has dispensed the quantity of petrol he requires he must go to the control point to make payment. The volume dispensed and the corresponding cost is automatically relayed to the control point by transducers.

SHELL

Left: self-service pumps at a filling station in Bremen, West Germany. There is a hose and nozzle for each grade of fuel, and the hoses are supported by counterweights to make them easier to handle.
Right: the layout of a modern petrol pump. Petrol is drawn up through the suction elbow from the storage tank by the action of the pump, and passed into the air separator. Air and vapour collect at the top of the main chamber, then escape through the orifice above the float, pass through the smaller chamber and are discharged to atmosphere through the flame trap. The petrol passes through the meter unit and down to the hosecock. The flow of petrol drives the coloured spinner in the sight glass to give visual indication that fuel is passing down the hose. The main valve in the hosecock is opened by the lever, allowing the fuel pressure from the pump to open the holding valve which closes again when the pump stops.

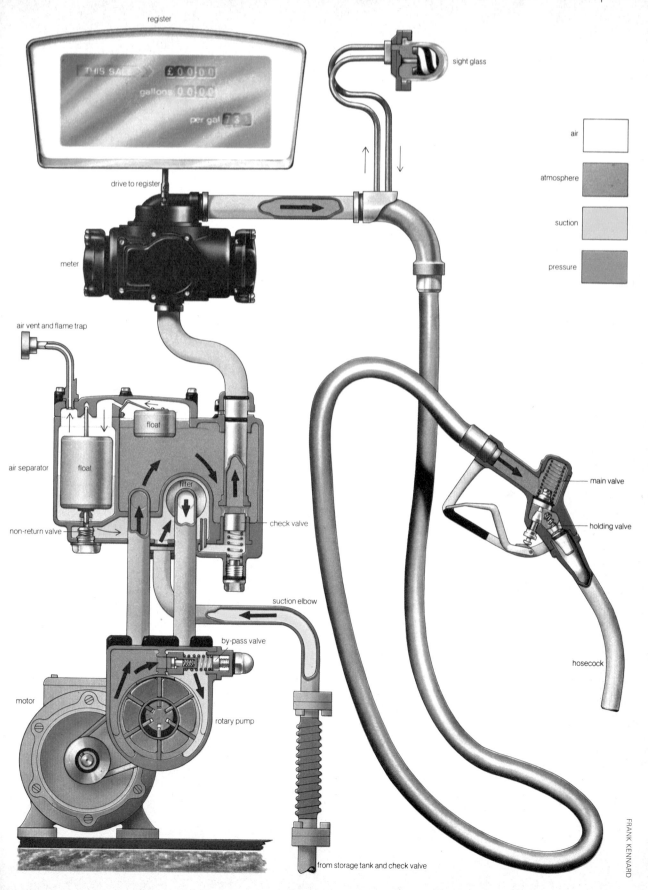

register

sight glass

air

atmosphere

suction

pressure

drive to register

meter

air vent and flame trap

float

air separator

float

filter

non-return valve

check valve

suction elbow

by-pass valve

motor

rotary pump

main valve

holding valve

hosecock

from storage tank and check valve

FRANK KENNARD

A customer using a pre-payment system must first insert the appropriate amount of money into the pre-payment counting mechanism. This mechanism then switches electrical power to a specific pump and allows that pump to be used until the corresponding amount of petrol has been dispensed. It then automatically switches the pump off.

Safety Every precaution is taken in the design of the electrical equipment used in petrol pumps, to ensure it cannot cause a fire or explosion. This can be accomplished by ensuring that the equipment cannot produce a spark that could cause such an explosion, even if the equipment is damaged or operated incorrectly. Alternatively, each piece of electrical equipment can be built into a separate box that is strong enough to withstand any internal explosion, caused by a spark generated by that equipment, without letting this explosion spread to the rest of the pump and possibly producing a much greater explosion or fire.

Below: a modern pump with its outer casing removed to show the pump and motor units, and the drive arrangements for the digital counter dials which indicate the quantity of fuel dispensed and its total cost. Some of the latest pumps use electronic readout devices.

PETROL, synthetic

Petrol [gasoline] consists of a mixture of HYDROCARBONS having an average of about eight carbon atoms per MOLECULE. Although petrol is normally manufactured by the DISTILLATION of crude oil (see OIL REFINING), it is possible to synthesize it from other hydrocarbon sources such as coal. Although nowadays the total volume of petrol produced from such sources is extremely small when compared with production from crude oil, in World War 2 coal was an important source of petrol, particularly in Germany.

There are two main processes for producing petrol from coal. The first involves breaking down the large coal molecules by a hydrogenation process, while in the second process, usually called the Fischer-Tropsch process, the coal is converted by controlled combustion into carbon monoxide, CO, which is then hydrogenated and built up into larger molecules.

Hydrogenation In the hydrogenation process, the coal is first separated as far as possible from any minerals which may be present, and is crushed to a fine powder. The powder is mixed with a heavy oil derived from a subsequent stage of the process and a small quantity of CATALYST such as *tin oxalate*, to form a slurry which can be pumped. This slurry, together with

hydrogen at a pressure of between 300 and 700 times atmospheric pressure, is heated to about 450°C (842°F) and then passed to catalytic converters where the hydrogenation takes place. The products from the converters are passed to a *hot catchpot* and then to a *cold catchpot* where the pressure is released and unwanted sludge is separated out. Unreacted hydrogen is removed at this stage and returned to the first step in the process to be mixed with more coal slurry. The liquid product from the cold catchpot is an oil product; it is passed to a fractional distillation column where it is separated into various fractions having different boiling points, including a petrol fraction.

Fischer-Tropsch process

Unlike the hydrogenation process, the Fischer-Tropsch process is carried out at pressures close to atmospheric pressure. This reduces the initial cost of the plant, but means that the ground space it occupies is greater because larger volumes of gas must be handled. The first stage in the process is the production of a mixture of carbon monoxide and hydrogen from coke and steam. The reaction can be written as follows:

$$C + H_2O \longrightarrow CO + H_2$$

coke   steam   carbon   hydrogen
monoxide

The proportion of carbon monoxide to hydrogen in the mixture is then adjusted until it is about 1 to 2 by volume, and the mixture is purified to remove sulphur compounds. The gases are then passed to a synthesis reactor where they come into contact with a granulated catalyst which converts them into a mixture of hydrocarbons. The temperature of the catalyst in the synthesis reactor is highly critical; if it is allowed to rise above 200°C (392°F) the feed gases will be converted to carbon dioxide and methane. The usual method of controlling the temperature is to employ a *fluidized* (finely divided so it moves fluidly) catalyst which can be circulated through the reactor. If the process is conducted at atmospheric pressure the catalyst is normally a mixture of cobalt and thorium oxide, whereas at a slightly higher pressure (10 to 20 times atmospheric pressure) an iron based catalyst is used. The proportions of the various hydrocarbons in the product mixture will depend on which type of catalyst is used. After leaving the synthesis reactor, the hydrocarbon mixture is separated from the unreacted gases and is passed to a fractional distillation column where petrol and other hydrocarbon fractions are separated out.

Left: a pilot scale plant for the Fischer-Tropsch process for making synthetic petrol. It has the advantage of operating at near atmospheric pressure although this means that it occupies quite a lot of space because of the volumes of gas required. The first stage is to produce a mixture of carbon monoxide and hydrogen which is passed to the synthetic petrol reactor where it comes in contact with a granulated catalyst and is converted to a mixture of hydrocarbons. These are separated from the untreated gases and the petrol is obtained from the hydrocarbon mixture by fractional distillation.

Right: a suitable soil pH is an important factor in plant growth, some plants preferring acid conditions and others an alkaline soil. Sugar beet, for example, needs a slightly alkaline soil, pH 6.5 to 7, so lime is spread on the fields (above) to reduce the acidity of the soil. Potatoes, on the other hand, are a crop which likes slightly acidic conditions so an ammonium sulphate solution is sprayed on the soil (below) to lower pH.

pH—MEASUREMENT OF ACIDITY

The pH scale was introduced by the Danish physicist Sørensen in 1909 as a method of expressing the acidity or hydrogen ION concentration of a solution. The p of pH stands for the German word *Potenz*, meaning power (in the mathematical sense) and the H represents the hydrogen.

Hydrogen ion concentration   An *acid* is a substance which ionizes in water to give hydrogen ions (H^+) and a *base* is a substance which ionizes in water to give hydroxyl ions (OH^-). Hydrogen ions and hydroxyl ions react together to form water.

$$H^+ + OH^- \longrightarrow H_2O$$

The strength of an acid or a base depends on the proportion of MOLECULES which ionize in the water. A strong acid is one in which most of its molecules are ionized and a weak acid is one in which few molecules are ionized. Since hydrogen ions or hydroxyl ions are always produced, the strength of the acid or base depends upon the concentration of hydrogen or hydroxyl ions. The concentration of hydrogen ions depends upon the concentration of acid or base molecules in the water, the proportion of these which ionize and the temperature.

Sørensen defined the pH scale as the LOGARITHM of the reciprocal of the hydrogen ion concentration:

$$pH = \log_{10} \frac{1}{[H^+]}$$

$[H^+]$ is the hydrogen ion concentration. For example, if the hydrogen ion concentration of a solution was 0.03 *moles* per litre:

$$pH = \log_{10} \frac{1}{0.03} = \log_{10} \frac{100}{3} = 2 - 0.477 = 1.523$$

One mole of a chemical compound has a mass equal to its molecular weight in grammes. For example, 1 mole of HCl (hydrogen chloride) has a mass of 36.46 g.

In pure water, which is neither an acid nor a base, very few molecules ionize. Since water is made of a hydrogen and a hydroxyl ion their concentrations are the same. At 25°C the concentration of both ions is only 0.0000001 moles per litre.

The pH of pure water is thus $\log_{10} \frac{1}{0.0000001} = \log_{10} 1 \times 10^7$ $= 7$ and because the higher the concentration of hydrogen ions, the lower the pH, it follows that pH values smaller than 7 are acid. When the pH is greater than 7, the concentration of hydroxyl ions is greater than that of hydrogen ions and the solution is a base—and is often referred to as being alkaline. pH 7 is a neutral solution.

Measuring pH
Some plant extracts and other chemicals change colour when exposed to acids and are therefore useful as indicators. Three common indicators are *litmus*, which is red in acidic solutions and blue in basic, changing colour between pH 6 and 8; *methyl orange*, which is red in fairly strong acidic solution, changing to yellow between pH 3 and 5; and *phenolphthalein*, which is colourless in acidic solutions and turns pink in basic conditions at pH 8 to 10.

Universal Indicator, however, changes colour gradually over the whole range of the pH scale. This enables the pH of a solution to be measured approximately.

More accurate measurements of pH can be made with a pH *meter*. All pH meters are based on a method originally developed by Sørensen. He measured the potential difference between the solution and a special electrode. The very small potential difference produced was equal to the hydrogen ion concentration. Nowadays a glass electrode meter is commonly used. It consists of a thin walled glass bulb. Inside this bulb is a solution of constant pH (a *buffer*) with a platinum wire dipping into it. There is also a reference electrode, usually a *calomel electrode*, which enables the potential difference to be measured by an accurate potentiometer when the two electrodes are dipped into an unknown solution, and the pH read directly from a scale on the meter.

Buffer solutions
A buffer solution is one of known pH, which does not vary with the addition of small amounts of an acid or a base. They are made by mixing together solutions of a weak acid (one that is only slightly ionized) and a SALT of the weak acid (which will be completely ionized).

For example, acetic acid and sodium acetate form a buffer solution when mixed. Acetic acid is only slightly ionized into hydrogen ions and acetate ions:

In this automatic titration a substance of unknown concentration is analyzed by adding measured amounts of a known solution which reacts chemically with it. The reaction is monitored by measuring the pH by means of electrodes immersed in the solution, the operation stopping by itself at the correct end point.

$$CH_3COOH \rightleftharpoons CH_3COO^- + H^+$$
acetic acid   acetate ion   hydrogen ion

Sodium acetate, however, is almost completely ionized:

$$CH_3COONa \longrightarrow CH_3COO^- + Na^+$$
sodium acetate   acetate ion   sodium ion

If an acid, such as hydrochloric acid (HCl) is added to the buffer solution the hydrogen ions from the acid will combine

with the acetate ions to form non-ionized acetic acid:

$$H^+ + Cl^- + Na^+ + CH_3COO^- \longrightarrow Na^+ + Cl^- + CH_3COOH$$

If a base is added to the buffer, the hydroxyl ions from the base, such as sodium hydroxide (NaOH), combine with the hydrogen ions from the acetic acid to form neutral water. Since any hydrogen or hydroxyl ions which are added to buffer solution combine with other ions, the concentration of hydrogen ions and hence pH stays constant.

THAMES WATER AUTHORITY

pH in biological functions

Buffer solutions play a vital role in plant and animal physiology, since a wide variety of chemical reactions can only take place in solutions of specific pH.

PROTEINS are large, complex molecules made up of a string of AMINO ACIDS joined together. These amino acids have chemical groups on them which can either give off hydrogen ions or accept them. Amino acids coil and twist around themselves so that the groups which gain and lose hydrogen ions are on the surface. Any change in the pH of a solution alters the shape of the amino acid chain.

Enzymes are proteins found in every cell of the body and it is their job to provide sites and catalyze (see CATALYST) a wide variety of chemical reactions in the cell. Any change in pH alters the enzyme activity, each enzyme only working within a small range of pH, and working best at one particular pH in the range. The pH in the cell is maintained by buffer solutions; phosphate buffers are an important example as are the proteins themselves.

Blood pH is maintained at 7.4 and at this value carbon dioxide reacts with water to form carbonic acid, which would be completely ionized. Carbonic acid is prevented from altering the pH of the blood by buffer solutions of phosphates and proteins in blood plasma, mainly by the haemoglobin itself. The blood returning to the lungs has a pH only slightly lower than the newly oxygenated blood.

Although the cell interior is maintained at a roughly neutral pH, animals' stomachs produce acids to aid digestion. Human gastric juice may have a pH as acid as 1.5 and the gastric juice of the carnivores may be even stronger. The acid is neutralized in the process of digesting food, and by the pancreatic juice, which has a pH of 8.0.

pH in plant functions

The main problem of plants is not one of internal pH, but of the pH of the soil from which it gets its supply of minerals and nitrogen. Extremes of pH can be survived only by plants which have specially adapted themselves: areas which have a high pH (chalk and limestone country) are markedly different to areas of low soil pH (peaty soils). Farmers raise soil pH and make it less acid by liming.

pH in industry

The most important use of pH is in chemical ANALYSIS, with acids neutralizing bases to find the strength of solutions, using indicators or pH meters to find the end point of a titration. Solutions of different pH are used to flush through ion exchange columns to dissolve out and indicate the presence of small quantities of different metals in solutions like river water.

The pH in sewage sludge tanks is initially at pH 5.5 to 6.5 in order that the maximum amount of methane (CH_4) is produced and the minimum amount of sludge is left.

Corrosion of metals costs the UK £600 million each year. Steel boilers have been found to suffer the minimum of corrosion if the pH of the water is maintained between pH 8.5 and 9.0. Aluminium is attacked at both high and low pH, and it is therefore advisable to maintain it at a neutral level.

PHASE (see sine waves)

PHASE (see matter, properties of)

When the incoming sewage reaches the works inlet it has a pH of about 7.3, which falls slightly to about pH 7.5 after primary sedimentation, when 50% of the suspended solids have been removed. This sludge may then be digested by the action of micro-organisms. The process begins at pH 5.5 to 6.5 falling to pH 7 at the end.

PHLOGISTON

The phlogiston theory was first conceived in the 17th century to explain what happened when materials were burnt, or *calcined*. It was put forward at a time when it was the usual practice in chemistry to ascribe various properties to the presence of 'principles'. There was a principle of solidity which was responsible for the solidity of substances, and principles of liquidity, acidity, and so on.

A principle of combustibility was suggested by J J Becher (1635–1682) in his book *Subterranean Physics* in 1669. He stated that the three fundamental principles (or 'elements') contained in all substances were 'fixed earth' (the principle of solidity), 'mercurial earth' (the principle of liquidity), and 'inflammable or oily earth' (the principle of combustibility). All combustible substances contained this last to a greater or lesser degree, and in combustion the oily earth was given off, leaving behind ash, composed of the other two principles.

Becher's theory was elaborated by his follower G E Stahl (1660–1734) in a long commentary on Becher's work in 1703 and in his own *Fundamentals of Chemistry* of 1723. He renamed the oily earth *phlogiston*. This was said to be contained in all combustible substances, such as oil, wood, and charcoal (which was nearly pure phlogiston, since it leaves practically no ash), and also in all metals, which can be 'burnt' to give *calxes* (oxides). Phlogiston was given off into the air in any combustion, or *calcination*, but the air had only a limited capacity for phlogiston before it became saturated and unable to support any further combustion, so a candle in a close space would soon go out.

The phlogiston theory slowly gained the support of chemists, and was generally accepted by the 1750s. Like any good theory it connected properties that had formerly been looked on as separate, for example, combustibility and metallicity, and it could explain many known facts and predict new ones. For instance, if the calcination (OXIDATION) of metals was the driving off of phlogiston, then treating with charcoal should replace the phlogiston, and the metal should be recovered. This is indeed what happens when many metal oxides are heated with carbon (*reduction*).

On the other hand, there were inconsistencies which made phlogiston less useful. The theory was based on the common-sense insight that during burning (of wood, for instance) something is given off; but why, then, did metals *gain* weight when calcined? Most supporters of the theory ignored this inconvenient fact, or argued that weight was not important in chemistry; some even went so far as to claim that phlogiston had negative weight! Worst of all, the phlogiston theory was not really very useful to chemists. Many took it for granted, but they found it of little help in suggesting what they should do in their everyday work in the laboratory.

As has often happened in science, the theory was only defended really forcefully (by Priestley, CAVENDISH and others) when it came under attack from a new theory. LAVOISIER's new view considered both combustion and calcination as combinations with oxygen, and gave consistent accounts of the weight changes. Lavoisier's other reforms of chemistry also provided a more fertile programme for chemical discovery, and the phlogiston theory was soon abandoned.

RONAN PICTURE LIBRARY

Above: an 18th century cartoon mocking Joseph Priestley for his defence of the phlogiston theory.

Left: apparatus used by Lavoisier to show the existence of oxygen. The volume of air in the bell jar diminishes as mercury in the retort is oxidized by heating.

PHOSPHORUS

In its most common form, phosphorus is a white wax-like ELEMENT which ignites spontaneously in air. It is a non-metallic element and occurs in the same group of the PERIODIC TABLE as nitrogen, arsenic, antimony and bismuth. Because it reacts with air, phosphorus is normally stored under water.

Phosphorus was first prepared in 1669 by the German alchemist Hennig Brand who used evaporated urine residue as the source of the element. It is surprising that such a reactive element was isolated by such an early date, and its discovery aroused much interest among the alchemists of the time who thought it might lead to the philosopher's stone, a material that would transform lead into gold. Phosphorus not only ignites in air, but it also glows in the dark because of a *chemiluminescent* OXIDATION process (see LUMINESCENCE).

In 1775 the Swedish chemist C W Scheele discovered a much simpler method of preparing phosphorus from bones, and his method was used for many years. In the 1840s a second form, or *allotrope*, of phosphorus, called *red phosphorus*, was discovered. This allotrope can be prepared by heating white phosphorus to 250°C (482°F) in a closed container and it is much more stable than white phosphorus; it does not ignite in air at room temperature. It was the discovery of red phosphorus that led to the invention of the safety MATCH. At very high pressures (12,000 times atmospheric pressure) white phosphorus is converted into a third allotrope, *black phosphorus*, a flaky crystalline substance which resembles graphite (see CARBON) and conducts electricity.

Manufacture
Almost all the phosphorus-containing compounds used today are derived directly from the ore, from white phosphorus, P_4, or from *orthophosphoric acid* H_3PO_4.

The most common phosphorus mineral is *fluorapatite*, $Ca_5F(PO_4)_3$, which is found in the USA, Morocco, Tunisia and the USSR. To prepare white phosphorus, the ore is mixed with gravel (silica, SiO_2) and coke and is heated in an electric FURNACE. The furnace has carbon rod electrodes and the ore, sand and coke are fed into the heating zone from a hopper. Phosphorus vapour distils off from the reaction mixture and is condensed under water. The calcium in the ore is converted into a molten silicate slag which is removed periodically and converted into granules by rapid cooling with jets of water. Iron impurities are converted into a metallic iron-phosphorus compound called *ferrophosphorus* which sinks to the bottom of the furnace. It is removed and cast into *pigs* (rough ingots), which are used for making certain iron ALLOYS.

Orthophosphoric acid can be prepared directly from the

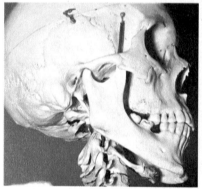

Top: an aircraft laying a smoke screen to hide troop movements. White phosphorus is a very effective smoke producing agent; dense white fumes are generated as soon as it is exposed to air.

Above: bones contain a high proportion of calcium phosphate and were once used as a source of elemental phosphorus.

Left: a formation of phosphate rock. This material is nowadays the chief source of phosphorus. It can be treated with either sulphuric or phosphoric acid to produce a fertilizer, or roasted with coke and silica to give phosphorus itself.

phosphate rock ore, or from white phosphorus. In the *wet acid process*, phosphate rock is treated with sulphuric acid to give a mixture of impure orthophosphoric acid and calcium sulphate, $CaSO_4$. Because the separation of these two components and the subsequent purification of the orthophosphoric acid is a relatively complex procedure, the acid is often made by burning white phosphorus in air to give phosphorus pentoxide, P_4O_{10}, and then treating the oxide with water.

$$P_4 + 5O_2 \rightarrow P_4O_{10}$$
phosphorus   oxygen   phosphorus pentoxide

$$P_4O_{10} + 6H_2O \rightarrow 4H_3PO_4$$
phosphorus pentoxide   water   orthophosphoric acid

Phosphorus itself does not have many uses, although it is employed in some metallurgical processes, in match manufacture, in the synthesis of certain organic compounds and in incendiary BOMBS. Incendiary bombs have a highly flammable filling such as petrol [gasoline] which is ignited by white phosphorus when the bomb bursts on impact. The phosphorus is often dissolved in *carbon disulphide*, CS_2, a volatile flammable liquid which evaporates quickly leaving behind the phosphorus. As soon as the phosphorus is exposed to the air in this way it ignites and sets off the main charge of the bomb.

Phosphorus compounds   Most of the phosphate rock mined each year is used to make agricultural FERTILIZERS. Millions of tons of 'superphosphate' fertilizer are made each year by treating rock phosphate with sulphuric acid; the phosphate component is *dicalcium orthophosphate*, $CaHPO_4$:

$$2Ca_5F(PO_4)_3 + 3H_2SO_4 \rightarrow 6CaHPO_4 + 3CaSO_4 + CaF_2$$
fluorapatite   sulphuric   dicalcium   calcium   calcium
          acid   orthophosphate   sulphate   fluoride

A more concentrated phosphate fertilizer can be made by treating rock phosphate with orthophosphoric acid. The product is called 'triple superphosphate', and the phosphate component is *monocalcium orthophosphate*, $Ca(H_2PO_4)_2$:

$$2Ca_5F(PO_4)_3 + 12H_3PO_4 \rightarrow 9Ca(H_2PO_4)_2 + CaF_2$$
fluorapatite   orthophosphoric   monocalcium   calcium
          acid   orthophosphate   fluoride

Another use of phosphates is in water softening. It is the presence of magnesium ions, Mg^{++}, and calcium ions, Ca^{++}, in water which makes the water hard and leads to the build up of scale in pipes. Addition of small quantities of phosphate, for example *sodium tripolyphosphate*, $Na_5P_3O_{10}$, will deactivate, or *sequester*, these ions and thus soften the water. Sodium tripolyphosphate is, for this reason, a major component of many detergent compositions. It is made by roasting a mixture of monosodium and disodium orthophosphates in a rotary converter.

There are many other applications of phosphates. Monocalcium phosphate and *sodium acid pyrophosphate*, $Na_2H_2P_2O_7$, are used as leavening compounds in cake mixes, self-raising flour and baking powder. Dicalcium phosphate is used as a polishing agent in toothpastes. Metal articles such as car bodies are usually dipped in a phosphating solution prior to painting.

Below left: a plant for separating phosphate from impure phosphate ore. The separation is achieved by flotation and the waste material, or gangue, is pumped to a tailings pond which can be seen in the background. The purified phosphate is passed to hoppers (left) for loading into railway trucks.
Below right: a sulphuric and phosphoric acid production plant. Phosphoric acid is one of the most important phosphorus compounds.

A thin layer of insoluble phosphates forms on the surface of the metal; this helps to prevent corrosion and provides a good surface for painting.

There are several chemical compounds containing phosphorus and HALOGEN atoms, for example *phosphorus pentachloride*, PCl_5, *phosphorus trichloride*, PCl_3, and *phosphorus oxychloride*, $POCl_3$. Phosphorus pentachloride and phosphorus trichloride are extensively used in organic chemistry to introduce atoms into organic compounds. Thus, acetic acid, CH_3COOH, will react with phosphorus trichloride to give acetyl chloride, CH_3COCl:

$$3CH_3COOH + PCl_3 \rightarrow 3CH_3COCl + H_3PO_3$$

acetic acid   phosphorus   acetyl   phosphorous
trichloride   chloride   acid

Phosphine, PH_3, a hydride of phosphorus, is a colourless poisonous gas with a faint smell of garlic. It is prepared by reacting white phosphorus with potassium hydroxide, KOH. The nerve gases Tabun, Sarin and Soman are organic compounds containing phosphorus. These compounds are extremely quick acting; they can be absorbed through the skin and produce vomiting, diarrhoea and nausea. Their main effect is on the central nervous system and they can cause death within 15 minutes. Similar compounds, such as Malathion, a powerful insecticide, have been made which are much less poisonous to warm-blooded animals.

Phosphorous compounds are vital constituents of living tissue. The organic phosphates *adenosine triphosphate* (ATP) and *adenosine diphosphate* (ADP) play a key role in the storage of energy in the human body. The conversion of ATP to ADP is accompanied by a release of energy which can be used by the body to promote other metabolic processes.

PHOTOCOPIER

There are a considerable number of copiers available today, and their use is steadily increasing. The total market for equipment and supplies in the UK alone is calculated at upwards of £100 million ($234.5 million) for 1974, and growing at over 10% per annum. The most familiar types of copier work on the direct electrostatic principle, of which the best known example is XEROGRAPHY, but the indirect electrostatic copier is very similar to the xerographic process, though instead of using a light sensitive drum the paper itself is coated with a zinc oxide compound that becomes light sensitive when electrostatically charged.

Xerography, however, is a comparatively recent invention, and a large number of photocopiers still use photographic processes, such as *diffusion* or *gelatin transfer*, or *thermographic* processes.

Diffusion transfer In the diffusion transfer process a negative is first made, then the positive is made by chemical means on a separate piece of material, in a combined developing and fixing solution. For this reason, the system is also known as *chemical transfer*, and is similar in principle to that used in a POLAROID CAMERA.

If the document to be copied were a single thin sheet, with the information to be copied on one side only, it would be possible to place the negative material under the document, and shine a light through to make an exposure. This is not usually possible, so to copy books and most other items it is common to use *reflex copying*.

Below: a dual spectrum dry copier, which uses coated paper. This machine uses an ultra-violet light source to obtain a copy image and an infra-red light to fix it on the copy paper.

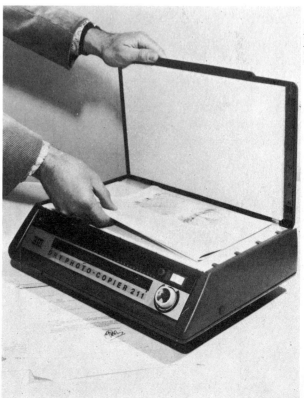

In reflex copying, the negative material is placed face down on the document, and a strong light shone through the back of it. Light parts of the document will reflect light back on to the negative material, while dark parts will absorb light, and so a latent image will be formed on the negative.

To make a copy, the negative is fed into a machine which contains the developing fluid, together with a sheet of positive paper in such a way that the image side of the negative is towards the face of the positive paper. After being coated with the fluid, the two are squeezed into contact by a pair of rollers.

During this operation the undeveloped silver halides in the negative dissolve and diffuse across to the positive paper, forming an image. The negative is peeled off and disposed of, although it is possible to obtain negative material that will produce several copies.

Gelatin transfer

This is a similar process to diffusion transfer, using unsensitized paper and a *matrix* coated on one side with an emulsion including developing and dye-forming agents. The original is exposed to tungsten light while in contact with the matrix. Again the reflex principle is used—the light passes through the matrix and is reflected back from the original. This reflected light hardens the emulsion. The light is not reflected back from the dark areas on the original which form the text or illustration, and thus the image areas of the emulsion do not harden. The exposed matrix is then passed through an alkaline activating solution which further softens the image areas and activates the dyes in these areas. The matrix and copy paper are then passed through a pair of squeegee rollers and the dye transfers to the copy paper. Up to six or seven copies can be obtained from one matrix, although matrices are available that will give as many as 15 copies.

With both diffusion transfer and gelatin transfer machines the exposure is carried out separately to the developing and copying process.

Thermography

In this method of copying the heat absorbing properties of the original are utilized, and so for best results the original should have as black an image as possible. Copy paper coated with ferric (iron) compounds and acids is necessary. This is fed into the copier in contact with the original. Infra-red light is passed through the copy paper and absorbed by the dark image areas on the original. The white areas reflect the heat so it is dissipated. The heat absorbed by the image areas causes a rise in their temperature which in turn affects the coating on the surface of the copy paper in contact with it, turning it black. This is usually referred to as the direct method. The use of a *transfer sheet* enables better quality to be obtained. The copy paper is sandwiched between the original and the transfer sheet, and the heated image areas affect the transfer coating which is impressed on to the copy paper.

Dual Spectrum copiers

The 'colour-blind' characteristics of the thermal method means it will not copy many common writing materials properly, such as blue ballpoint

Below: a simplified diagram of a direct electrostatic photocopier, such as the Copycat. Zinc-oxide coated paper from a roll is cut to length and negatively charged, then exposed to light from the face-down original by means of a sliding lens and mirror system. Non-image (white) areas lose their charge, but image (black or coloured) retain it. The paper then passes through a bath of liquid toner—carbon particles—which is attracted to the charged image areas, turning them black. Finally, the paper is squeezed and air-dried.

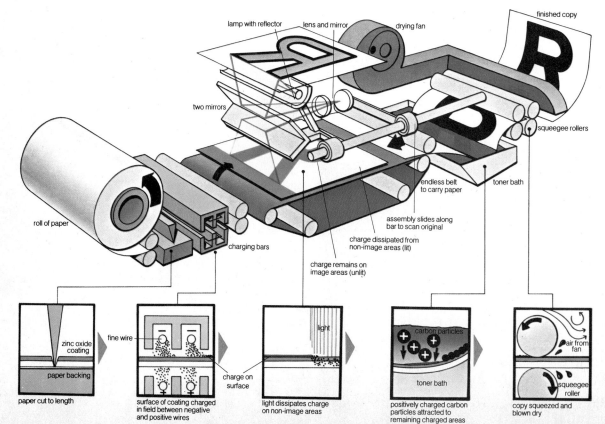

lamp with reflector   lens and mirror   drying fan   finished copy

two mirrors

squeegee rollers

roll of paper

charging bars

endless belt to carry paper   toner bath

assembly slides along bar to scan original

charge dissipated from non-image areas (lit)

charge remains on image areas (unlit)

zinc oxide coating   fine wire   light   carbon particles   air from fan

paper backing

charge on surface

toner bath

squeegee roller

paper cut to length

surface of coating charged in field between negative and positive wires

light dissipates charge on non-image areas

positively charged carbon particles attracted to remaining charged areas

copy squeezed and blown dry

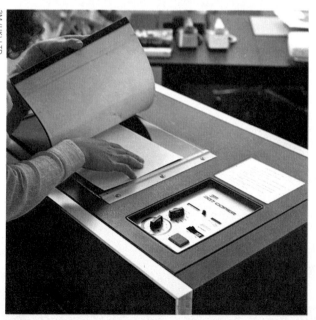

ink. *Dual Spectrum* was developed by the 3M Co to overcome this, and uses ultra-violet light. Again, the coating used is one which decomposes in light. The ultra-violet light passes through the back of the coated paper on to the original. The non-image areas reflect the light, causing decomposition of the coating. The paper is now passed into the developing unit with a sheet of copy paper. The developing unit uses infra-red heating at a temperature of about 100°C (212°F). The non-decomposed areas react with the coating of the copy paper to give a black image which corresponds to some of the blues and reds as well as to the blacks on the original. The image is not sensitive to heat after development.

Stabilization Similar in principle to PHOTOGRAPHIC PROCESSING, there are two methods of stabilization. The reflex method uses a negative and a positive, one sensitized paper and two solutions. The original is exposed to strong light while in contact with a sheet of copy paper. The copy paper is then passed through the baths of developer and stabilizer in the processor to form a paper negative. This negative can then be exposed with another sheet of copy paper to give a positive print. For many applications, however, the negative may be the end result.

The direct positive method does not require a negative to be made. A different type of copy paper is used in which the white parts of the original reflect light on to the copy paper and cause it to be exposed as white, leaving the image areas dark and giving a direct positive. This technique is not suitable for double sided originals.

Stabilization materials are sensitive to a wide range of colours and have the further advantage that the intermediate negatives can be altered or amended before the final print is made. Although similar to photographic techniques, and using similar materials, stabilization is simpler and quicker in use. Instead of fixing the image it is 'stabilized' so that it is no longer light sensitive, but does not have the long-term permanence of the fixed image. It is possible to subsequently fix stabilized images, however. The quality obtainable is very good with this method, and copy life is adequate for most purposes.

All methods of copying in the office have some drawbacks, either in quality, the range of colours that can be reproduced, or in the number of copies that can be used to prepare plates for offset LITHOGRAPHY, and although electrostatic copying and diffusion transfer are probably most popular in this application, stabilization is gaining ground.

Dye-line copying, using paper sensitized with diazonium salts and usually developed in ammonia or ammonia vapour, is widely used for reproducing engineering drawings and is also used with translucent originals for some office copying in Germany, but is not normally considered to be photocopying.

Top left: servicing an Ozalid copier.

Centre left: the inside of a modern electrostatic copier, a plain paper copier which works on the indirect electrostatic principle. The original image is transferred to an electrostatic tape by a xenon flash and a lens unit. Imaging powder is attracted to the latent image on the tape, and this copy image is then transferred to the copy paper and fixed by applying heat and pressure.

Left: this machine works on an electrostatic principle, but the copy image is made permanent by the application of pressure alone, without heat, and so there is no warm-up time.

PHOTOELECTRIC CELL

Photoelectric cells are useful sensing devices for a variety of applications ranging from simple counting to the control of STREET LIGHTING, depending on the intensity of daylight. The simplest counting device consists of a beam of light which is directed, across the path of the moving objects, at a photoelectric cell, which is connected to an electromagnetic counter. The photoelectric cell senses when the beam is interrupted and after suitable amplification activates the counter. For high speed work transistors may be used instead of electromagnetic devices. Other applications for photoelectric cells include door openers, printing (in colour printing to ensure correct registration), measuring the density of smoke from chimney stacks or turbidity (cloudiness) in a fluid, and ensuring the correct level of a lift [elevator] when stopping at a particular floor.

The photoelectric effect
Under certain conditions, the current flowing in an electrical CIRCUIT may be affected by the action of LIGHT falling on some suitably prepared part of the circuit. This influence of radiation on electrical behaviour is termed the *photoelectric effect,* and various *photoelectric cells* or *photocells* have been developed which enable the detection and quantitative assessment of radiation to be carried out. Photoelectric cells or photocells are divided into three categories depending on their action: photoemissive (the normal photoelectric effect), photoconductive and photovoltaic cells.

Below : photovoltaic cells require no external power supply but are less sensitive than the other types. With suitable materials, photoresistive cells can simulate spectral response of the eye but are slow. Photodiodes are fast and replace photoemissive cells.

Photoemissive cells
Photoemission is the emission of negatively charged particles, ELECTRONS, from the surface of a material illuminated by light or other ELECTROMAGNETIC RADIATION.

The effect was first observed by the German physicist Hertz in 1887 but was not fully explained until EINSTEIN in 1905 extended the QUANTUM THEORY of radiation which had been postulated a few years earlier by Max PLANCK. Planck had suggested that radiation such as light is emitted and absorbed in 'packets' or bundles which he termed *quanta.* Einstein went on to state that the radiation itself consisted of quanta or *photons.* Light striking the surface of a metal does so as a stream of particles, or photons, each having associated with it a discrete and individual amount of energy. This amount of energy can be transferred to an electron associated with an ATOM of the bombarded metal. A minimum amount of work must be done to enable the escape of an electron from the metal, termed the *work function* of the emitting material. Thus, if absorption of a photon excites an electron to an energy in excess of this work function, emission occurs. The rate of emission is proportional to the rate at which photons strike the material; that is, the beam intensity.

If the emitted electrons are made to flow in an electrical circuit the resulting electrical current can be used as a quantitative measure of the light intensity. The material used in a photoemissive device is chosen to have a small work function to maximize electron emission.

A typical cell consists of an evacuated glass envelope containing two electrodes. One of these, the *cathode,* consists of a semicylindrical metal plate coated with a photoemissive material. The material is selected according to the type of

photoemissive & photo conductive cell circuit operation

no light • photo cell • resistor • battery • dark voltage

light • photo cell • active current • battery • large voltage

photovoltaic cell circuit operation

no light • photovoltaic cell • no voltage

light • photovoltaic cell • voltage created by light on cell radiation being measured. An alloy of antimony and caesium works well with daylight, but with artificial lighting a layer of caesium deposited on silver oxide is often used. The other electrode, the *anode,* consists of a straight wire or wire gauze.

Radiation striking the photosensitive cathode causes electrons to be emitted. A positive voltage is applied to the anode, which attracts these electrons, and a current is established. The sensitivity is often enhanced by filling the bulb with an INERT GAS, such as argon, at low pressure. The electrons emitted at the cathode collide with atoms of the gas to liberate additional electrons and so increase the current flow. The maximum output of such a cell is too low to be of immediate use and must be amplified electronically.

Among the main uses of this type of cell are the reading of film soundtracks in a PROJECTOR and the conversion of optical signals to electrical signals in TELEVISION cameras.

Photoconductive cells
Changes in the intensity of light falling on certain materials cause changes in the ability of these materials to conduct electricity. This effect is known as *photoconductivity.*

Materials capable of conducting electricity do so because a certain number of the electrons associated with each atom of the material can be readily induced to move from one atom to a neighbouring one by the application of an external voltage termed *electromotive force,* emf. When radiation strikes a photoconductive material such as selenium, absorption of photon energy sufficiently excites a certain number of electrons to enable them to overcome the influence of their atoms and become free to move in the electric field established by the voltage (electric field is voltage per unit distance).

Thus if selenium is connected in an electrical circuit con-

taining a battery and a meter to indicate current flow, the current flow will increase when light strikes the selenium cell, that is, the electrical RESISTANCE falls. The resistance of the cell in the total absence of light is termed the *dark resistance,* and a disadvantage of the system is that variations in dark resistance occur with changes in temperature, humidity and the degree and duration of any previous exposure to light.

A time delay, the *response time,* occurs between light striking the cell and the change of resistance. This response time is typically greater when light levels are decreasing than in increasing light levels. This effect matters little in gradually changing light conditions but becomes a significant disadvantage when sudden changes in light levels need to be detected.

Other semiconducting materials that exhibit photoconductivity include thallium sulphide, germanium, lead sulphide and cadmium sulphide and these have largely replaced selenium in present day devices. These are sometimes called photo-DIODES. Such cells respond to a wide range of radiations and are used in switch-on relays for street lighting, and instruments for low temperature heat-radiation measurements.

Below left: a fast response photodetector. This is a photoconductive type for detecting radiation in the wavelength range 0.1 mm to 8 mm, and must be cooled to a low temperature for effective operation.

Below centre: this is an indium antimonide photoconductive cell and is used extensively in the analysis of infra-red radiation.

Below right: a photoemissive cell. This is a highly sensitive device (20 μA/lumen) — a caesium and antimony cathode is used.

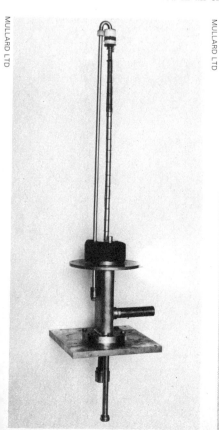

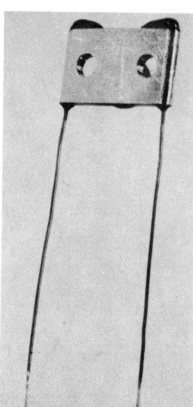

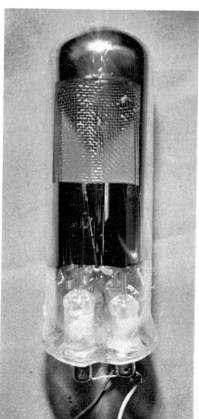

Photovoltaic cells When light strikes the junction between certain materials a small voltage or emf is produced. This is the *photovoltaic effect*.

A typical cell employing this principle consists of an iron plate coated with a thin layer of selenium. A thin transparent layer of gold is deposited on the front surface of the selenium to enable electrical contact to be made. Light passing through the gold film strikes the selenium and raises the energy of the electrons, which become free to move. These electrons move into the gold film and, if the cell is connected in circuit with a low resistance meter, the electrons flow round the circuit to the iron base plate via the meter.

The cell thus generates its own emf, this produces an electron flow in the circuit and the current recorded by the meter is proportional to the illumination on the cell. This type of device is very efficient and has the considerable advantage of requiring no external power supply.

Photovoltaic cells are widely used in EXPOSURE METERS for photographic work and as 'electric eye' detectors for the operation of RELAYS, but are less useful than photoemissive cells as accurate quantitative measuring instruments.

Below : a cadmium sulphide cell used in camera exposure meters.

Bottom : a silicon phototransistor suitable for applications in character recognition, tape and card readers, velocity indicators and encoders. They are compatible with TTL and DTL logic circuits.

PHOTOFINISH CAMERA

Some permanent record of the order in which the horses (or any other competitors in a race) actually cross the finish line has been attempted over many years by making use of photography. A single still photograph can be tripped at the exact moment the first horse crosses the line but this will not show the order in which succeeding horses pass. A high speed motion picture film can likewise be used but consumes a great deal of film which is slow to handle, and can miss the exact time of crossing because the shutter which opens and closes as the film passes is not open at the critical moment.

The photofinish camera was therefore developed to use a continually moving film the speed of which is geared to the scaled down speed of the reduced image of the competitors as seen through the camera lens. This principle was invented as early as 1906 as the *panoramic camera*—the sort which is used to take pictures of large numbers of people together, such as a school. In this, the pupils are arranged around the camera, which then rotates while taking the picture so that the beginning and end are taken at different times. It is not unknown for pupils at one end to sprint round the back of the others, and thus appear twice in the same photograph.

The same principle was adopted during World War 2 for AERIAL PHOTOGRAPHY at low level, where the ground movement is quite rapid. In this case, the subject and film had to move in step with each other. It was realized about this time that this was the answer to the problems of photofinish cameras.

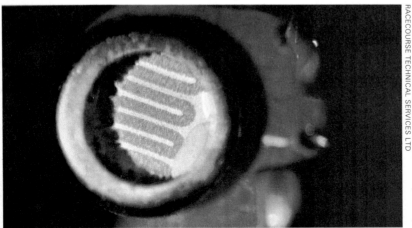

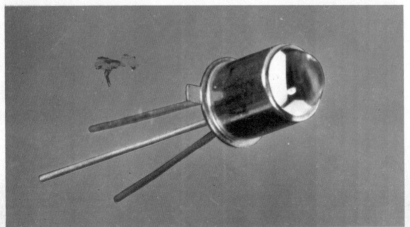

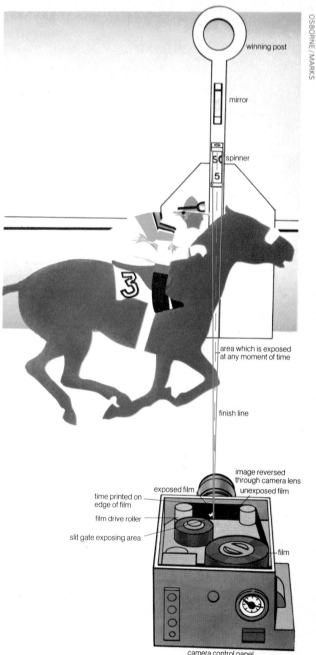

winning post

mirror

spinner

area which is exposed at any moment of time

finish line

image reversed through camera lens

exposed film

unexposed film

time printed on edge of film

film drive roller

slit gate exposing area

film

camera control panel

Above left: the winning post at a racetrack, showing the mirror and spinner, which is reset after each race with the next race number. Reflected in the mirror can be seen the camera box with its two ports: two cameras, with different focal lengths, are used.

Above: as the horses approach the finishing line, the photofinish camera operator selects the film speed to be used, on the basis of experience. A different setting has to be used if the horses are bunched on the near or far rails, for example. The rate of the spinner is not critical as the words will be visible even if they are stretched or bunched up. The film is unperforated 35 mm stock: if sprocket holes were used to drive the film, the result would be a slight unevenness, with a regular pattern of vertical stripes. At left is a typical photofinish. Time is recorded from left to right. Note that horses 9 and 5 have apparently bent legs.

The normal intermittent shutter of the movie camera is replaced by a very narrow exposing gate which is always open and limits the horizontal angle of view of the camera to a very narrow vertical band. This is aligned over the finish line.

Events which occur before or after the finish line cannot be observed by the camera because of the limited view. As the gate is always open, however, every event on the line can be recorded. A horse crossing the line will first show its nose and then its head and ears to the camera film and finally its tail as it passes the finish but the whole horse is never seen simultaneously. A second horse which crosses later than the first and whose nose is behind that of the first will appear after the first and therefore further back on the continuously moving film. The camera is in fact recording on its moving film a time sequence of events on the finish line.

Because of this sequential time recording, time can be printed on the edge of the film against which the time of every horse to cross the finish line can be read. A spinning drum at the far side of the track carries information about the race, date and track to avoid identification errors, and a mirror above this gives a view of the horses from the other side in case the direct view is obscured by another horse. In this way, a complete record of the finish of the race is available on a strip of film—its length varies according to how spread out the horses are, but is commonly about two feet (60 cm) long.

The judge will want to see the record of a close race as soon as possible, so the film must be processed instantly. The film used is pre-hardened, and so can be processed at temperatures of 110°F (43°C). The development takes just 8 seconds, and the film is available for projection to the judge, who usually sits in a booth below the camera room, 30 seconds after the finish of the race.

PHOTOGRAPHIC MATERIAL MANUFACTURE (see film)

PHOTOGRAPHIC PROCESSING

Exposing photographic materials normally does not produce a visible image, merely an invisible or *latent* image consisting of silver bromide (see HALOGEN) crystals, some of which contain specks of silver produced by the action of light (see FILM). Processing is the name given to the sequence of chemical treatments needed to convert the latent image into a stable, visible one. There are only a few basic different steps: *development*, *fixation* (or *stabilization*) and *bleaching*, but a wide range of different effects can be obtained by combining the steps in a different order or carrying them out in different ways.

The first, and most important, step is development, in which exposed silver halide grains are reduced to SILVER (see OXIDATION AND REDUCTION):

$$AgBr + developer \rightarrow Ag + Br^- + oxidized$$

silver bromide + developer → silver + bromide ion + oxidized developer

while unexposed grains are not affected. The ability of a small latent image centre, which is formed during exposure and may consist of only about 10 atoms of silver, to initiate the reduction of the whole grain, which may contain up to about 10^{10} (10,000,000,000) atoms of silver, is the fundamental reason for the high sensitivity of the photographic system.

A developer therefore contains a suitable reducing agent or mixture of two agents. Hydroquinone, *p*-aminophenol and *p*-phenylene diamine are typical members of three different classes of developing agents commonly used. Since the reducing power of such agents increases with the alkalinity of the solution, it is controlled by incorporating a suitable alkali, such as borax, sodium carbonate or caustic soda, in the developer. Since the bromide IONS released by the development reaction reduce the rate of reaction, potassium bromide is usually incorporated to minimize the difference between fresh and

Inside a photofinish camera. The lens chosen is screwed into the aperture on the left. The film can pass directly into a processing tank (white lid) after shooting, without using a darkroom.

Roll films are usually developed in tanks either individually or in frames such as this. Each film is held by the edge in a stainless steel spiral. The frame is transferred from tank to tank in the dark.

To illustrate stages in film processing, a copy negative has been made on sheet film and is being developed in a dish. This shows the film's appearance after a short while in the developer.

used developer. It also decreases the tendency to reduce some unexposed grains.

Developers also contain sodium sulphite which acts as an anti-oxidant, suppressing the oxidation of the developing agent by atmospheric oxygen and thereby extending the shelf-life of the developer. Sulphite also reacts with the oxidized developer, which is unstable in alkaline solutions and decomposes to give coloured products, to give colourless products which do not stain the photograph.

In black and white photography, the silver, which is formed as a tangled mass of very fine filaments and appears black, is the primary product and the oxidized developer is removed during subsequent processing steps. In colour photography, on the other hand, the silver is unwanted while the oxidized *p*-phenylenediamine developer produced in the development reaction reacts with *colour coupler* to form an image dye. In normal development (both black and white and colour) no reaction occurs in unexposed areas and most darkening is produced in the most fully exposed areas. The image therefore is a *negative*; one in which the tonal values are reversed.

Fixing

The silver halide that is not reduced during development is slightly coloured and, being photosensitive, darkens further on prolonged exposure. It must therefore either be removed from the layer (*fixation*) or converted to a colourless inactive material (*stabilization*). Fixing agents are compounds which form soluble *complex* SALTS with silver compounds and which therefore dissolve silver halides as a complex salt. Fairly concentrated solutions of *sodium* or *ammonium thiosulphate* are usually used; the former compound is frequently called 'hypo', an abbreviation of its old name *sodium hyposulphite*.

$$AgBr + 2S_2O_3^{--} \rightarrow [Ag(S_2O_3)_2]^{---} + Br^-$$

silver bromide — thiosulphate → silver thiosulphate complex ion + bromide ion

Fixing solutions used in black and white processing are usually made acid to diminish the reducing power of any developing agent carried over from the developing tank which might otherwise reduce part of the silver halide as it dissolves to produce *dichroic fog*. Such baths also contain sulphite to diminish the decomposition of the thiosulphate into sulphite and sulphur.

After fixation, the film or paper must be thoroughly washed as any residual fixer left in the print decomposes to give coloured products and attacks the developed silver on long storage.

Stabilization is intrinsically less satisfactory than fixation. The final prints are less stable and, since they contain insoluble white silver compounds, are confined to prints on paper. The process is used when convenience and speed of access is more important than the quality of the final image, and is commonly used in print processing machines. Stabilizers are usually organic *sulphur* compounds, such as *thioureas*. After development, the unreacted silver halide is converted into a white inactive compound by bathing in a solution of the stabilizer. Stabilized prints are not washed as this would remove the excess stabilizer and make the print less stable. A stabilized print will, however, last for several years without discoloration; if at any time a permanent print is wanted, it can be fixed and washed in the normal way.

Bleaches

Bleaches are used to eliminate developed silver from photographic materials. Although very many different formulations are used, they fall into three main classes. Simple bleaches, such as a solution of *potassium dichromate* and *sulphuric acid*, convert the silver to a relatively soluble silver salt (silver sulphate) without affecting the undeveloped silver halide. Rehalogenizing bleaches contain a milder oxidizing agent, such as *potassium ferricyanide*, together with *potassium bromide* and reconvert developed silver back to silver bromide. They are frequently used in colour processing, where the reformed silver bromide is removed in the fixing bath which removes the undeveloped silver halide.

Finally, bleach-fixing solutions contain an oxidizing agent, such as thiosulphate. They remove both developed silver and undeveloped silver halide simultaneously and are used to eliminate a step in some colour processes.

Continuing the sheet film process: left, a fully developed neg, with the emulsion still showing white. Normally this is only viewed by a red light. From the back, the image is hardly visible through the emulsion: the centre picture shows it half in the fixer, so only the lower part has cleared. The neg is then washed and dried (right).

Negatives and reversal Photographic systems in which the original photograph is used to give an enlarged print, such as most black and white photography, or in which one master is used to make several copies, such as most professional cinematography, necessarily involve two photographic steps which may either both involve negative processing, with light and dark tones interchanged, or may both involve *reversal* processing in which the film is processed to give a positive result, with the tones correct. Negative processing is usually used because it is simpler. For black and white photography, development is followed by fixing, washing and drying, and for colour, colour development is followed by a bleach step to remove the developed silver before fixing and washing.

Reversal processing is usually reserved for photographic systems in which the original photograph is the final product, such as in colour transparencies for projection and amateur cinematography. In these cases the increased complications in processing are compensated for by the elimination of a second photographic step. In black and white reversal processing, the exposed emulsion is first developed to give a negative image and then bleached in a simple bleach. The undeveloped emulsion grains are fogged, or rendered developable, by exposure or by chemical means and then developed in a second developer. In colour reversal, the exposed emulsion is first developed in a black and white developer to give a negative silver image but no dye, then the remaining grains are fogged and developed with a colour developer to give a positive dye image. The developed silver and any residual silver halide is removed by bleaching and fixing.

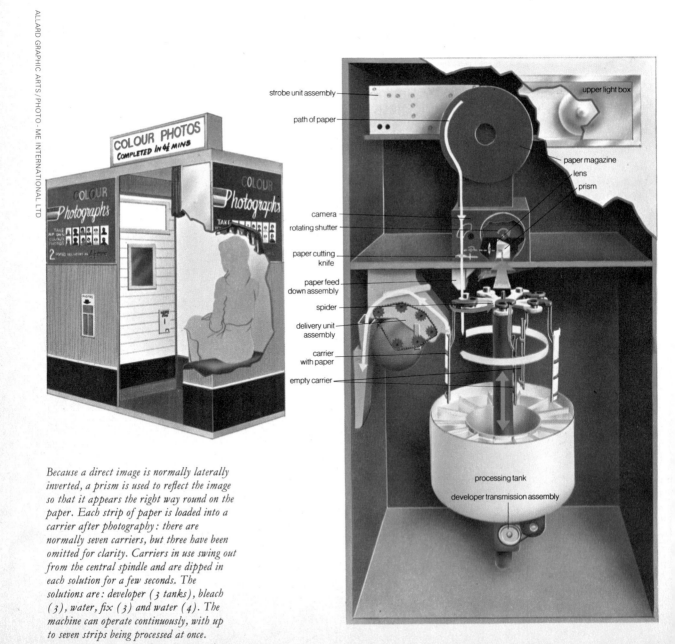

Because a direct image is normally laterally inverted, a prism is used to reflect the image so that it appears the right way round on the paper. Each strip of paper is loaded into a carrier after photography: there are normally seven carriers, but three have been omitted for clarity. Carriers in use swing out from the central spindle and are dipped in each solution for a few seconds. The solutions are: developer (3 tanks), bleach (3), water, fix (3) and water (4). The machine can operate continuously, with up to seven strips being processed at once.

strobe unit assembly

path of paper

upper light box

paper magazine

lens

prism

camera

rotating shutter

paper cutting knife

paper feed down assembly

spider

delivery unit assembly

carrier with paper

empty carrier

processing tank

developer transmission assembly

Other methods A *monobath* consists of a combined developer and fixer. A very active developer is needed so that development is complete before too much silver halide has dissolved. Since the process goes to completion in one step, the results are insensitive to the time of treatment. An adaptation of a monobath is used in *image-transfer processing* for black and white POLAROID prints, the preparation of some printing plates, and other processes such as some PHOTOCOPIERS. The exposed film is developed in a monobath while being sandwiched against a *receiver layer* containing suitable nuclei on which the dissolved silver halide can be developed by the developer in solution. A normal negative image is obtained on the exposed photographic film, but on the receiver sheet, where the developed silver is derived from the (unexposed) silver halide grains that dissolve in the fix, a positive image is obtained. Again the process goes to completion and is insensitive to processing time.

One type of processing which is widely used, yet which many photographers rarely come across, is *lith* development. This is used in the graphic arts industry, particularly from the point of view of REPRODUCTION IN PRINTING. Printing processes can only handle plain black or white tones; except for the GRAVURE process, any *half tones*, or greys, have to be broken up into dots which look like a grey tone when seen from a distance. To make a negative of some subject for printing, therefore, a process is needed which can transform greys into either black or nothing at all: that is, with very high contrast.

The developer used for this process has very few free sulphite ions and is usually supplied as two solutions which are mixed just before use, to prevent oxidation. The lack of sulphite results in production of *quinone* by the first grains to be developed, which stimulates nearby grains to develop faster. In this way, development takes place rapidly in areas which have had a heavy exposure, and very slowly in the areas with less exposure. The development appears to spread out from the highlights of the picture, and is known as *infectious development*. The films used in graphic arts are designed with this in mind. A number of interesting special effects can be obtained in this way.

Processing methods The mechanical procedures used to carry out the required processing steps depend on the scale of the operation. On a small scale, films and papers can be processed in dishes or held on frames and dipped into a succession of tanks for the required time. Roll films are usually wound on spirals and placed in a small light-tight box into which the processing solutions are poured.

Processing on a large scale is fully automated. Photographic paper is processed in continuous rolls several hundred feet long and only cut up into separate prints when processing is complete; roll films are spliced together into long lengths. These long lengths of material are fed continuously on a system of pulleys in and out of a succession of deep tanks containing the processing solutions. The time spent on any processing step is controlled by the rate at which the strip moves and the number and depth of the tanks devoted to that step.

PHOTOGRAPHY (see camera, film etc)
PHOTOGRAVURE (see gravure)

Right: the interior of a professional darkroom which produces individual prints of high quality. On the bench at right are two enlargers. When a print has been exposed (10 to 15 seconds) it is developed in the far dish (about 2½ min) then transferred to running water in the next dish (about 30 sec). The centre large dish contains fixer, the nearest one being water again. Fixing takes about 10 minutes, and the print is then washed for about 15 minutes. From the ceiling hang safelights which can be fitted with dark red or yellow filters which do not affect the paper. Small prints for family snapshots are not made in this way but are produced in an automated plant on rolls of paper.

Left: simplified view of an automatic photo machine, making colour photographs within a few minutes. This uses a direct reversal system, with the image shot straight on to the paper. Chemicals are used to 'fog' the paper in place of light: the interior is normally dark.

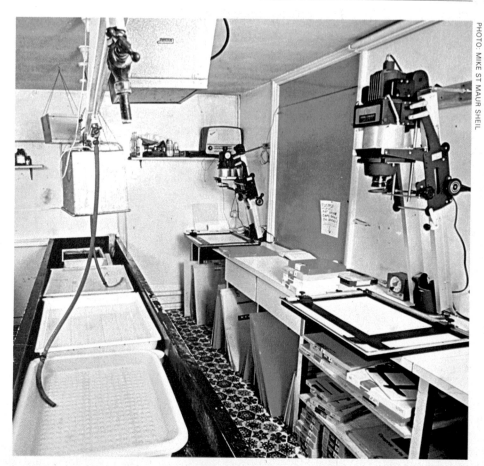

PHOTO: MIKE ST MAUR SHEIL

PHOTOMETRY

Many people are familiar with one part of the science of photometry when they use an EXPOSURE METER to measure the brightness of a scene when taking a photograph. Photometry is the measurement of quantities of light, and has many more practical uses, from making sure that offices and work floors are adequately lit to determining the visibility of a lighthouse beam. The exposure meter is a simple example of a *photometer*, used to measure light.

There are four types of measurement involved. 'Candle-power' is one well known type, referring to the *luminous intensity* in a particular direction of, say, a car headlamp. The total light output (*luminous flux*) of the source itself is another quantity; there are also brightness (*luminance*) of a bright surface and the illumination (*illuminance*) falling on a factory bench or office desk. All four are involved in STREET LIGHTING design, while data on sky luminance helps architects to provide good daylighting of interiors.

Units and standards These four measurements each have their associated units, some of which have alternative names, depending on the system of units being used. It might be thought that the standard unit of power, the watt, would be suitable, but this is rarely the case. An electric light bulb consuming 100 watts of electricity may indeed give out as much as 95 watts as radiation; but much of this will be in the INFRA-RED region, and therefore invisible to the eye, so that it may appear no brighter than a 40 watt fluorescent tube whose radiation is given out mostly in the visible region. The units

used in practice are therefore based on a source of standard brightness and colour distribution.

The earliest intensity standard was a *standard candle*, made to specified instructions. Throughout the 19th century, various standard lamps were produced, but in 1940 the present primary standard was adopted internationally. This involves a small furnace which radiates as a *black body*—that is, one which absorbs and radiates perfectly (see ELECTROMAGNETIC RADIATION)—at the temperature of freezing platinum. The luminous intensity of 1 square centimetre, in the perpendicular direction, is defined as 60 candles (cd), making the candela equal to 1 old candle. This standard is complicated, however, so national laboratories maintain special tungsten lamps calibrated against it, as secondary and working standards.

The unit of luminous flux, the lumen (lm), is defined such that a source having an intensity of 1 cd in all directions emits 4π lumens ($\pi = 3.142 \ldots$). This is because a sphere has 4π steradians, the steradian being a solid angle, just as a circle has

These pictures were taken at the British Standards Institution's photometric lab. At lower left is a photometric bench with a car's rear light at the end, seen through a lens which makes its light parallel. Baffles ensure that only light from the lamp reaches the photometer in the foreground. Bottom left: a rotating two mirror system reflects light from the streetlamp to the photometer in the background, so the light can be measured at all angles without turning the lamp upside down. Below: an integrating sphere, for measuring the total luminous flux from light bulbs.

360°. The source therefore has 1 lm per steradian. The unit of illuminance, the *lux*, is 1 lumen per square metre. Other units have been proposed for luminance, such as the *lambert*, the *foot-lambert*, and the *nit*; there are also various other units of illuminance, such as the *foot-candle*.

Any unit can be combined with time when appropriate— for a FLASHGUN, for example, 10 lumen seconds would mean the equivalent of a total output of 10 lm maintained for 1 second, or 10,000 lm for 1 millisecond. Some photoelectric photometers are designed to measure such time-integral value directly; but if the 'time shape' (the way the brightness varies with time) of the flash must also be known, an *oscilloscope* is also required to display it.

Photometers

As a detector of light, or photometer, the eye has two drawbacks. First, it cannot measure precisely, but can only set two brightnesses to be equal. The old Bunsen photometer had mirrors by which both sides of a white disc were seen as if side by side, and two lamps to be compared

were set on opposite sides, but at different distances, so as to make the two sides equally bright. Portable luminance meters worked similarly, but the white comparison surface, with a small variable-distance lamp to illuminate it, was built in. The same instrument was used to measure illuminance, by placing a white disc on the spot in question and measuring its luminance. The illuminance could then be calculated, using the previously known reflection factor of the disc.

The second drawback of the eye is that it is fooled if there is much colour difference between two sources being compared. Different observers get different answers anyway, because no two eyes have exactly the same colour response.

The modern photocell eliminates both drawbacks. It can accurately compare unequal lights and, not seeing colour, is not fooled by it. Further, its spectral response can be matched with the curve for the *standard photometric observer* (internationally adopted in 1933) by a suitable colour FILTER in front of it.

For intensity comparisons, two sources may be placed, successively, at the same distance from the filtered photocell, and two readings are taken. For luminance measurements a telescope system images the desired small area on the photocell. The luminance for calibration is produced by a standard white reflecting surface, such as magnesium oxide, placed at a known distance from an intensity standard. For luminance measurements, a PHOTOMULTIPLIER TUBE is often used, because the amount of light available is small. For illuminance, a selenium or silicon PHOTOELECTRIC CELL is convenient, because it can be placed where the measurement is required.

Below : on the left is the standard colour sensitivity curve used in photometry. It corresponds to the eye's colour response, and to the Sun's light output. Our eyes evolved to see this colour spread as white, that is colourless, light.
On the right are two elementary photometers, which use the eye as the light detector. The observer simply has to move the lamps so that the shadows, or translucent spot and paper, are equally bright. The square roots of the lamp distances gives the ratio of their intensities, since light fades with the inverse square of distance.

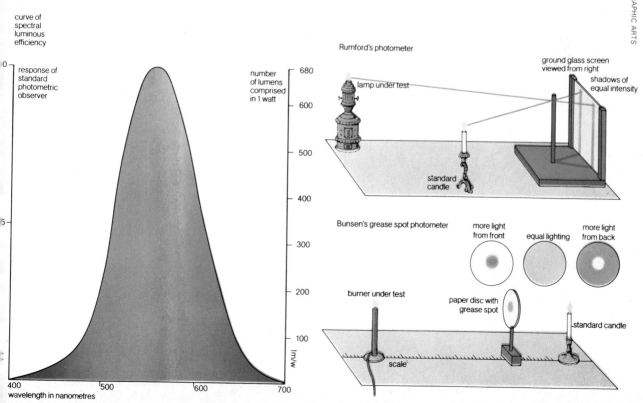

curve of spectral luminous efficiency

response of standard photometric observer

number of lumens comprised in 1 watt

680
600
500
400
300
200
100
lm/w

400   500   600   700
wavelength in nanometres

Rumford's photometer

lamp under test

standard candle

ground glass screen viewed from right

shadows of equal intensity

Bunsen's grease spot photometer

more light from front

equal lighting

more light from back

burner under test

paper disc with grease spot

standard candle

scale

ALLARD GRAPHIC ARTS

PHOTOMICROGRAPHY

When the compound MICROSCOPE was first introduced at the beginning of the 17th century, the image could only be recorded by sketching or tracing. Such records were called *micrographs*. Nearly 250 years were to pass before advances in photography enabled microscopists to produce a permanent record of the magnified image. The word *photomicrography* was coined to describe the production of such a record. A precise definition would be 'photography through a microscope'.

For those magnifications up to about ten times, the term *photomacrography* is preferred. Confusion often arises between the terms *photomicrography* and MICROPHOTOGRAPHY, but the latter refers exclusively to the recording of an object as an image greatly reduced in size.

Apparatus The basic apparatus consists of an illuminating source, a compound microscope and a camera. The camera has no function other than to contain the photographic recording medium, usually film. No lenses or diaphragms are required, since these parts are already present in the microscope, but a ground glass screen makes the focusing of the final image easier. A shutter can be located either in the camera or the microscope.

A photomicrographic set-up can be constructed from the simplest of instruments, and will function perfectly well, provided that it is aligned so that the optical axes of the microscope and camera coincide. A further requirement is that it should be supported and clamped so that it is absolutely free from vibration effects, since long exposure times are often necessary, especially when opaque objects are photographed using reflected light, or when high magnifications are employed.

Modern apparatus tends to be designed on a modular basis, permitting components and accessories to be added, substituted or adjusted with the minimum of inconvenience.

Photographic film There are many factors to consider when selecting the photographic film that will give optimum results with a given specimen under given lighting conditions. It is normal practice first to decide upon the combination of light source and colour filters (if any) required to reveal the details of interest in the specimen, and then to select the appropriate film to record the range of the visible spectrum being used. There is no point in selecting a *panchromatic* film, sensitive to all visible colours, with all its difficulties in darkroom handling, if a blue-sensitive film can be used just as effectively.

The brightness range of the image will determine whether the film is to be of high or low *contrast*. If the range is short, then a high contrast material may be used. Conversely, a low contrast film is required to record an image of long brightness range. The greatest attention should be paid to the reproduction of detail in the darker areas of the specimen, which will be represented as light areas on the negative. More overexposure

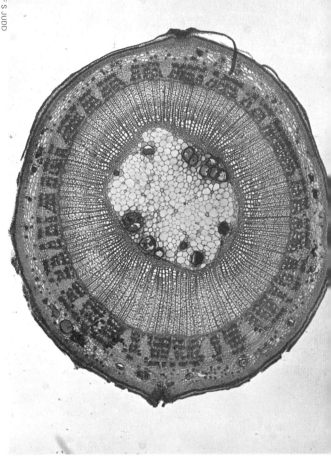

F S JUDD

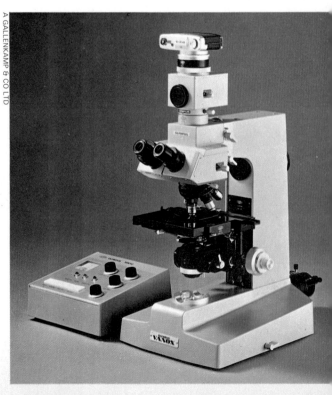

A GALLENKAMP & CO LTD

Above right: a thin section of a lime tree stem, magnified 28 times. Specimens such as these are cut to a thickness of a few microns with a microtome—at its simplest, a flat table with a blade and a fine screw adjustment. Such thin sections are quite often colourless, so dyes can be used to colour specific parts of the section. Certain dyes will only affect certain parts of the plant fibres, thus enabling, say, starch regions to be picked out.

Right: apparatus designed for photomicrography. Above the objectives is a mirror which directs some, or most, of the light into either the eyepieces or the camera at will. An electronic shutter exposes the film for the correct time automatically.

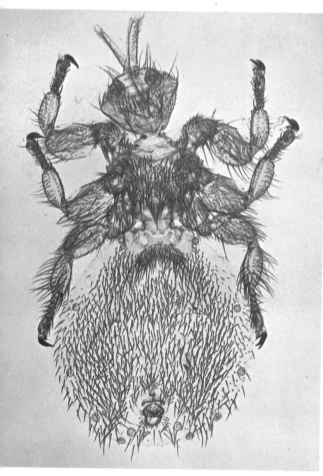

F S JUDD

than underexposure can be tolerated with negative materials, but the opposite is true for colour reversal films (producing colour slides directly).

The colour output of a light source varies with its temperature, and this is of importance in colour photomicrography. The lower the temperature of a source, the richer the light is in the red; the higher its *colour temperature* (as it is known), the more blue light it emits. Colour films are manufactured to give a true colour rendering of a subject with light of a specific colour temperature. Where it is necessary to match the light source with the colour film, colour-correcting filters are employed which absorb either the red or blue region of the spectrum. As an example, a film which is balanced correctly for daylight illumination can be exposed successfully to tungsten illumination by using a red-absorbing filter in front of the light source.

Resolving power   The resolving power (RP) of a system is a measure of its ability to reveal or record very fine detail. The higher the RP, the smaller is the detail revealed or recorded. The maximum RP of the optical microscope is fixed by the wave nature of light at about 1500 angstroms (0.00015 mm), and under good viewing conditions the eye can resolve 0.1 millimetre. This means that, provided the highest quality lenses are used, a magnification of about 700 times will reveal the smallest detail resolvable with an optical microscope.

The size of the smallest detail in the image at 700 times magnification is therefore 0.1 millimetre. All photographic films are capable of recording detail of this size, so resolution in photomicrography does not depend on the RP of the photographic material. The quality of the image cannot be improved photographically. The film merely records what the microscope makes visible.

Applications   Nearly all branches of science have benefited from the application of photomicrography. In medicine it is used as a tool for routine analysis. The examination of cervical smears for the early detection of cancer, and the study of chromosomes, are just two examples of its usefulness.

Photomicrography also plays a vital role in nuclear physics. The photographic emulsion has been used as a PARTICLE DETECTOR for many years, and much fundamental information can be obtained by the study of the tracks that these particles make through the emulsion. In another field, the photomicrographic record presented as evidence in legal proceedings should leave no room for ambiguity. The photographing of fingerprints, signatures, fibres, bullets, and so on, should be done as accurately as possible. FORENSIC photography is therefore regarded as one of the most exacting disciplines of the photomicrographic technique. Many other fields of science, such as metallurgy, biology and geology make wide use of photomicrography.

PHOTO: PAUL BRIERLEY

PHOTRI

Top left: an enlarged view of a female sheep ked, of the species Melophagus ovinus, magnified $13\frac{1}{2}$ times. Knowledge of the behaviour of these pests is of great importance to sheep farmers.

Middle left: some of the most important developments in any field of technology in recent years have been in microelectronics. This is a photomicrograph of a microcircuit which replaces dozens of conventional components, compared in size with common salt grains.

Left: a photomicrograph of acetanilide crystals, viewed by polarized light to reveal differences in crystal thickness. This drug is used to dull pain and fight fever by lowering body temperature.

PHOTOMULTIPLIER TUBE

The intensity of a beam of LIGHT can be measured using PHOTOELECTRIC CELLS in which the energy associated with light radiation is converted into electrical energy. An important type of photoelectric cell is that which operates on the principle of *photoemission*. The output current of such a cell is, however, low and substantial electronic amplification is required. This low output also limits the range of detection of such a cell.

The *photomultiplier* tube has been developed to overcome these limitations. In this device the initial photoemission is increased, or multiplied, by a *secondary emission* process. When an electron, moving at a sufficiently high velocity, strikes a surface the emission of further electrons from that surface can occur. This process is called *secondary emission*.

Basic principles
When a beam of light (photons) strikes certain materials, the energy associated with the beam raises the energy of the electrons of the bombarded material, enabling them to overcome the influence of the atom that they are associated with. These electrons are thus emitted from the atom and can then be induced to flow in an electrical circuit resulting in an electrical current proportional to the intensity of the incident light beam. This is the principle of the *photoemissive cell*.

A typical photomultiplier consists of a metal plate, the *cathode*, coated with a photoemissive material contained in an evacuated glass bulb. An alloy of caesium and antimony is an example of a photoemissive material suitable for the monitoring of visible light. The electrons liberated at the cathode by photoemission are attracted towards a second (positive) plate called a *dynode*. Each electron striking this dynode gives rise to the emission of a number of electrons by secondary emission.

A series of such dynodes is arranged in the photomultiplier tube and the negatively charged electrons released from the first dynode, by secondary emission, can be attracted towards the next plate by the application of a higher positive voltage to this next plate. This process continues throughout the series of dynodes, each one being at a higher voltage than the previous one.

Amplification
If each electron striking a dynode causes four electrons to be emitted, by secondary emission, then at the first dynode four electrons will be released; at the second dynode 4×4 (4^2) or 16 electrons will be released; at the third dynode $4 \times 4 \times 4$ (4^3) or 64 electrons will be released. If the cell contains eleven such dynodes, the number of electrons available to produce an electrical current in an external circuit is 4^{11}, or just over four million times the number of photons striking the cathode. The greater the number of secondary electrodes, the larger will be this multiple effect or amplification.

All the 'multiplied' electrons are attracted finally to the last plate in the system, the *anode*, from which they are passed to the external detecting circuit. The sensitivity to light of such a system is extremely high and a typical photomultiplier can detect and respond to very much weaker light intensities than can be detected by the human eye.

The dynodes are usually arranged in the form of slats forming a venetian blind-type structure. The voltage difference required between each successive dynode to sufficiently accelerate the electron motion is of the order of 100 volts. With the number of dynodes usually incorporated into such a device the overall operating voltage is high and consequently there are certain hazards associated with its use. Consequently the use of a photomultiplier tube is generally confined to situations where adequate sensitivity for light measurement cannot be

MULLARD LTD

M M RATHORE

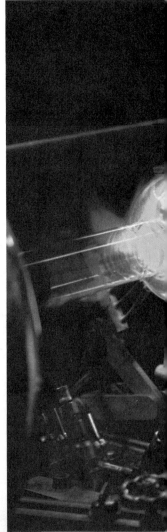

Top: ten-stage photomultiplier tubes. They are intended for use in the detection and measurement of nuclear radiation with scintillators and counters. The dynodes (which liberate more than one electron for every electron striking them) have a 'venetian blind' structure to improve stability.

Above: photomultiplier tube with dynode secondary emitting surface made from caesium and antimony. Operating voltage is 1250 volts, sensitivity 80 A/lm.

Right: welding a face plate on photomultiplier glass envelope.

achieved by other means. The very high sensitivity also requires that ambient light be rigorously excluded from striking the system.

Applications One of the most important areas of application of photomultiplication is the detection and quantitative assessment of radiation emitted from radioactive materials. The radiation to be measured is arranged to strike a glass screen coated with a *phosphor*, a material which emits light when irradiated. The screen is placed in close contact with a photomultiplier tube and the emitted light from the phosphor is arranged to strike the photocathode. This impact gives rise to one or more photoelectrons. The photomultiplying action then increases the electron flow by a factor of a million or more.

The resulting current is measured and by scaling this figure down by an amount related to the amplification of the photomultiplier, the quantity of radiation originally striking the phosphor can be assessed. Each 'flash' of light produced by radiation striking the phosphor is called *scintillation* and the device is a *scintillation counter* (see PARTICLE DETECTOR).

PHOTON (see quantum theory)

PHOTOTYPESETTING

Phototypesetting (also called *photocomposition* or *filmsetting*) is a process for the automatic selection and projection on to photographic FILM of alphabetical characters, figures, punctuation marks, and other symbols in the correct sequence to produce the sort of text that you are reading now, ready for the various printing processes (see LETTERPRESS PRINTING and LITHOGRAPHY). The characters are most commonly stored in the machine in a manner similar to slides in a projector and the machine receives instructions such as particulars of the size and style of the characters, the order in which each character and space must be exposed, the length of the line of type to be set, the vertical space between each line, and many other factors, from a punched paper tape, 7 or 9 track magnetic tape, or magnetic disks (see DATA STORAGE).

One of the main differences between typeset (printed) matter and typescript (ordinary typing) is that, while in the latter there is a straight margin on the left hand side, the lines are ragged on the right; whereas in most printed matter every line is exactly the same length. This is accomplished by stretching out a line which falls slightly short of the required width by increasing the value of the spaces between the words, ensuring at the same time that all the spaces in any given line are of identical value. The process is known as *justification*.

Another difference between print and typescript is that most TYPEWRITERS allocate a uniform width to each character, irrespective of whether the letter is as wide as this capital W or as narrow as this l, or even the full stop at the end of this sentence. In print, however, much careful attention is paid to character fit, which improves the appearance of the text matter but requires that each character is given only as much space as its width demands.

Justification and character fit are, in fact, common to the alternative (hot metal) typesetting method which uses cast metal type, but are mentioned because in phototypesetting one of the most important items of data to be fed into the machine is that which specifies the 'set feed' for each character.

Projection systems There are only two methods of arranging type matter across the page: either the source remains stationary and the page is moved (as with the carriage of most typewriters) or a system must be devised to project each successive image in its correct position along the line. Various manufacturers of filmsetting machines have their own methods of doing this, but most use one of two systems of mirrors.

Both systems are substantially similar, the main differences being the light source and the method of storing, selecting and presenting the characters. In the first type, 400 film *matrices* (each carrying a character image) are arranged in a square grid of 20×20 with each character located by a simple two-part address which defines column and row as in a map reference. The matrix case is moved simultaneously in both directions to locate the required matrix beneath a single constant light source which is controlled by a mechanical shutter. The beam of light carrying the image passes through a condenser lens (see PROJECTOR), is turned through 90° by an angled mirror, projected through a ZOOM LENS (which controls character size and focus) and then to a system of moving set feed mirrors which are used to expose the images of the characters in their correct sequence and spacing across the page.

In the second system, the film matrices are disposed around the periphery of four discs. Characters are selected by rotating the discs in either direction to align them accurately in the

BPIF

optical path of the light source. Each disc has its own xenon flash tube and the four projection paths are merged by means of a multi-mirror block of semi-reflecting surfaces so that the character images on any disc can be centralized on a common optical target. The indexing and arrest of the discs, to locate the selected matrix prior to exposure, are carried out at high speed, which is further improved by the way in which the characters are grouped around the four discs. Characters are assessed for their frequency of occurrence (e being the most common character, a the second, t the third and so on) in conformity with a system which makes it unlikely that two consecutive characters will be exposed from the same disc. By such means matrices can be selected and presented for exposure in advance, and the matrix discs operated in sequence. The image then passes through sizing lenses to set feed mirrors in a manner similar to that described for the grid system.

These two systems share a common characteristic, namely, that the character is exposed on the film from a stationary matrix. This system claims the advantage of offering very good typographical quality, though the speed of setting is not so high as that for machines which do not hold the matrix still during exposure. The second system, which uses the four discs, will expose some 35 characters per second, which represents the practical limit if the disc is to be arrested and the matrix kept still at the moment of exposure.

Where quality may be of less significance than the speed at which the setting must be performed, the matrices can be arranged on glass discs which spin at very high speeds and exposure depends on the very accurate aiming of a strobo-scopic flash which fires and 'freezes' the selected character as it passes through the optical path. Machines using this system are capable of setting up to 75 characters per second.

Above: a paper tape reader and the punched tape containing the text to be set. The tape punch has a keyboard similar to that of a typewriter but with extra keys for punching in instructions to the photosetting system.

Below: a set of matrix discs. The matrices, similar to photographic slides each carrying the image of a single character, are arranged around the peripheries of the discs.

Bottom: an alternative method of storing the character matrices is to arrange them on a grid. This one holds 400 characters.

MONOTYPE CORPORATION LTD

MONOTYPE CORPORATION LTD

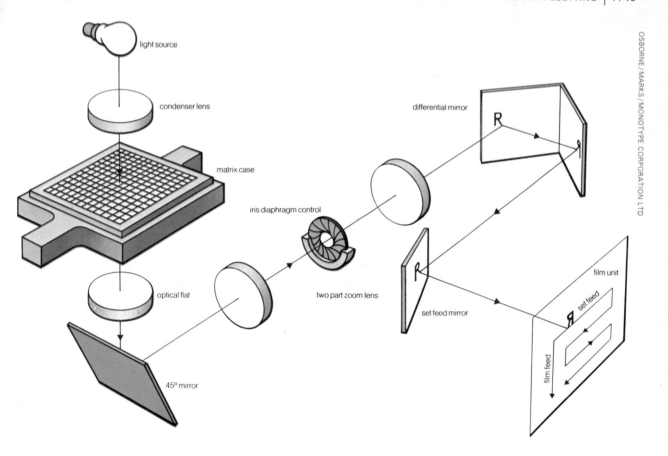

OSBORNE / MARKS / MONOTYPE CORPORATION LTD

light source

condenser lens

matrix case

differential mirror

iris diaphragm control

optical flat

two part zoom lens

45° mirror

set feed mirror

film unit

set feed

film feed

B P I F

Left: a machine for preparing punched tapes. It is based on a modified electric typewriter, and has two extra keyboards for punching the instruction codes.

Above: in this phototypesetting system the film matrices are arranged in a grid on a matrix case which is moved beneath the light source so that the light shines through one character at a time in the correct order. The character images are then projected through the lens and mirror system on to the film. The machine is programmed in a similar way to a small computer by loading the program, carried on 31-channel tape, into its memory unit. The character selection is controlled by another 31-channel tape, which contains the copy information. The matrix case is positioned by two pneumatic rams which precisely align the required character with the fixed light source. Other machines of this type use 6 or 8 channel tapes.

Crt setting   Yet another system dispenses with a complete image of the characters but instead stores in a COMPUTER memory masses of individual terms of data which describe the configuration of parts of the letters. Thus, the image to be projected never, in fact, exists in complete physical form, but is generated from a great number of discrete parts. The data are used to control an electron beam, which, by its scanning action, 'paints' the character on the screen of a CATHODE RAY TUBE (crt) in the same way as a picture is composed in a television receiver, and the character image is recorded on to film.

Other 'crt' machines use a combination of the systems previously described in that they employ an electron beam to scan film masters in a grid type matrix case and project the image through an optical system on to the film.

Line feed   On the completion of a line the filmsetter receives a *line feed* signal, in response to which the film is 'wound-on' an accurately specified distance to produce the required inter-line spacing. In normal text matter this would be constant from line to line, but subject to variations to divide paragraphs, leave space for sub-headings, chapter titles, and footnotes, for example, which may appear in different type styles. When a complete section has been exposed on the photosensitive material which, despite it being referred to as film, can also be opaque paper, the cassette in which it is contained is removed from the machine and processed.

The final product is then arranged according to the design of the page with text matter, headlines, chapter titles, page numbers and illustrations in the positions allocated by the designer. The result is camera copy from which printing blocks or lithographic plates, for example, are produced.

PHYSICS

To many people, physics *is* science. All the most famous names in science—Newton, Galileo, Einstein, Archimedes, for example—belong to people whose major discoveries were in physics. Physics is concerned with the laws that govern Nature—in other words MATTER and ENERGY. CHEMISTRY, which is concerned with the composition of substances and their interaction with each other, is considered to be a separate subject, but it has relied heavily on advances in physics to clarify and explain the constituents of matter and their subsequent interaction on the chemical level. The same is true for biology and biochemistry; in fact, physics pervades our understanding of the Universe and of life.

The rise of physics Something like half a million years ago our pre-human ancestors were already using simple hand-made tools and fire; the palaeolithic men who made the famous cave paintings had bows and arrows some 20,000 years ago, and even today there are still races whose technology is still at the Stone Age level of evolution. By 10,000 years ago, the first farmers were tilling the soil, and 5000 years ago the signs of basic science were emerging in Babylonia. Despite some laws discovered by the Greeks, technology in everyday life was very much the same in the Middle Ages as it was in Roman times—indeed, the Romans had better plumbing. It was not until the 17th century that science as we know it really got under way; then in the 18th and 19th centuries came the industrial revolution, and in the 20th century physics plays such a large part in our lives that it takes a considerable effort to adopt a life style which does not depend on it. It was in the 17th century that the real beginnings of 'classical' physics

came. GALILEO, KEPLER, BOYLE, NEWTON, HOOKE, HUYGENS, GUERICKE, TORRICELLI—these men and many others all laid the foundations of physics. By this time the level of civilization had risen sufficiently for this to become possible.

The 17th century also saw a divergence between philosophy and physics. Physics was then called natural philosophy—this is why doctors of science are given the title 'Ph D'—'doctor of philosophy'. While Galileo got into trouble with the Church for his notions which were opposed to the doctrines of Aristotle, the northern European schools of science no longer had to worry about whether their findings were philosophically acceptable.

Scientific method The scientific method is not an infallible way of finding out the truth: sometimes it fails completely, and what is needed is some rare insight to interpret the results in a new way. The basis of the method, though, lies in experimentation or observation; recording the results accurately; the assumption of *cause and effect*—that every natural phenomenon has a cause which must be investigated; the forming of a theory; and the use of that theory to make predictions about the behaviour of other things.

The principle of cause and effect, while it seems to be a perfectly obvious notion, was not always recognized as such. Early explanations of natural phenomena usually involved the action of a god, and while it is true that modern physics merely pushes the level of understanding rather deeper, the point is that one should always try to find out a more underlying cause.

The first people to record the phenomena around them were the Babylonians, living between the rivers of Tigris and Euphrates, in what is present day Iraq, around 3000 BC. They

had the use of writing, and catalogued the motions of the heavenly bodies. The stone circles of north western Europe, such as STONEHENGE, show that the inhabitants of that part of the world, at around the same time, were trying to do the same thing despite their lack of writing, by laying out an analogue of the celestial motions on the ground.

The Babylonian and early Egyptian records came down to the Greeks, who first attempted to establish some sort of order. Some elementary notions in mechanics and statics—such as ARCHIMEDES' famous bath episode, and his lever experiments —were laid down. The most important contribution the Greeks made was to establish some principles of MATHEMATICS, which has played an essential part in the development of physics. The actual techniques of algebra on which physics is based did not come along until rather later, though the basics were laid down by Diophantus at the end of the 3rd century AD.

After the Greeks, it was the Arabs who took over the development of science. Some original ideas can be traced back to the Arab scholars, particularly al-Haytham's work in OPTICS, and in the symbols used for mathematics, but by and large they merely kept the fire alight until the growth of European learning, first in Italy and then in northern Europe.

Seventeenth century Galileo (1564–1642) was the first physicist of note. His basic experiments in dynamics, and his use of such primary instruments as the TELESCOPE, MICROSCOPE and THERMOMETER, were the first shot in the battle against the dogmas of the Greek Aristotle.

It was Galileo who first talked lucidly in terms of forces and motions of bodies which could be measured. He took the first steps towards finding the laws which related these quan-

tities, rather than just saying, as Aristotle did, that stones fall to the ground, and heavier stones fall faster than lighter ones. Galileo proved Aristotle wrong on this count, and showed how one could calculate the way in which stones do fall.

After Galileo came the work of Newton, Huygens, Boyle and so on. The principal centre was the Royal Society in London, of which all these men were Fellows. Apart from physicists there were such names as Edmond Halley the astronomer, Christopher Wren the astronomer and architect, Evelyn and Pepys the diarists, and John Locke the philosopher.

Newton's work on dynamics, mathematics and optics led the way; in fact he laid the foundations of physics. He found that there is a constant factor which must be included in any equation concerning gravity: what we now call the gravitational constant, G. This was the first of three constants which are essential to our understanding of the properties of matter.

Eighteenth century For the next century or so, scientists consolidated Newtonian (or 'classical') physics, and a textbook on mechanics and dynamics would contain pretty much the same sort of information as one today. 18th century research concentrated on research into heat and its effects, leading up to the development of steam engines, and the first links between science and technology. It also saw the first experiments in static electricity by FRANKLIN and COULOMB.

Nineteenth century In the early 19th century a much more important discovery was made: current electricity was produced and studied by VOLTA, OERSTED, AMPERE and OHM, including its links with magnetism for which FARADAY is famous. This all culminated in MAXWELL's equations in the 1860s, linking such apparently diverse phenomena as ELEC-

Far left: early Greek scientific thought in Athens followed Plato's deductive approach: 'Astronomy, then, like geometry we shall pursue by the help of problems and leave the starry heavens alone.'
Second from left: another school of Greek thought arose later in Alexandria which followed the empirical approach of Aristotle; such technological achievements as Hero's embryonic steam engine had been developed by the 1st century AD.
Above: during the Middle Ages lack of political stability and the repression of non-theological study allowed no real progress. As Boyle was later to observe, Man until Copernicus had been like a spider in a palace interested only in her own web.
Third from left: some consolidation of ideas did take place in the Arab world, mainly in mathematics and optics. This extract from an Arabic script depicts a simple structure for water control and shows a working knowledge of pulleys and axles.

TRICITY, MAGNETISM and LIGHT. Maxwell's equations show that there is another important constant, the speed of light, c.

The increasing use of steam engines in the 19th century led to investigations into the relationships between heat, work and energy. Sadi CARNOT first established that work and heat are linked, the essence of the science of THERMODYNAMICS. The mechanical equivalent of heat was studied by JOULE, and was followed up by Helmholtz and Lord KELVIN.

After this, it was believed that physics was essentially complete, and that all that had to be done was to tie up a few loose ends and calculate everything to a few more decimal places. Sadly for this view, some of the loose ends proved remarkably difficult to tie up, such as the distribution of the light emitted by glowing incandescent bodies.

20th century physics

According to the classical theory, there should be more and more energy given off as one looks further and further towards the ultra-violet end of the spectrum. This does not happen—something seems to be limiting the amount of short wavelengths emitted, which avoids what would be an 'ultra-violet catastrophe'.

Max PLANCK suggested that all this could be explained if energy comes in discrete 'packets' or *quanta*, just as matter is not continuous but is composed of atoms. The QUANTUM nature of radiation is the limiting factor. Einstein went on to show that this idea tied up some other loose ends as well, such as the PHOTOELECTRIC effect.

Others, notably BOHR and RUTHERFORD, extended its influence to the field of atomic physics, showing how the electrons exist only in certain energy levels, governed by the third basic constant, Planck's constant, h. Maxwell's work was not overthrown, but merely amended.

Far from rounding off classical physics, these discoveries opened up the 'new physics'. This took into account all the work on radioactivity done by people such as BECQUEREL and the CURIES, and linked them with the discovery of the electron by J J THOMSON. This, together with Einstein's theory of RELATIVITY which takes over from Newtonian mechanics at speeds approaching that of light, led via the famous equation $E = mc^2$ to atomic power.

Future developments

Physicists no longer believe that all they have to do is to calculate things to more decimal places, though it is generally accepted that our knowledge of basic physics is now unlikely to suffer any upheavals. Fundamental research today is in two apparently widely separated fields, those of PARTICLE PHYSICS and astronomy.

In particle physics, attempts are being made to find the most elementary particles, which all other matter consists of, and to perceive how they interact. In astronomy, it is possible to study matter on a large scale, under conditions impossible to reproduce on Earth, and at very early times in the history of the Universe, as a result of the time taken for the light to reach us from distant objects.

The light from the stars is produced by thermonuclear reactions taking place at a microscopic level, though involving vast numbers of atoms. The action of the weakest force FIELD known, the gravitational force, only manifests itself over astronomical distances. Attempts are currently being made to find a unified field theory, which will link all the four force fields known, and will maybe explain why the constants G, c and h have their particular values.

It is possible that in the process of doing this, new fields and constants will turn up, revealing new aspects of physics which are as yet unsuspected.

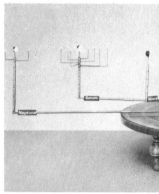

Contemporary theories of celestial mechanics: Descartes' vortex theorem (see right) and Newton's laws of motion. Above: Experiment illustrating Newton's Third Law: every action has an equal and opposite reaction. While both theories appeared plausible at the time, the increasing maturity of the scientific method required prediction. As Descartes' idea could not be mathematically developed, Newton won the day.

SCIENCE MUSEUM

M M RATHORE

SCIENCE MUSEUM

SCIENCE MUSEUM

The 17th century saw major advances on two fronts: celestial geometry and mechanics.

Far left: The earth at the centre of the universe shown by an armillary sphere on the shoulders of Atlas.
Near left: Kepler reordered the solar system and placed the sun at its centre; he also devised mathematical laws to predict the motion of the planets. Shown here is an orrery.

Above left: Priestley's cylinder electrostatic machine.
Left: Natural magnetic lodestones with keepers.
Below: in the 19th century, Maxwell unified electricity and magnetism. Shown here is an early use in the synthesis of sound.

PIANO and its history

The complexity of the modern piano is second only to that of the ORGAN. This complexity arises from the nature of its sound production compared to its ancestors, the *clavichord* and the *harpsichord*. They share the fact that the strings are activated through the depression of a key, but the means of striking the strings is different.

Clavichord   The clavichord became prominent among instrumentalists in the 16th century and was obsolete by 1800. The right-hand (*treble*) end of the box-shaped case contains the sound board, the bridge and the tuning pins; the left-hand (*bass*) end contains the keyboard. The strings are stretched horizontally across. The action is a simple tangent action; that is, the key is pivoted in the middle and when it is depressed a small brass blade called the *tangent* rises on the other end and strikes the string smartly. When the string is struck, it is divided into two parts between the *hitch pin* and the *bridge*. The right-hand part vibrates and the left-hand part is damped by a felt.

The clavichord has a soft sound best suited for domestic music making, but it is unique among pre-piano keyboard instruments in that dynamic range is possible. The muscular action of the player, however, is different, and a pianist will have some trouble adapting himself to the clavichord. Increasing the velocity of the tangent by striking the key *sharply* will increase the volume of the clavichord, but increasing the *pressure* of the touch on the key will raise the pitch of the string, thus playing out of tune.

Harpsichord   The harpsichord reached its peak of popularity in the 17th and 18th centuries. When a key is depressed, a *jack* carrying a *plectrum* and a *damper* rises past the string. The end of the plectrum is angled upward so that it plucks the string as it rises. The top of the jack is hinged and lightly spring-loaded with a bristle, and the string turns it aside as it falls. A felt damper just above the plectrum prevents the string from sounding when this happens.

A simple harpsichord, with one set of strings, was known as a *spinet* or a *virginal* in England; more usually, the harpsichord has two, three or four sets of strings, each with its own set of jacks. The sets of strings are tuned in unison and the player can select or stop out different sets by means of slides which move an entire set of jacks to hit or miss the strings. This varies the tone as well as the volume of the instrument. There may be a separate set of jacks to strike the strings near the ends, producing a sharp sound like a guitar string plucked near the bridge. Stops with leather or felt pads may partially damp the strings; some jacks may have leather and others quill plectrums. All of these devices are operated by the player by means of hand, knee or pedal controls to vary the tone of the instrument.

Piano   Early in the 18th century, instrument makers began trying to build an instrument with a more variable tone than that of the harpsichord. In 1708, Cuisinié devised a keyboard instrument which vibrated the strings by means of a revolving resined bow, in the manner of a violin. A *clavecin à maillets*, invented by Marius in 1716, shows an attempt at a percussive action, a sort of harpsichord with hammers. The invention of the instrument which is the ancestor of the piano is generally credited to Bartelommeo Cristofori, a Paduan who was Keeper of Musical Instruments for a Medici prince. A letter written in 1711 praises 'the piano and forte (soft and loud) in the theme and its answer, (and) the gradual lessening of the tone little by little, and then suddenly returning to the full power of the instrument'. By 1731 music was being especially written for the new instrument.

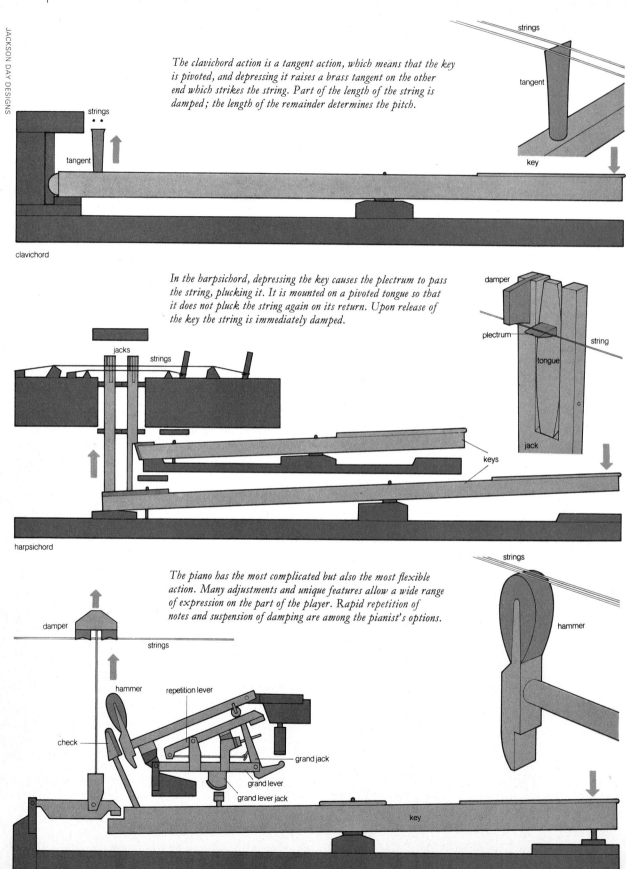

The clavichord action is a tangent action, which means that the key is pivoted, and depressing it raises a brass tangent on the other end which strikes the string. Part of the length of the string is damped; the length of the remainder determines the pitch.

strings

tangent

key

strings

tangent

clavichord

In the harpsichord, depressing the key causes the plectrum to pass the string, plucking it. It is mounted on a pivoted tongue so that it does not pluck the string again on its return. Upon release of the key the string is immediately damped.

damper

plectrum

string

tongue

jack

jacks

strings

keys

harpsichord

The piano has the most complicated but also the most flexible action. Many adjustments and unique features allow a wide range of expression on the part of the player. Rapid repetition of notes and suspension of damping are among the pianist's options.

strings

hammer

damper

strings

hammer   repetition lever

check

grand jack

grand lever

grand lever jack

key

piano

Piano action The essence of the piano's individuality is that a felt-covered hammer is thrown up at the string and rebounds immediately, regardless of the action of the player. Since the hammer is projected rather than carried, it is necessary for it to move faster than the key which sets it in motion. The intervening levers between the key and the hammer are called the *action*, though in common usage the action has come to mean all the parts, including the hammer.

For maximum control of the dynamic level created by the velocity of the hammer, a device called the *backcheck* is fitted which catches the hammer on its return, preventing rebound which might damp the sound. The *escapement* moves aside the lever which lifts the hammer so as to allow the hammer to fall back further than it was lifted, regardless of whether the key is kept depressed or not. Modern grand pianos have a *repetition action* or *double escapement* which stops the return of the hammer at an intermediate stage, allowing for rapid repetition of the same note.

The keys control not only hammers but also *dampers* which rise with the depression of the key and return to damp the sound when the key is let loose. The dampers are also connected to rods at each end of their rank which are operated by another rod connected to the right pedal, called the *damper* or *loud* pedal. This raises all the dampers at once, allowing firstly that all the strings can vibrate whether struck or not, giving added resonance and tone quality, and secondly that the player may move from one note or chord to another without a break in the sound caused by damping. The left pedal, called the *una corda* or *soft* pedal, moves the whole mechanism to the right, so that the hammer strikes only two (instead of all three) of the (treble) strings. The name 'one cord' survives from the time when a choice of one, two or three strings could be made; the device produces a thin, softer tone which is used sparingly for a coloristic effect. Most concert grands today have a third pedal, called the *sostenuto* or *sustaining* pedal, which holds off only those dampers connected to the keys being struck, allowing the player to sustain a note while he moves to another, or to mix sustained and detached notes.

Strings While Christofori's first instrument used the new method of making the strings vibrate, the sound produced was not very different at first from that of the harpsichord. The harpsichord action was very efficient in terms of energy transference, because the strings were light and able to absorb all the energy from the plectrum. This lightness, however, meant that the ability to vary the speed (and therefore the force) with which the hammer struck the string was negated by the limited ability of the light string to absorb the new energy. Until 1834, the wire was made from iron or brass, producing a biting though relatively quiet tone. Steel wire was introduced by a maker from Birmingham; the firm of Webster and Horsfall vied throughout the 19th century with the Viennese firm of Muller. Steel has a tensile strength which approaches the theoretical limit, and this is responsible for the power of the modern grand piano.

At its simplest, if the length of a piece of wire is halved, its pitch will be an octave higher than the original. In practical terms this would mean that the low bass notes of the piano would need a string as long as sixteen feet; in order to overcome this problem the bass strings are made thicker and have copper wire tightly coiled around them. String tension, on the

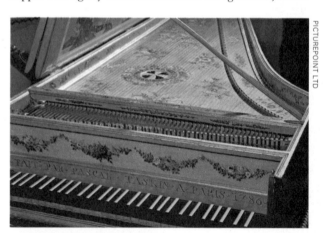

Far left: a 'giraffe' upright piano, about 1800. Early uprights were really grand pianos on edge, with the strings stretching upward from behind the keyboard. Later designs took the strings down to the floor, making the piano more compact for small rooms.

Left: a Broadwood piano from 1782. Note the drawstops.

Above: a French harpsichord from 1786.

other hand, works the opposite way; a doubled tension produces a note an octave higher. Increases in thickness and tension of the strings meant that throughout the 19th century the frame of the developing instrument was constantly having to be strengthened.

Construction The piece of wood (actually made from several pieces) above which the strings are strung is called the *soundboard*. As this controls the amplification of the small displacement of air caused by the vibration of the strings, it is an important element in the tone of the instrument. The chosen wood must transmit sound quickly and with little absorption; the best woods, such as Rumanian pine, Canadian Sitka and Norway spruce, and silver fir, transmit sound at up to fourteen times the speed through air. The position of the strings relative to the soundboard is also important.

Early pianos were of wooden construction, like harpsichords. But as the piano developed, thicker strings and tighter stringing made stronger frames necessary, and metal bars were introduced into the piano cabinet. Before and after 1800 patents were filed for various designs using metal braces, although the reason may originally have been to save space. In 1820 a design was patented using a combination of metal bars and plates of different metals. Based on the principle of thermal expansion of different metals suggested by pendulums in clocks, this frame allowed the hitch pins holding the strings to move slightly according to their temperature. The first casting of an all-metal frame complete with hitch pin block was carried out in Boston in 1825. Three years later pianos were made with cross-stringing, so that the long bass strings passed over the others. This design is commonly used today and adds greater richness to the bass tone, as well as making possible a more compact cabinet design.

A German single action design lasted through the 18th century, and many pianos had a hand stop for raising the dampers. Andreas Stein (1728–92) invented the escapement mechanism, and in England, John Broadwood patented the damper pedal in 1783. John Isaac Hawkins developed the soft pedal; by grading the thickness of strips of cloth or leather from one edge to the other, the player was allowed to 'fake' a diminuendo or a crescendo by gradually introducing or withdrawing the pedal. By the end of the 18th century Broadwood became pre-eminent among English makers for the introduction of an up-striking grand action as well as for experiments with regard to the striking place of the hammers on the strings. During the early part of the century, there was a vogue for special effects, and pianos were made with as many as eight pedals. Composers such as Beethoven and the Scottish musician John Field, who was a great influence on Chopin, influenced the development of the piano; Beethoven admired the English instruments for their sonority, especially the Broadwood.

During the 19th century America began to make an impact on the industry, such firms as Chickering and Steinway showing their wares at international exhibitions. America also possessed the Merino sheep whose wool was found to be best for compression into felt for hammers, although much work on hammers was also done by the English makers Whitehead and Naish.

As the piano became a popular household instrument, experimental designs inevitably followed. There were pianos with double keyboards for piano duets and square pianos disguised as tables. The most useful design was the upright, which created design problems through not having the help of gravity to assist the action. The first uprights were very tall, like grands on edge, and had strange shaped cabinets. In 1800, Hawkins took the strings down to floor level, giving the low, square shape of the modern upright. Robert Wornum was another important designer of uprights, and by 1860 they had replaced square pianos for home use. The composer Chopin actually preferred uprights to concert grands for their more intimate tone. Many modern uprights still have a type of soft pedal which reduces the striking radius of the hammer, thus reducing its force.

PIANOLA (see player piano)

Left: an overstrung, underdamped upright piano. Overstrung means that the strings cross over each other diagonally, saving space. Underdamped means that the dampers are located under the striking line, or hammer line, so that the damping is done where the string excursion, or vibration, is greatest.

Above: balancing the checks, which prevent hammer rebound.

PICK-UP

'Pick-up' is a general term for a TRANSDUCER that converts signals—usually associated with music and musical instruments—into an electrical form. In RECORD PLAYERS and the *transcription units* of HI-FI SYSTEMS, the pick-up converts the mechanical vibrations of the stylus moving in the record groove into an electrical signal for amplification. Such devices are more commonly known as *cartridges* and described as being either ceramic, capacitive or magnetic, depending on the method of conversion. The term 'pick-up' is usually reserved for electric guitars and related stringed instruments.

The guitar pick-up

These devices pick up the vibrations of the strings by the principle of *induced magnetism*. The strings must consequently be of steel or some other magnetic material. A steel string, when placed in a magnetic field, will distort that field. The reason for this is that the magnetic flux will take the path of least *reluctance*, that is, least 'resistance' to the flow of flux, and steel has a lower reluctance than air (see MAGNETISM). In the vicinity of the string is placed a coil of wire. When the string moves the magnetic field the flux pattern will change, thus inducing a voltage in the coil (see *inductance*). By connecting the coil terminals to an amplifier a manageable signal can be obtained.

In practice, a small permanent magnet is placed under each string—six in all for a guitar and four for a bass guitar. Around these is placed a coil consisting of many turns of light gauge insulated copper wire. The coil terminals are taken to a socket on the instrument for connection to amplifier and speakers.

This is the simplest arrangement possible and in principle the best. There is however, one major drawback with this system. Given the environment of the electric guitarist, situated as he is amongst a mass of electronic equipment, the pick-up will respond to any stray magnetic fields, and mains 'hum' becomes a problem.

Eliminating mains hum

As it is not possible to eliminate the stray magnetic fields emanating from mains cables at source, it must be eliminated at the pick-up. This is achieved by an arrangement of two coils such that the hum in one of the coils cancels out that in the other, while the signals in each add together to make a stronger signal.

In this arrangement, rather than having 12 separate permanent magnets (six for each coil) one long and slender bar magnet is used. This is arranged so that the poles are along the two opposite narrow faces of the bar, which is mounted flat under the strings with its long axis across them. Along the pole faces are, mounted vertically, 12 soft iron pole pieces which concentrate the field in the vicinity of the strings. The north pole pieces form one line and the south poles a second line, so that there is one north and one south pole to each string. The coils around the two sets of poles are wound in opposite directions and connected together in series.

The nett signal is the sum of the signals in the two coils because, although they are wound in opposite directions, the poles associated with each are likewise opposites. With stray external magnetic fields, however, the winding arrangement

Below: the guitar pick-up works on the principle of induced magnetism. When a magnet is placed near a steel string there is a concentration of magnetic flux lines in the vicinity of the string and when the string vibrates there is a vibrating flux pattern which induces a similarly oscillating voltage in the pick-up coil. Mains hum is eliminated using two coils wound in opposite directions.

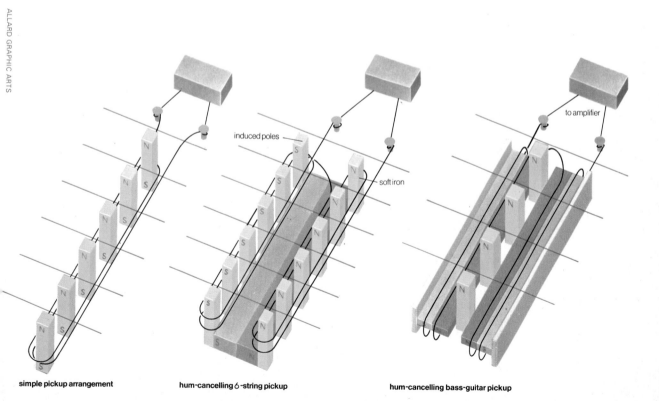

simple pickup arrangement

hum-cancelling 6-string pickup

hum-cancelling bass-guitar pickup

causes cancellation of any hum.

A similar arrangement is made for the four-string bass guitar pick-up, but it is usually of a sturdier construction so that low frequency vibrations do not create a 'fuzzy' signal. Two bar magnets are used instead of one, placed side by side in a south-north-south configuration with two coils (again wound in opposite directions) lengthwise around the two bars. The flat soft iron pole pieces are attached to the outer south poles and four vertical pole pieces, concentrating the field near the strings, positioned along the central north pole.

Design

One problem is that—particularly with bass pick-ups—vibrations in the pick-up and between it and the guitar body lead to a low quality signal. These devices are therefore mounted firmly on a solid brass plate which is attached to the instrument. With bass guitars, this is usually placed in a recess in the wooden body of the instrument.

Because the coil has an associated inductance, this, coupled with any stray capacitance in the system, leads to a characteristic resonant frequency determined by the values of capacitance and inductance. This means that the circuit offers less resistance to an oscillating current at one frequency than at any other. If this resonant frequency occurs somewhere in the instrument's range of notes then one note will be louder. Consequently, the pole pieces can be adjusted to obtain a fairly uniform signal at all frequencies. With the double coil arrangement, one set of poles is adjustable while the others are fixed.

Below: a modern six-string electric guitar pick-up. This has two coils so arranged that any stray magnetic fields from mains currents cancel each other out. Mains hum is a problem with single coil pick-ups.

Bottom: single coil pick-up. The coil forms a resonant circuit and the frequency response is corrected by adjusting the pole heights.

PICTURE RESTORATION

Although picture *restoration* is the better known term, emphasis is placed nowadays rather on CONSERVATION—that is, maintaining a painting in a stable state by correct storage and treatment. Restoring a picture to its original appearance is only one aspect of the conservation of paintings.

Structure of paintings

Paint consists of a coloured material, often a natural mineral, ground into a powder (the *pigment*) and mixed with a liquid which, in time, sets to a hard film (the *medium*). The main structural layer of a painting is known as the *support*.

Watercolours have a support of paper and a paint layer of pigments ground in a medium of gum. Wall paintings in Renaissance Italy, called *buon fresco*, consisted of pigments ground with pure water painted on to wet lime plaster: as the plaster set (by combination with atmospheric carbon dioxide) the pigments became physically bonded to the calcium carbonate layer.

In easel paintings the support is usually a wooden panel, or canvas stretched over a wooden frame, prepared for painting with layers of plaster or paint called the *ground*. The paint itself might be a single layer or many layers superimposed. In early Italian pictures there are often areas of gold under which are preparatory coloured layers (usually red) called *bole*. Paintings were usually varnished, when dry, with a natural resin dissolved in an organic liquid. Natural resins (such as *copal* or *dammar*) discolour badly with time, which is one of the main reasons why paintings have to be cleaned.

Watercolours

A common problem of watercolours on paper is that they are easily stained by contact with materials such as animal glues and inferior types of backing boards. Often, watercolours have been mounted on cards with glues which are breeding grounds for all sorts of moulds and small insects,

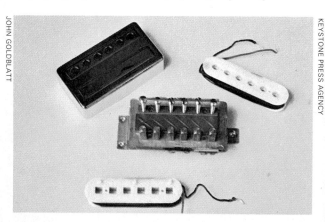

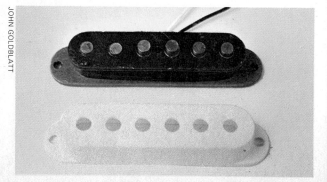

and the first task of the restorer will usually be to remove everything from the reverse of the paper. Stains are then removed by local or overall treatment with very mild BLEACH solutions, followed by extremely thorough washing with pure water to remove all traces of the bleach. Overall bleaching can be done by spraying, or by total immersion of the water-colour laid on a glass plate—but first it is vital to carry out detailed tests on any colours and inks which might run or alter chemically under the action of water and bleach.

After treatment the water colour is lightly attached to best quality card with hinges of thin paper, before framing. Water colours must never be exposed to strong light as the delicate colours are often fugitive and will easily fade.

Wall paintings

Mural, or wall paintings pose unique problems for the conservator because treatments almost always have to be carried out in situ, without the refinements of the restorer's studio. Centuries of neglect, damp and damage by war have made many wall paintings into pale fragments, and such catastrophes as the Florence flood of 1966 made the problem that already existed infinitely worse. Conservation techniques must be simple, effective and able to be operated on a huge scale.

Until the mid-19th century, decaying areas of frescoes were merely demolished and modern paint substituted, more or less matching the missing original. When the importance of trying to preserve the original paint became paramount, adhesives were used in an attempt to fix flaking paint and plaster: however, many frescoes were ruined by the use of wax which made the delicate chalky surface irreparably greasy and dark, and made later conservation virtually impossible. The main enemy of frescoes is damp, soaking down from the roof of the building, or upwards from the earth bringing with it SALTS which crystallize out within, and on the surface of, the painting. These may be nitrates from decomposing buried organic matter, or calcium sulphate formed by the action of acidic sulphur oxides (always present in polluted city air) on the calcium carbonate of the plaster. The crystals not only obscure and eat away the surface of the fresco, but the physical pressure of their formation within the plaster can cause whole areas to disintegrate. The coloured surface swells and falls off, revealing large pockets of powdery calcium sulphate.

To solve this particular problem, the fresco is treated with solutions which precipitate barium sulphate throughout the plaster layer—this is insoluble, inert and forms a hard, strong network protecting and reinforcing the plaster. The technique is to apply the solutions in a cellulose pulp to ensure prolonged contact and maximum penetration.

Sometimes the only way of saving a fresco is to remove it from the wall and mount it on a stronger support—a process known as *transfer*. The technique is simply described, but requires great skill to carry out without damage: two layers of cloth are stuck on to the face of the fresco with animal glue, left to dry, and then pulled away from the wall, bringing the fresco with them. There are different degrees of transfer called *strappo* and *stacco* depending on whether only the colour layers

Far left: a restorer working on a panel from Hampton Court Palace, England. X-ray examination of the panel had revealed two earlier paintings beneath the top one, a 17th-century painting of the entry into Jerusalem. The first painting dated from the 15th century.

Below: the picture on the left is a normal holographic image of a 15th-century Italian painting of St Catherine. The picture on the right is a holographic double exposure of the same painting, the two exposures being taken at different temperatures. Irregularities in the interference pattern reveal detached areas of paint.

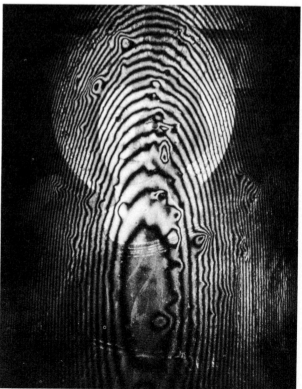

APPLIED OPTICS

APPLIED OPTICS

are removed, or the outer layer of plaster as well. A bonus of *stacco* transfer is that the preliminary drawings for frescoes are often revealed: these are named *sinopie* after the red pigment used and are sometimes very beautiful works of art in their own right.

Easel paintings Conservation and restoration of easel paintings fall into two main categories: treatment of the support and treatment of the painted surface. In most cases, the support layers must be made secure before working on the front of a painting.

Wood panels used for painting have a problem in common with all wooden objects in that they expand and contract widthways across the grain as the humidity of the air changes. This movement can lead to warping, cracking and loosening of original joins in the panel. However, more damage is done in trying physically to prevent the movement, than in allowing it to proceed under controlled atmospheric conditions. Thus, in the past, bars of wood and complicated slotted wooden grids (called 'cradles') were stuck on to the back of panels to prevent them warping. When the panel tried to move, it strained against the restriction, and splits and corrugations developed at the weakest points. Nowadays restorers favour removal of all such restrictions, and the panels are flattened under their own weight in conditions of high humidity. The moisture content is then made stable by sealing the back of the panel with a water impervious layer known as a *moisture barrier*. Various methods have also been devised for joining splits and strengthening or supporting weak panels without restricting their movement.

Canvas supports are less susceptible to atmospheric changes than wood, but they have the disadvantage of being easily torn or dented. Also, their flexibility can cause brittle paint to flake, curl or crack. Weak or torn canvases and loose paint are often treated by *lining* the painting: this involves sticking a new piece of canvas on the back of the original canvas, using a suitable adhesive. In cases where the paint is loose, the adhesive is made to penetrate through both canvases to fix the paint in place.

If a support is so weak that it cannot effectively be consolidated, then *transfer* to a new support might be carried out. As in the transfer of wall paintings, layers of material are attached to the paint surface: then the painting is laid face down and the support is carefully cut away until the reverse side of the ground is reached. In a *complete transfer* the ground, too, is removed and the restorer sees the astonishing sight of the back of the paint layers—the whole painting in mirror-image. This operation is so delicate and exacting that it is only very rarely carried out as a last resort.

When the support is secure, the paint layers may be treated. The 'cleaning' of a painting means removal not only of dirt, but also discoloured varnish layers and retouchings put on in the past to cover older damage. The fault of old retouchings

Far right: the original canvas support of a painting is carefully cut away with a scalpel. To hold the paint layers intact while the canvas is removed, the front of the painting is attached to a temporary support by means of adhesive. Once a new canvas backing has been secured, the temporary support can be removed.

Above right: restoration in progress on a painted ceiling and wall at the Royal Naval College, Greenwich, England.

Below right: a painted section is removed from a ceiling before cleaning and restoration.

is that they often became dark and unsightly, and frequently extend beyond the area of damage and cover original paint. The technique of cleaning is to apply suitable solvents or solvent mixtures on small swabs of cotton wool which absorb the varnish and retouchings as they dissolve. Cleaning must be rigorously controlled so that no original paint is removed. Sometimes retouchings will not yield to suitable solvents and are split away from the original paint with surgeons' scalpels.

After cleaning, old losses are retouched using pigments ground in a clear synthetic resin. How retouching is done varies from country to country and with the type of picture—ranging from complete matching to filling in the missing area with a single neutral colour. Resins used for retouching and also for the final varnish should remain colourless and soluble in the mildest possible solvents, so that they may be removed at any time.

Scientific examination of paintings

The restorer of today is increasingly guided by the methods of analytical science. A well-known example is the use of X-rays to detect forgeries, overpainted pictures or changes of composition by an artist. Also important are simple colour photography for recording all stages of treatment, INFRA-RED *photography* for showing underdrawings and ULTRA-VIOLET *fluorescence photography* for observing changes on the surface of a painting.

Microscopes are much used, both for observing the painting directly and also for examining minute samples taken from the edges of old damages. These samples are often embedded in a clear resin and ground down in such a way that a cross-section of all the paint layers is visible. Study of cross-sections gives a great deal of information on the technique and technical history of a painting. Microchemical analysis to identify pigments and media can be carried out directly on them, using both simple classical methods and instrumental techniques.

PIEZOELECTRIC MATERIALS

'Piezo' is derived from the Greek word meaning 'press' and the *piezoelectric effect* is the production of electricity in a material by the application of pressure. This effect only occurs in electrical INSULATORS and results in the appearance of electrical charges (see ELECTROSTATICS) on the surface of the mechanically deformed material. The converse effect to piezoelectricity also exists. When an electric field is applied to a piezoelectric crystal, it distorts mechanically. All piezoelectric materials can be used in either way.

The piezoelectric effect only occurs in materials where the atomic BONDS are *ionic*—that is, where the atoms are arranged in positive-negative pairs called *dipoles*. Pressure applied to the material distorts these dipoles, causing a separation of the positive-negative pairs and creating an electrical field. The dipoles must either be naturally orientated or be capable of orientation in an electric field in the form of an ELECTRET, usually a *heteroelectret*.

Whether or not the piezoelectric effect is observed depends upon the arrangement of positive and negative ions in the material. This restricts the effect to crystalline materials having no *centre of symmetry*, that is, not perfectly symmetrical (asymmetrical), since for a crystal with perfect symmetry no combination of uniform stresses will produce a charge separation.

An example of a substance with a perfectly symmetrical crystal is sodium chloride, common salt, where each positive charge is surrounded symmetrically by negative charges and vice versa. Barium titanate, however, is a substance with an asymmetrical crystal and exhibits piezoelectric properties. Crystal can be divided into 32 types depending on how the atoms are arranged (see CRYSTALS AND CRYSTALLOGRAPHY). Of these, 20 possess the property of piezoelectricity because of their asymmetry.

Associated effects When substances are heated they usually expand. If a crystal is heated and the crystal structure is asymmetrical it may expand differently in different directions. This effectively causes a mechanical stress on the crystal. The production of a charge on the surface of a crystal by heating is called *pyroelectricity*. All pyroelectric crystals are piezoelectric but the converse may not be true because not all piezoelectric crystals have different thermal expansions in different directions. Of the 20 piezoelectric crystal types only 10 are pyroelectric. Pyroelectric materials have applications in heat and infra-red detection devices. They are being used increasingly for infra-red cameras and for night viewing devices.

Piezoelectric properties Piezoelectric activity can be defined in a number of ways but the most useful practical measurement is the change in polarization or dipole orientation produced for a given applied stress (pressure). This, the piezoelectric constant, is given the symbol d. d is also obtained by determining the strain (change in shape) produced for a given applied electric field. Another measurement which is required is the fraction of the energy which may be transferred from mechanical to electrical energy or vice versa. This is the electro-mechanical coupling constant K.

Materials In the past two decades, much development has taken place. The first piezoelectric material was quartz, but this has a low efficiency of mechanical to electrical conversion and a low charge produced for a given applied force.

Ammonium dihydrogen phosphate, known as ADP, can, like quartz, be produced in large crystals and has many advantages over quartz. *Sodium potassium tartrate* (Rochelle Salt) has for many years been the most common material in cheap commercial application.

All these single crystal materials need to be cut along particular crystal axes to achieve maximum effects, which is a jeweller's art. Apart from quartz, the other single crystal materials already mentioned present problems in use because of their water solubility and mechanical weakness. Until recently, therefore, quartz was the most popular piezoelectric material because of its chemical stability and mechanical strength.

The largest class of piezoelectric materials in use today are the CERAMIC oxides. These materials offer the advantages of providing strong, stable oxides at a lower cost than the water soluble single crystals. Furthermore since the polycrystalline ceramic materials can be made in any size or shape and do not require to be oriented along preferred crystal axes, like the single crystals, they offer great versatility of design.

A ceramic consists of a compact of very small crystals which have their axes oriented in random directions. Ceramics, like the single crystal, have no net polarization in their normally prepared state and must have their intercrystalline dipoles oriented to produce heteroelectrets and thus induce piezoelectricity. This process of polarization is carried out by 'poling'. In poling a high voltage (about 10 kV) is applied to the crystal or the ceramic material in order to drag all the small dipoles into the same direction. The force necessary to do this is sufficiently high to prevent random rearrangement on removing the voltage. Often the material is heated, to make the dipoles more mobile, and cooled with voltage applied.

Many ceramics have been investigated for use as piezoelectrics, but *barium titanate* and *lead zirconate titanate* (PZT) are the most common. These materials form the basis for two families of materials whose properties may be modified by changes in chemical composition or preparation procedure.

One property that has not been mentioned so far is the *Curie temperature*. This is the temperature above which all the dipoles that make up the electrets become randomly oriented and thus cause all piezoelectric activity to be lost. The process is reversible, but on cooling below the Curie temperature the material would require 'poling' again. It is thus essential that the Curie temperature of a material lies outside the working range. Curie temperature is very sensitive to chemical composition and only minor changes need be made to produce satisfactory Curie temperatures. The Curie temperature of

ITT/PHOTO: PAUL BRIERLEY

Left : quartz crystals for piezoelectric applications such as oscillators are cut and polished with very high precision.

Right : when a piezoelectric material (such as a heteroelectret) is distorted, charge separation occurs which produces an external electric field. Conversely, an external field causes distortion. Because of the symmetry of common salt (top right), piezoelectric behaviour cannot occur. Common salt (NaCl) is built from Na$^+$ and Cl$^-$ ions arranged in cubic form with perfect symmetry. Each Na$^+$ or Cl$^-$ is surrounded symmetrically by six ions of the opposite charge. Barium titanate, BaTiO$_3$ (bottom left) on the other hand, does exhibit piezoelectric behaviour. This shows how it is built up asymmetrically from Ba^{2+}, Ti^{4+} and O^{2-} ions in an elongated cube. The Ti^{4+} ion sits at centre of six O^{2-} ions, where the distance c is greater than a. Two piezoelectric ceramics in parallel form a gramophone pick-up (bottom right).

barium titanate is around 110°C and that of PZT above 300°C.

Applications Piezoelectric materials are used wherever mechanical and electrical energy must be interchanged—they are therefore used in TRANSDUCERS—devices which interchange types of energy, for example microphones. In principle piezoelectric transducers can compete with all other electromechanical transducers including motors and generators. In practice they are limited to small mechanical displacements and small amounts of electric charge per cycle. With repetitive operation in the ultrasonic range they can nevertheless develop acoustic or electrical power in the 1 to 10 horse power range. Because they become more useful the higher the frequency of the operation cycle, piezoelectric materials are found in the field of acoustics and are even better suited to ULTRASONIC applications.

Record player pick-ups The most common use of a piezoelectric material is in record player pick-ups. Until 1950 the single crystal Rochelle Salt dominated the market, but has since been replaced by ceramics such as barium titanate and PZT. The forces available from the record groove are of the order of 1 to 5 grammes and this produces an output from the ceramic element of from 0.1 to 0.5 volts.

Ultrasonics Piezoelectric ceramics are invaluable in the generation and reception of sound waves in water or other liquids. The applications include ultrasonic cleaners working in the range of 20 to 100 kHz. In ultrasonic devices, the vibrating piezoelectric causes 'cavitation' in the liquid effectively agitating and 'sucking off' dirt from contaminated surfaces. Sonar devices working in the same frequency range comprise an active emitter and a detector so that the position

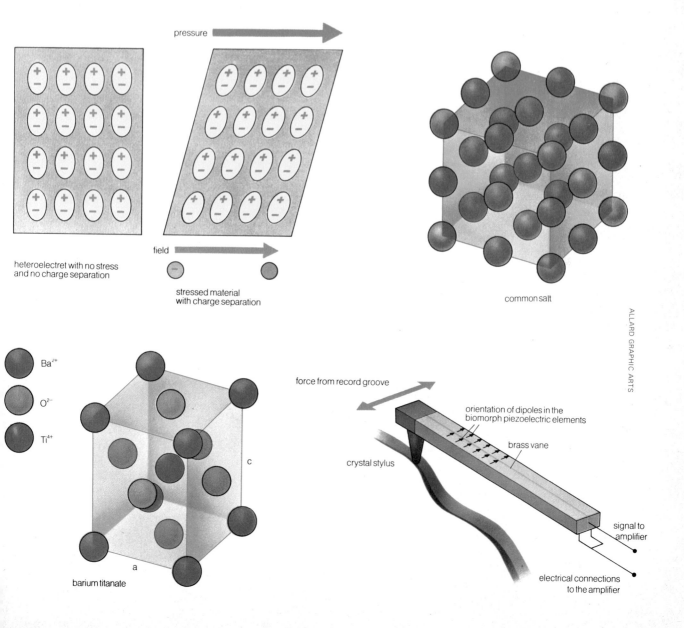

pressure

heteroelectret with no stress and no charge separation

field

stressed material with charge separation

common salt

Ba²⁺

O²⁻

Ti⁴⁺

barium titanate

force from record groove

orientation of dipoles in the biomorph piezoelectric elements

brass vane

crystal stylus

signal to amplifier

electrical connections to the amplifier

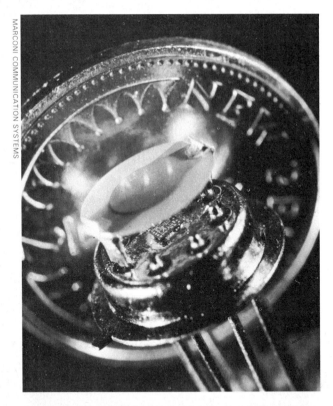

MARCONI COMMUNICATION SYSTEMS

ITT / PHOTO: PAUL BRIERLEY

of objects which reflect the ultrasonic beam can be found from the time difference between the transmitted and reflected signal. This technique is used for fish detection, echo depth sounding, and sonar underwater devices (see ASDIC and HYDROPHONE).

Low amplitude and high force motion is required in devices such as ultrasonic cutters, welders and soldering irons. Welders have been developed for both plastics and metals. Ultrasonic waves can also be used in flaw detectors and medical diagnosis, where the reflection of the sound waves at interfaces between body tissues or at cracks in bones is recorded like a depth sonar signal.

High voltage sources A study of piezoelectric constants shows that practical levels of compression, say up to 7000 psi (482 bar), will produce voltages in the range 5 to 15 kV per cm. Such devices could provide the spark for gasoline motor ignition although at present this application is not possible owing to the depolarization of the ceramic element under continuous stress. A unique advantage of a piezoelectric compared with a conventional magneto or induction coil system is the independence of voltage from the engine speed, which would make for excellent starting. Commercial applications of sparks from the high voltages has come for butane and natural gas igniters for heaters, cooking stoves, brazing torches and even cigarette lighters. Both impact and gradual squeezing are used as sources of compression of the ceramic.

Displacement transducers Distance can be measured by piezoelectrics, as the voltage produced will be proportional to the amount of compression. Miniature transducers have been placed in blood vessels to record periodic pressure changes associated with heart beats. Special purpose transducers can be developed as blast gauges and noise sensing elements to detect boiling of water in nuclear reactors.

Electronic applications Data handling systems and computers require the delaying of signals by known amounts of time ranging from one second upwards. The propagation of sound in solids provides delays in signals, using conveniently sized elements. The signal propagates through the solid by generating a new electric signal as it passes by distortion of the ceramic crystal. Sound travels at about 2500 metres per second through PZT. For frequencies of 30 MHZ the requirement is for devices with a thickness of about 0.05 mm.

Piezoelectric crystals have major applications in devices determining or limiting the operating frequency of electric circuits. In these devices the mechanical RESONANCE frequency of the piezoelectric crystal influences the electric signal. Electric energy is converted to elastic energy and then back to electric with a particular resonance frequency. These devices are used as filters in the IF (intermediate frequency) stage of radio receivers and transmitters. Piezoelectric ceramics are an order of magnitude poorer than quartz in the stability of resonant frequency. Quartz is thus used where high accuracy is required, such as quartz stabilized clocks (see QUARTZ CLOCK), where accuracies of one part in 10,000 or better can be achieved.

Top left: this tiny device, no larger than a pea, is a complete quartz crystal oscillator with microelectronic integrated circuit. The crystal is designed to operate at its natural frequency.

Left. quartz crystals (SiO_2) are grown artificially under high temperature and pressure. The solvent used is water with alkali.

PILEDRIVER

A piledriver is a machine used to install *piles*, which are sheets or columns, usually of steel, driven into the ground to support a building or other structure. It is some 4000 years since the first piledriver was used to install stakes to support primitive lakeside dwellings, and in other periods, in the days of the Romans for instance, piles were used to form the foundations of many known historic buildings still in existence today. The early piledrivers operated on the simple drop hammer principle, dropping a heavy weight (such as a rock held by a rope) on to the pile to drive it into the ground.

Drop hammers used today are made of cast iron and weigh from half a ton to five tons. They are fitted with guides which slide in vertical members to ensure that the hammer remains central on the pile. Although this method is still in use it is rather slow compared with more modern drivers which are powered by air, diesel, or occasionally steam. Some drivers are available which operate by hydraulic or electrical systems.

Piles fall into two main categories. Steel *sheet piling* is used to withstand horizontal forces, which occur in docks and on temporary works. *Bearing piles* are used mainly to build upon, and skyscraper blocks are founded on these except where soft ground makes other types of foundation necessary.

Below: this MENCK-MRBS 7000 pile hammer is designed for use in offshore oil or gas production platform construction work. It is a single acting, steam powered hammer, with a falling weight of 154,000 pounds (70,000 kg).

Air hammers   There are two main types of air hammer, *single acting* and *double acting*. The single acting driver is similar in action to a drop hammer, but the heavy falling *ram* is raised by air or steam pressure instead of by a CRANE.

When the desired stroke (height) has been reached the pressure is released, letting the ram fall and knock the pile into the ground. The rams vary in weight between 2.5 and 15 tons, and the single acting driver is somewhat more efficient than the drop hammer. Single acting hammers are used to install bearing piles.

The double acting air hammer is a somewhat lighter tool used to install sheet piling. It normally operates on compressed air, and has a light ram rather like a piston, which moves up and down within a cylinder, the bottom end of which is the *anvil* that rests on the top of the pile. Air is admitted to the cylinder to lift the ram, which on its upward journey actuates a valve arrangement that cuts off the air supply to the lower part of the cylinder and transfers it to the upper part above the

Below: an early form of piledriver, a heavy weight which is raised to the required height and then dropped on to the pile, hammering it into the ground. This arrangement was designed to drive piles into a river bed or a harbour to form the foundations of a bridge or a dock.

Bottom: driving H-section steel piles. When steel piling is used for temporary support work it can be removed for re-use by means of a piling extractor which acts like an inverted piledriver.

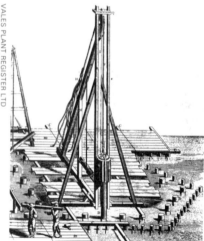

VALES PLANT REGISTER LTD

BSP INTERNATIONAL FOUNDATIONS LTD

ram. This forces the ram back down the cylinder to strike the anvil, which in turn strikes the pile, and the air is expelled through exhaust ports.

Diesel hammers Unlike the air and steam hammers which require an auxiliary source of power (COMPRESSORS or

Below: in the single acting hammer the air or steam passes down through the piston and lifts the ram, then the valve is closed and the ram falls and strikes the pile. In the double acting hammer, the air raises the ram and is then diverted up the transfer tube to force it back down on to the anvil. The ram of the diesel hammer is raised by a crane and then released. As it falls it operates the fuel pump which sprays diesel fuel into the chamber. Just as the ram strikes the anvil the fuel-air mixture ignites, driving the ram back up to restart the cycle.

steam generators), the diesel hammer is a self contained unit. Like the double acting air hammer, the ram is in the form of a piston moving within a cylinder. The hammer is started by lifting the ram with a crane and releasing it when the required height has been reached.

On the downward stroke the ram actuates a cam-operated fuel pump which injects a measured amount of diesel fuel into the combustion chamber at the bottom of the cylinder. The ram continues downwards, closing off the exhaust ports and compressing the trapped air. The ram then strikes the anvil, thus driving the pile, and at the moment of impact the fuel-air mixture (which has been highly compressed in the combustion chamber at the bottom of the cylinder) ignites, and the resulting explosion drives the ram upward to start the cycle again (see DIESEL ENGINE). It is stopped by turning off the fuel.

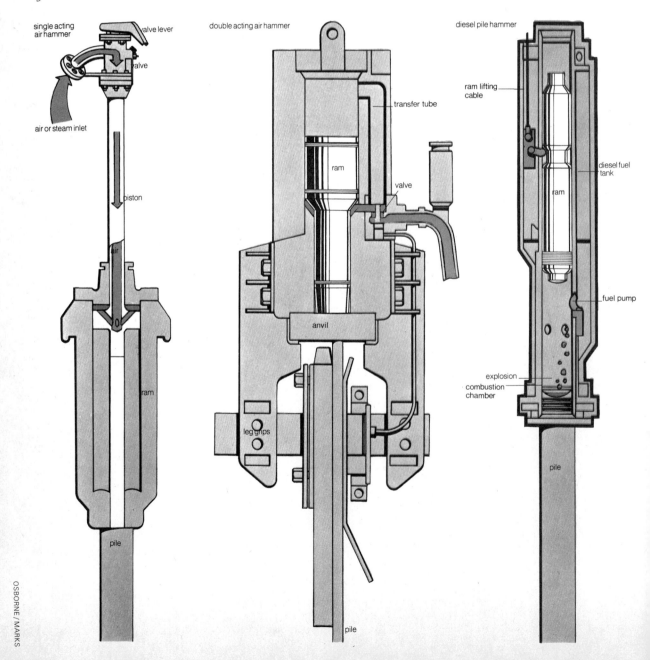

Above: an example of an air launched RPV used for weapons delivery. This is a Teledyne Ryan BGM-34A with a Maverick missile, carried on a pylon beneath the wing of a DC-103E launch aircraft.

Right: a Short Skyspy remotely piloted surveillance vehicle. Powered by a piston engine, it takes off vertically, converts to horizontal flight until it is over the target, and then hovers above it photographing it or sending TV pictures or other information back to its ground base. It can also be used for missile guidance.

PILOTLESS AIRCRAFT

A pilotless AIRCRAFT, like a guided MISSILE, is an unmanned self-propelled airborne vehicle; its flight may be guided either by remote control or by preset equipment carried on board. Unlike missiles, most pilotless aircraft are designed to be recovered after a mission and used again.

The first aircraft to be flown 'hands off' was a Curtiss flying-boat of the US Navy, tested in 1913 with a gyroscopic stabilizer designed by Lawrence Sperry. This device formed the basis for the first practical autopilot. Pilotless aircraft were, and are, used chiefly as targets for fighter aircraft and anti-aircraft weapons. Some are otherwise-standard full-sized aircraft, converted to be flown by remote control, but most are smaller and specially designed for the purpose. Known as *target drones*, they account for the greatest number of pilotless aircraft built today, but increasing use is being made of a class known as *remotely piloted vehicles* (RPVs).

The basic components of a pilotless aircraft, as of a missile, are the airframe, motor, and onboard control, command and guidance systems. In operation, these are supported by launch, remote control and (usually) retrieval systems; and, for target use, require target augmentation and scoring systems.

Airframe and motor Almost without exception, airframe design and construction is similar to that of a piloted AIRCRAFT or air-breathing missile. Conventional aerodynamic control surfaces (wings, ailerons, elevators, fins) are fitted, and the motor may be a piston, turbojet, turboprop or rocket engine. Piloted aircraft converted for drone use normally retain the cockpit (often with provision for a human pilot to monitor the instruments) and the wheeled undercarriage. Some other drones and RPVs also have an undercarriage, but most are designed not to need one.

Command guidance system Most pilotless aircraft have a RADIO command guidance system, in which an onboard radio receiver collects and decodes signals transmitted by the remote control operator and interprets these signals to activate RELAYS for manoeuvring the aircraft, switching the scoring equipment on or off, or other required functions.

Because most targets are comparatively small, their RADAR 'signature' (the energy reflected by the metal skin of the aircraft) is normally too low for radar tracking to be reliable. The signature can be augmented by an onboard radar beacon receiving a PULSE-CODED signal from the tracking station and responding with a coded reply at a fixed power output.

Complementary to the command guidance system is the TELEMETRY equipment on board the drone which relays information back to the remote controller to indicate whether his commands are being carried out correctly. It can also send back data (such as drone speed, altitude and fuel remaining) to guide him in formulating subsequent instructions to the drone.

Launch system Target drones and RPVs (other than conversions from piloted aircraft) are launched either from a ground or ship launcher, or from a carrier aircraft in flight. The surface launcher is usually a short, rail-type structure (fixed or

pitot   fairing

vertical stabiliser

6935

engine fairing

wing

elevon

fairing

fuel tank fairing

engine

pyrotechnic parachute
ejection system

auto-pilot

batteries

parachute pack

fuel tank

boost separation swing links

nose

fairing

solid fuel boost motor

engine air intake

fairing

wing

elevon

mobile) from which the drone is launched at an upward angle, either under its own power or boosted by a JATO (Jet-Assisted Take-Off) bottle which fires for a few seconds and drops away once its fuel is expended. For an air launch, drones or RPVs are suspended from pylons under the wings of a 'parent' aircraft. As in a ground launch, preflight systems are checked and the engine started via umbilical connections which are retracted before launch. No boost motor is normally needed: the drone simply drops away from the pylon, and the remote controller assumes command a few seconds later. Drones converted from piloted aircraft, and some larger RPVs, have a conventional undercarriage for normal runway take-off and landing.

Remote control system This consists of the transmitting portion of the radio command guidance system; a control box through which flight and other commands are fed to the drone; a radar tracking unit with facilities for plotting the drone's course and displaying its position; and equipment for receiving, interpreting and displaying the data telemetered

Above: the major components of the Turana RPV built by GAF in Australia. Designed for gunnery and guided weapons target use, it has a Microturbo Cougar turbojet engine which gives it a top speed of 450 mph (724 km/h) and a range of 374 miles (602 km). Based on the Ikara missile, it is a successor to the Jindivik target drone of which almost 500 have been built.

Right: a sequence of pictures showing the mid-air retrieval of a Supersonic Firebee II. The automatic parachute system in the tail is activated and when the main 'chute has fully opened the recovery helicopter moves in to snare the drogue 'chute. The main 'chute is then discarded, leaving the Firebee suspended below the helicopter.

back from the drone to the controller. It is usually located at the ground (or ship) control centre, but may be installed in the launch aircraft.

Retrieval system   Pilotless aircraft which have no undercarriage to land on at the end of a mission generally have some form of PARACHUTE recovery system, actuated automatically or by remote control. A small drogue 'chute and larger main 'chute decelerate the drone and lower it to the ground or water for pickup. Inflatable airbags may be fitted to cushion the landing or to keep the drone afloat. The most widely used method, however, is the helicopter mid-air retrieval system (MARS). In this, a load line attached to the drone extends upward above the main parachute to a smaller engagement parachute. A hook lowered by the helicopter snares this third 'chute, and once the helicopter is safely supporting the drone's weight the main 'chute disconnects automatically, the helicopter returning to base with the drone suspended below it. If the command radio signal is lost, or is interrupted for a given time, a safety device can activate the recovery parachutes automatically.

Target augmentation system   Because a drone has realistically to represent a full-size aircraft target, yet is relatively small itself, its size must be augmented artificially to the attacking pilot. Augmentation may range from a simple smoke-dispensing system, making it easier for him to see when aiming his weapons within visual range, to electronic systems to make its image appear larger on his cockpit instruments. Against heat-seeking missiles, for example, a heat source can be carried to enlarge its infra-red signature. Target identification can be assisted by an onboard radar beacon, similar to that used in the tracking system, as a semi-active homing aid. A MICROWAVE amplifier system, using a transistorized power supply, can increase the natural radar signature emitted by the airframe.

Scoring system   In most missile-firing situations, since the target is outside the interceptor's visual range, the drone carries equipment to record the accuracy of weapons fired against it; these include both 'direct hits' (which do not actually hit the drone but pass very close to it) and those which come within a specified 'miss-distance' which would be lethal in a combat situation. Typical systems use either the DOPPLER effect principle or a series of separate transmitters in the drone, the interceptor and the missile, all feeding data to a computer at the remote control centre.

RPVs   This new class of pilotless aircraft has developed from the target drones in current use. Their attraction lies in their small size, and therefore their relatively low cost; their suitability for active military roles in situations where a human pilot in the cockpit is not essential, or where his presence would endanger his life; and their ability to perform strenuous manoeuvres unhampered by the physical limitations of having a man in the cockpit. Already they have been used successfully for photographic and electronic reconnaissance (eg, in Vietnam); sensor dropping; radar intelligence-gathering; electronic countermeasures (as jammers or decoys); and for weapons delivery. One type can fulfil a pathfinder role, locating and 'locking on' to a target with its TELEVISION CAMERA and LASER designation system, and relaying details of the target to a backup strike force of weapon-carrying RPVs—all under remote control. Recent developments also include 'mini' RPVs, which are no bigger than ordinary radio-controlled model aircraft yet can carry miniature cameras, scanners and other sensors over short battlefield ranges.

PINBALL MACHINE

The pinball machine, often called *pin table* in Britain, is an amusement device in which the player obtains the highest score possible on a display board by causing a steel ball to travel around a wooden playing board, negotiating obstacles.

Construction   The working units are contained in a rectangular wooden cabinet measuring 22 × 54 inches and 16 inches deep (about 56 × 137 × 41 cm). It is mounted on four steel legs, giving a sloping playing field 36 inches high by 38 inches (91 × 96 cm) wide with the low end where the player stands. The display board is at the other end of the cabinet facing the player and is 28 inches (71 cm) high.

The working components are electrically operated by 24 volts AC, and the lighting display by 6.8 volts AC, the power being obtained from a double-wound transformer. The basic working units fall into four categories: fractional hp motors, relays, solenoids and switches. The motors are used to drive cams which cause switches to pulse. Relays are used to transfer voltage links to different circuits, and solenoids are used to turn power into mechanical movement.

Operation   Upon insertion of a coin, switches close, starting a motor which turns a wheel carrying painted numbers, and a certain credit is shown on the display board through a little window, according to the value of the coin. The player pushes a start button, which delivers a ball to the playing board, causes the machine to light up, causes all the electrical devices to home to zero and again operates the credit device, this time removing a credit.

Next the player pulls a spring-loaded plunger at the right-hand corner of the table, which sends the ball up to the high end of the sloping board, and the ball then rolls back down the board, negotiating obstacles. Runways and obstacles have rubber rings around them to give rebound to the ball. The chief mechanical obstacle is the *bumper*, a round device several of which are mounted on the playing board. When the ball rolls against a thin plastic ring around the base of the bumper, a vertical rod in the centre of the ring, extending below the surface of the table into the well of a contact blade, moves in the well, causing a switch to make contact. A solenoid creates a magnetic field which pulls down sharply on an assembly of plunger and yoke around the top of the bumper, and the ball is pushed sharply away from the obstacle, careering across the table to hit other obstacles. Each time the ball strikes an obstacle a

Below : the works of a pinball machine are a maze of electromagnetic devices and wiring. These are relays, which are switches controlling a circuit by means of another circuit.

score is registered on the display board.

The other important device is the *flipper*. There are two, at the low end of the table, operated by buttons on each side. If the ball rolls between them, it goes down an *exit hole*, but the player can use the flippers (pivoted arms) to bat the ball back up into the obstacle course, and he can shake (*tilt*) the table to make the ball roll towards the flipper. If he shakes the table too much, it is sensed and the game is over.

There are also two runways at each side of the table, one of which is called the *out-hole*. These are provided because otherwise a skilful player might be able to keep a ball in play for a long time, and then the table would not make much money.

Normally, a player gets five balls, and bonus scores for achieving a certain number of points; if he gets above a certain score, he may receive an extra ball or a free play (five more balls). As each ball disappears down the hole, a new ball becomes available and the player uses the spring loaded plunger again to bring it into play. Normally also, bells ring each time a ball strikes an obstacle but the bells are often disconnected because of the noise factor.

The display board is screened (painted) with a garish design, and the games are called such things as *Delta Queen*, *Skylab*, *Lucky Ace* and so on, although they are all essentially the same. Hidden within the design are 'ghosted' areas which appear only when illuminated, giving a message to the player such as 'game over', 'ball to play' or 'tilt'. If the tilt limit has been exceeded the game cannot continue unless the player inserts a new coin.

Above right: the advance unit, which causes various units to light up when the balls strike them. Bells are also supposed to ring, but they are often disconnected to keep down the noise.

Right: a pinball machine, or pin table, with the glass top removed and the works open.

Below: the bumper, one of the scoring devices on a pin table. When a ball strikes the plastic ring, the vertical rod in the centre moves in the well, causing an electrical contact. A magnetic field pulls sharply downward on the yoke at the top of the bumper, pushing the ball away, and the bulb lights up.

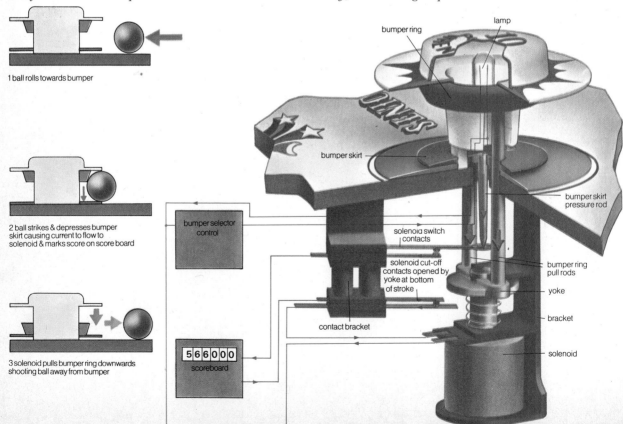

1 ball rolls towards bumper

2 ball strikes & depresses bumper skirt causing current to flow to solenoid & marks score on score board

3 solenoid pulls bumper ring downwards shooting ball away from bumper

bumper ring

lamp

bumper skirt

bumper selector control

solenoid switch contacts

solenoid cut-off contacts opened by yoke at bottom of stroke

bumper skirt pressure rod

bumper ring pull rods

yoke

bracket

contact bracket

566000
scoreboard

solenoid

PIPELINE

The transport of fluids by pipeline has been known since early civilization. The Chinese are believed to have used pipes made from bamboo or clay about 5000 BC. Evidence can still be seen in Italy of the large aqueducts and the lead pipes constructed by the Romans about 2000 years ago to bring fresh water to the cities. Until the mid-19th century pipes made from wood or lead were mainly used for this purpose, laid to a fall so that the water could flow under the force of gravity. Cast iron or asbestos cement pipes are now used, joined together with spigot and socket joints, permitting water flow under pressure.

With the development of commercial crude oil production, which commenced over 100 years ago in the USA, pipelines became necessary. The first, 6 miles long and of wood, was soon superseded by cast iron pipes. Steel pipes were later introduced, mechanical joints being used until recent years when the all welded system was adopted. Steel pipes are not, however, very suitable for carrying water as corrosion can occur on the inside wall of the pipe, and where these are used, it is necessary to provide a suitable internal lining.

Oil pipelines

When the world consumption of crude oil began to increase rapidly, pipeline systems were developed in the producing areas, mainly in America and the Middle East for the movement of large volumes of oil either to the centres of consumption, or to the coast for shipment by tanker. The Trans-Arabian pipeline, which connects the oilfields of Saudi Arabia with the Mediterranean port of Sidon, is 1000 miles long. It began operating in 1950 and cost about £80,000,000. There are, however, many shorter pipeline systems throughout the world.

Gathering pipelines from distant well heads in the desert converge on the gathering centre at Zelten. Here the unwanted gases are removed before the crude oil is pumped 100 miles to the Mediterranean coast.

In Europe steel pipeline systems were slower to develop as most of the demand for petroleum products was met by the import of crude oil from the Middle East, there being little indigenous crude production. Refineries were usually located near to the coast and close to major areas of consumption, product transportation being via road or waterway. The last 25 years has, however, seen a considerable growth of pipeline networks in Europe for moving crude oil or oil products, and natural or manufactured gas. This has been partly brought about by the increasing size of tankers used for crude shipment, which in many cases can only berth at terminals which have water depths in excess of 60 ft (18 m). The discovery in recent years of vast deposits of crude oil and natural gas off the shores of Europe, has also led to the demand for transportation systems both inland and offshore.

Materials and production

Pipes can be made from a number of materials including steel, cast iron, asbestos cement, aluminium, plastic or even pre-stressed concrete. Mechanical joints are normally used for most of these materials but steel and aluminium pipes can be welded together. Distribution systems for the handling of crude oil, products or gas are invariably constructed from high quality steel pipes with welded end joints.

Early steel pipes were produced by ROLLING from plate and joined by electric resistance WELDING; later a solid drawn system without a seam was adopted. The increasing demand for large diameter pipe led to the development of the submerged

Left: construction of a 30-inch (76 cm) marine pipeline with flotation drums as it is manoeuvred ashore off the barge.

Below left: welding 30-ft (9 m) lengths of pipe. A pneumatic clamp inside the pipes locks them in alignment and the welder seals the pipe into a continuous bore. Laying gangs (right) with side-boom tractors trench the pipeline.

Next page bottom: pipelines for bringing crude oil ashore from supertankers. Once the pipes have been laid the countryside will be restored to its former state.

Far right: a pipeline for bringing ashore natural gas from the Leman Field, N. Sea.

arc butt welding process to produce pipe up to 48 inch (122 cm) in diameter, rolled from plate and providing pipe of extremely high quality to close tolerances. A more recent development is spirally welded pipe which is made from steel strips wound spirally to any desired diameter. Modern production methods are now capable of producing pipe with high, but permissible, stress values, enabling considerable economy in pipe thickness for the same operating pressure. Strict quality control is imposed at all stages of production to ensure acceptable pipe capable of operating at very high pressures (from 1500 to 2000 psi—103 to 138 bar) with complete safety.

Construction
Almost all pipelines laid across country are buried, usually with a depth of cover of about 1 metre. This not only provides protection for the pipe, but allows the normal use of land where it passes through agricultural areas. The technique of laying a steel pipeline with welded joints involves the use of highly specialized equipment and trained personnel. Pipeline construction is undertaken by several teams working in unison, usually known as a *spread*. Each team has a specific duty ranging from clearing the route of any obstacles, excavating the ditch for the pipe, welding the pipes together and laying them in the ditch, the final operation being the restoration of the ground to its former condition. Special crews deal with particular areas such as major road or river crossings.

The laying of steel pipelines offshore involves a very special technique, particularly for large diameter pipelines in deep water such as the North Sea. Lines must be designed to ensure negative buoyancy so that they will remain on the sea bed; this is usually achieved by applying a reinforced concrete coating to the pipe which also provides extra protection. A careful analysis is required of the stresses expected during the laying of a submarine pipeline to ensure that the pipe will not suffer any damage during this operation. Sea lines of a few miles in length close to land may be installed by welding sections ashore, then hauling into position by a winch aboard a ship. For longer lines, the pipeline is usually installed by means of a lay barge which moves along the route laying the pipe behind it along an inclined submerged support which projects from the barge. Wherever possible, offshore lines are buried in the seabed to provide greater stability to the line and reduce the risk of damage caused by fishing operations or from ships' anchors. Considerable development has also taken place in recent years on the construction of barges capable of laying large diameter pipelines in increasing water depths under adverse weather conditions.

Pumping stations
Single or multi-stage centrifugal PUMPS are normally used in liquid pumping stations, operating either in series or in parallel. Other types of pump such as reciprocating or rotary are sometimes used, but the centrifugal pump is usually the most suitable for general duty. The purpose of a pump is to provide the force or pressure required to move the fluid along the pipeline, overcoming friction and any adverse

static head. For a long line it may be necessary to install a number of pumping stations at intervals to provide the overall pressure requirements. Flow conditions for gas lines are more complex as a result of the compressibility of gas and compressors are used for this purpose. On average, over flat terrain, pumping stations are 20 to 30 miles (32 to 48 km) apart.

The choice of drivers partly depends upon local conditions and the availability of fuel. They can be electric motors, steam turbines, gas engines, large diesel engines or gas turbines. Electric motors usually prove to be the most acceptable.

Control systems Complex pipeline systems are normally designed for fully automatic operation on a fail safe basis. Operation of a system, including all the principal equipment, can be initiated from one central control room. All essential operating data is transmitted back to the control centre on a continuous basis so that the controller is always fully informed of the operating conditions of the pipeline. Communication is normally by microwave radio or direct cable, although public utility circuits are sometimes used.

Many pipeline systems make use of COMPUTERS to assist in batching schedules, that is, the predetermined cycle of liquid products. Some of the latest systems are now designed so that the control of all operations can be linked directly to a computer.

Corrosion control Buried steel pipelines are protected externally by the provision of a wrapped coating on the outer pipe wall, and it is usual for a cathodic protection system to be applied by means of an impressed current or sacrificial zinc anodes (see CORROSION PREVENTION). Should a fault develop in the coating, this diverts corrosive action away from the pipe.

Testing All cross country steel pipelines are tested for tightness and resistance to pressure before they are put into operation. The testing medium is usually water and the test pressure is always higher than the actual maximum operating pressure. Before putting a pipeline into operation it is also usual to pass a 'go devil' or 'pig' through its entire length, pushed through the pipe by air or water. A go devil consists of a short length of rod with circular steel plates attached at both ends, the front plate being made just a little smaller in diameter than the inside of the pipe. When passed through the whole line it clears the pipe of any obstructions and demonstrates that the pipe has been laid without damage. To enable easy location a pig can be fitted with a short life radio-active capsule for detection above ground. Batching pigs or inflatable spheres can also be used while pumping products through a pipeline to maintain separation between different products.

PIPE manufacture

Pipes nowadays are manufactured from various materials for the building, chemical and mining industries, as well as for agricultural and motorway drainage, and other public works applications such as pipelines for gas, water and sewage.

Clay pipes were used as early as 4000 BC for drainage systems and lead pipe was manufactured in Roman times, the metal *plumbum* (Latin; hence 'plumbing') having a conveniently low melting point of 327°C (620°F). In Crete, Egypt and Rome, evidence of ancient clay drainage systems has been found, and the Romans left evidence of their clay drainage and lead pipework in Britain. Examples of gravity flow water pipes made from bored tree trunks can be seen in a remarkable state of preservation, notably at Kingussie in the Scottish Highlands.

After many centuries of squalor and ill-health, especially in cities, caused by lack of sanitation, it was only in the 18th century that pipes were again used in any quantity for the conveyance of sewage. In modern times pipes have been made from paper fibres during times of shortage, from cement combined with various materials, and increasingly from plastics.

Lead pipe From the 18th century, lead pipes and gutters were used, being highly resistant to corrosion. Water pipes of smaller diameters were installed in buildings until the 1930s, when copper tubing (see TUBE MANUFACTURE) proved more economic and gave better damage resistance and serviceability in cavity walls and floors. In any event, the toxic properties of lead pipes mean that they are no longer considered suitable for water service, and they are becoming obsolete. They are made from long, flat sheets of lead, rolled over and soldered.

Clay pipe In 1845 Henry Doulton began producing salt glazed stoneware pipe at Lambeth in South London, and after the Public Health Act of 1848, resulting from an inquiry into bad sanitary conditions in Britain, there were eventually some 200 small companies making this type of pipe. As increasing population has made necessary the piping of effluent over longer distances, pipe diameters for sewage lines have increased from the 4 and 6 inch (10 to 15 cm) sizes to a range of 10 to 18 inches (100 mm to 450 mm) in clayware pipes and even larger in other materials.

The clay is quarried at seam levels up to 300 feet (91 m) below ground. It is ground to a powder and brought to a plastic state with water and other additives in troughs by mechanical means (for example, twin parallel knife-carrying shafts revolving in opposite directions). The clay passes through a vacuum chamber to remove entrapped air and is fed to hoppers serving extruders. The EXTRUSION process for clay pipes forces the clay by means of a rotating auger or ARCHIMEDEAN SCREW through the space between a solid core of circular cross section and a larger cylindrical opening; the annular space between the two represents the thickness of the pipe wall. The extruded pipes are trimmed and dried. In drying, warm air is circulated round the pipes as they roll in the insulated drier, which may be several hundred feet in length. An older method was to allow the pipes to rest on slatted floors in rooms into which air was drawn from nearby kilns.

Tunnel kilns over 200 m (more than 650 feet) long accommodate pipes on rail-mounted cars which pass successively through pre-heater, firing and cooling zones, before reaching the off-loading station. The preheater is fed by warm air from the cooling zone and reaches a temperature of about 200°C (360°F). In the firing zone the temperature is increased by burning oil or gas to about 1100°C (1980°F), at which point the clay *vitrifies*; that is, the constituent elements fuse together. During the 1960s the industry passed from glazing of all the product to acceptance of unglazed as the British Standard specification, resulting from technological advancement to a much improved clay body density. Where glazing is still applied, it is either an overall salt glaze or a ceramic glaze applied to the inner surface only. During firing the salt glaze is imparted by volatilization of common salt in the kiln.

Pitch-fibre pipe   Pitch-fibre pipe was introduced following World War 2 when the run down clay pipe industry was unable to meet the requirements of the period. Pitch-fibre had the advantage of lighter weight, being a combination of bitumen and paper. The manufacture involves a mixture of paper fibre and water transferred from an endless felt (term for a felt belt) to the surface of a polished mandrel. After drying in an oven, the paper tube is plunged into a bath of hot pitch and cooled in water.

Concrete pipe   *Spun concrete* pipe is made by a centrifugal casting process in which the outer mould is spun rapidly so that the wet concrete is compressed to the mould by CENTRIFUGAL FORCE.

Pre-stressed concrete pipe can withstand greater compression forces. Steel wires are bedded into the concrete; during hardening, the core is expanded by a sealed flexible liner being subjected to high water pressure, so putting tension on the wires. After hardening the pressure is released and the liner removed, reducing tension on the wire and imparting a corresponding compression stress to the concrete. Usually this type of pipe is made in large diameters up to 47 inches (120 cm) for trunk mains conveying water supplies.

Asbestos cement pipe is manufactured in $1\frac{1}{2}$ to 35 inches (3.8 to 90 cm) diameters from a mixture of selected asbestos fibres and Portland cement, providing a combination of

Below left: production of 2 m × 375 mm diameter ($6\frac{1}{2}$ ft × 15 in) vitrified clay pipe for use as main drains and sewers.

Below centre: die formers in storage. These are the female dies which form the inside diameter of PVC pipe in the extrusion process.

Below right: the Anger extrusion line which makes 12 inch (about 300 mm) PVC pipe. The pipe is cut to 9 m (about 33 feet) and will withstand 12 bar pressure, a British Standard requirement.

flexibility and strength for water and sewage mains and irrigation applications. A thin film of wet cement and asbestos fibre is transferred, as in pitch-fibre pipe manufacture, from an endless felt on to a polished mandrel, but the mandrel rotates and continuous layering takes place. The layers are consolidated by means of hydraulic pressure over the pipe length until the required wall thickness is reached. The mandrel is removed and the pipe is matured in water for several days prior to end trimming, followed by a further period of air maturity. Joints are in the form of asbestos cement sleeve couplings with rubber sealing rings. Cast iron detachable flange joints are an alternative where access to the pipeline may become necessary.

Plastic pipe   PLASTICS have been developed as pipe materials since the 1950s. Thermoplastic materials used for making pipe are *polyethylene*, *polypropylene* and *polyvinyl chloride* (PVC). *Thermoplastic* means that they will soften and flow under sufficiently high temperatures and harden again upon cooling. This is an essential feature of the extrusion process used in making plastic pipe.

Polymer materials are made of large molecules by combining smaller molecules called *monomers*. The materials, containing additives such as fillers, plasticizers, stabilizers, pigments and lubricants, are stored in a granular form in silos, and are pneumatically conveyed to the extrusion machinery as needed. The extruder applies heat, variable between 160 to 220°C (320 to 428°F), and pressure to the powder to *gelate* it into a homogeneous mass which can be formed into the desired shape. It is first semi-gelated and goes through a decompression zone for removal of volatiles; then further heat and pressure are applied to complete gelation before the mass reaches the diehead.

The inner part of the extrusion die is held by streamlined metal strips projecting inwards from the outer die body; this part of the die is called the *spider*. A well-designed die has enough length and compression beyond the spider to ensure

HEPWORTH POLVA PLASTICS

fusion of the melt and avoidance of *spider memory*—traces which might cause splitting. The final parts of the die are the mandrel and the female die, determining the inside and outside diameters respectively. The exact outside diameter is determined by a cooled calibration jacket against which the pipe is forced by internal air pressure; a piston attached to the mandrel retains the air, which is supplied through one of the spider legs. For smaller diameter pipe this is accomplished by an external vacuum applied to the jacket.

The extruded pipe is cooled by water jets and automatically cut to length. It is supplied either with plain or pre-formed socket ends for push-fit joints. The joins can be welded, cemented or push-fit using rubber sealing rings. Couplings made of cast metal are also used, and these can be plastic coated for corrosion resistance.

Thermoplastic pipe is light and easy to handle. Polyethylene (PE) pipe is flexible and in small diameters is used for gas mains and cold water service. Polyvinyl chloride is increasingly used; without a plasticizer additive, it has good rigidity and strength and is known as uPVC (unplasticized polyvinyl chloride). uPVC pipe is used for gas mains, sewage trunk and water mains, household drainage, conduit for electric and telephone wiring and other uses. Slotted or perforated uPVC pipe is now being used for agricultural and motorway drainage. Being highly resistant to corrosion above or below ground, having excellent flow characteristics and being easy to handle, uPVC pipe will continue to find new applications.

PISTOL (see automatic pistol revolver)

Below : overhead view of the Anger extrusion line for making PVC pipe. The machine applies heat and pressure to the polymer to make a soft homogeneous mass and then pushes it through dies.

HEPWORTH POLVA PLASTICS

PITOT TUBE

A pitot tube [impact tube] is primarily used for the measurement of speed or velocity of a fluid, either gas or liquid. The instrument is named after Henri Pitot, who recorded work in 1732 on the measurement of water flow (see FLOWMETERS). In principle, if an open ended tube faces the flow of the fluid, a pressure will build up which will increase with the velocity of flow; thus, if a PRESSURE GAUGE is attached to the outlet of the tube, the gauge will indicate fluid velocity.

The tube facing the fluid is known as the *head* and is required to sense a *total pressure*, which is the addition of the surrounding (*static*) pressure and the pressure due to flow (this is called *dynamic* pressure). The face of the tube creates an obstacle to the flow; this is known as a *stagnation point* which creates a *stagnation pressure*, and it requires very careful design to make the stagnation point give the required *total pressure*.

To derive an indication of velocity a pressure difference must be measured between the total pressure and the surrounding static pressure, which is sensed by *static vents*. In a simple system the vents are holes pierced in the side of the outer tube assembly, but in large installations such as aircraft, the airflow is complicated and therefore static vents are placed at a number of positions and the average pressure is taken.

Total pressure is directly dependent upon the density of the fluid, which is directly dependent upon *absolute temperature* (temperature measured in Kelvins, where 0°C is 273 Kelvins—273°K). The error on measured velocity due to temperature change is approximately 0.2% per °C in air and therefore compensation must be included for high accuracy. Aircraft air speed indicator (ASI) systems do not usually have temperature compensation because first the error is not serious in this application and second the aerodynamic properties which control flight are all affected in the same manner.

Design features A typical design is the L shaped tube, which is satisfactory where the fluid flow is straight and not swirling, that is, there is no turbulence. This design will begin to give significant error if the flow deviates more than about ± 10°, but by shaping the inlet hole, flow angles of up to ± 60° are acceptable. A general purpose pitot static tube would be about 8 mm (0.3 inch) diameter and have a smooth surface. The nose must be carefully tapered or shaped to give both minimum disturbance to flow and achieve a good total pressure. Smaller and larger versions are made for special purposes, often with in-built temperature sensing elements; also, very special shapes are necessary for supersonic conditions. A number of pitots may be grouped to measure angles of incidence or turbulent flow and if icing is probable, electrical heating may be added.

The basic tube is usually metallic, either non-ferrous or stainless steel and the mounting and surrounding assembly is often plastic or of a fibrous material. In conditions where damage may occur a protective shield may be added but this must not interfere with the flow; additionally, the nose may be hardened to prevent abrasive action disturbing the shape.

Aerodynamic properties In subsonic conditions, the pressure difference sensed by the pitot-static system is proportional to velocity squared, that is, every time the velocity is doubled the pressure difference increases by a factor of four

Right : the first diagram shows the basic principle of measuring the pitot pressure of moving air or liquid. In the pitot-static arrangement shown underneath pressure from the forward flow is compared with lateral static pressure. The third diagram shows the position and appearance of the tubes on an aircraft.

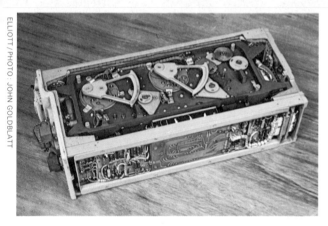

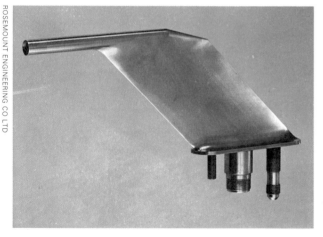

(see HYDRO- AND AERODYNAMICS). As velocity increases towards the speed of sound in the fluid, shock waves begin to build up until supersonic conditions are reached, where the pressure can in some circumstances decrease with increased velocity. At these speeds, there is a need for special tube shapes.

At low air velocities, the pressures are extremely small, for example, at 2 mph (about 3ft/sec, 1 m/s) the pressure is only about 0.0001 psi; at 200 mph (100 m/s) this increases to about 1 psi. Thus for faster moving vehicles such as aircraft, the pitot becomes a practicable method of air speed indication. Complications arise, however, because, due to air density changes with altitude and temperature, the indicated air speed (IAS) is not the true air speed (TAS). At 3000 ft, the TAS is approximately twice the IAS.

Calibration To obtain accurate calibrations, the pitot system must be placed in a fluid flow which is directed accurately along the axis of the tube, without disturbance or turbulence. This is known as *laminar flow*. A common method is to use a *whirling arm rig*, which consists of a rotating arm, perhaps 10 to 20 ft (3 to 6 m) long, whose outer end travels in a circular trough. The pitot is mounted on the outer end of the arm and although the travel is circular, the radius is large enough for the fluid flow to be considered laminar. This method is useful for the lower velocity calibrations and has the advantage that the fluid velocity is known directly from calculation of the arm speed and does not require reference to any other fluid flow instruments.

Top left : this static and pitot-static transducer unit measures the pressure of the airstream and static air pressure—providing signals for computing airspeed (these are fed to an air data computer). Connections are made by pipe to the pitot tubes.
Left : this is a fuselage mounted pitot tube with built-in de-icer.

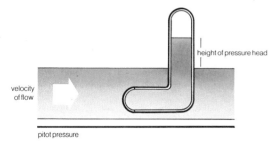

velocity of flow

height of pressure head

pitot pressure

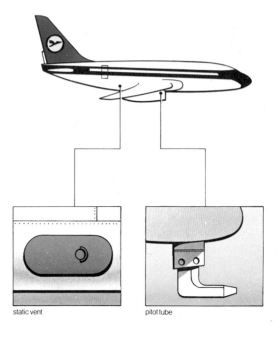

static vent

pitot tube

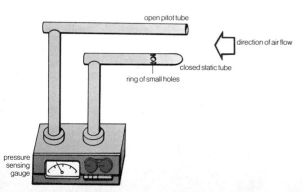

open pitot tube

direction of air flow

closed static tube

ring of small holes

pressure sensing gauge

pitot-static pressure tube

The WIND TUNNEL is another method for calibration and can be more useful for higher speed air flow. The tunnel is usually rectangular and can range from a few inches to many feet across with a length which is many times the aperture. This, plus careful design of the air driving fans, creates laminar flow. In a wind tunnel, the velocity calibrations must be compared with an instrument of known calibration.

Both of the above rigs are means of generating fluid velocity and, apart from calibration, they are frequently used for conducting flow experiments where pitots would be the means of determining the resultant velocities.

Associated equipment
Some sort of pressure measuring instrument is required to indicate the pressure difference sensed by the pitot-static system. The *liquid manometer* is widely used for experimental purposes, where the pressure may be conveniently fed to each end of the classic U tube configuration.

Differential pressure gauges are more practicable for many purposes, for example, the aircraft air speed indicator; in this case the linkage within the gauge is mechanically designed to compensate for the square law (where pressure is proportional to the *square* of velocity of the fluid) and provide readings on a linear scale. Where an electrical signal is required for control or computation, a *differential pressure transducer* would be used. In this case, the compensation for the square law would be done electrically.

Typical uses
One of the greatest uses is for the measurement of velocity of airborne vehicles, aircraft, missiles, and so on, where the higher speeds and the requirement for aerodynamic information make the pitot ideal. Considerable use is found in research and development where 'clusters' or 'rakes' are often fitted to rigs, to test pumps, turbines, compressors and so on, and establish both velocity and direction of flow.

Below : pitot-static pressure tube probe mounted on the nose of an HS Harrier. Speed is determined from the dynamic and static pressure.

SMITHS INDUSTRIES LTD

PLANCK, Max (1858–1947)

Max Planck is best known for his QUANTUM THEORY of ELECTROMAGNETIC RADIATION which he first presented to a meeting of the German Physical Society in December 1900.

Born in Kiel in 1858, Max moved with his family to Munich where he attended school and university, later transferring to Berlin University to be taught by great physicists of the day, Herman Von Helmholtz and Gustav KIRCHHOFF. Throughout his long life Max Planck was interested in the study of heat, known as THERMODYNAMICS. It was in this subject that he presented his doctoral thesis and published papers which led to him becoming a professor at Berlin University on Kirchhoff's death.

Unlike most scientists the breakthrough in scientific thought for which Planck is today remembered came rather late in life when he was 42. This was his discovery of the quantum theory of energy for which he was awarded the Nobel Prize in 1918. Planck was the first to realize that the energy of all electromagnetic waves (including light, heat and radio waves) can exist only in the form of discrete packages, or *quanta*, rather than being continuously distributed in a wave-like form. In this he returned to the 'corpuscular' theory of light which NEWTON had rejected.

Ironically Planck was both worried and frightened by the theory he proposed. A mild man descended from a long line of lawyers and civil servants, he was cautious in his speech and believed totally in the classical theories of electromagnetic radiation as explained by MAXWELL, which were shown by his theory to be inadequate at short wavelengths. Also he was not satisfied with the mathematical formulation of the quantum theory, as it gave the energy of a quantum of radiation as the product of the frequency of the radiation and a small constant. Planck firmly believed that this constant could be removed. *Planck's constant*, h, as it is now called, is one of the fundamental constants of nature (like the velocity of light in a vacuum) and is vital to the understanding of the nature of atoms themselves and how they absorb and emit radiation.

Thus Planck was rather annoyed when his quantum theory was championed by an unknown Swiss clerk in a paper on the theory of RELATIVITY. The clerk's name was Albert EINSTEIN. After this bad start a firm friendship grew between the eager young Einstein and Planck, who was, by now, middle-aged. It was said that neighbours often heard them playing chamber music together, Einstein on his violin and Planck at the piano.

Perhaps it was partly this friendship as well as Planck's faith in God which enabled him to withstand the many trials in his life. He continued to teach physics in the decadent and crumbling Berlin and even to visit Hitler, in his capacity as secretary of the Prussian Academy of Sciences, until the age of seventy. Sadly, for Planck and for German science, many of his colleagues, including Einstein, had to flee from the Nazis and Planck's son, Erwin, was executed as an accomplice in the July plot against Hitler.

Max Planck's greatest sorrow was the rift in physics he felt he had caused. Until his death, at the age of almost ninety, he strove to reconcile the classical physics he believed and taught the modern physics he had founded.

PLANCK'S CONSTANT (see quantum theory)

Right : a photograph of Max Planck and an extract of a letter he wrote in May 1916 to Arnold Sommerfield. The letter deals with electron transitions in Planck's theory of the atom.

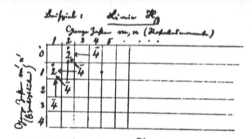

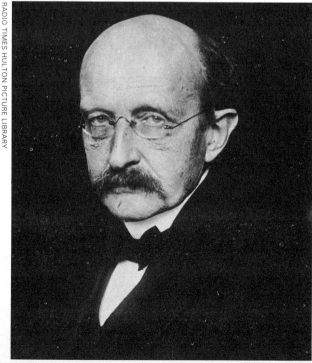

PLANETARIUM PROJECTOR

A planetarium projector is a device capable of projecting, on to the inside reflecting surface of a hemispherical dome, a realistic view of the night sky as seen from any place on the surface of the Earth. It is also able to demonstrate, in a few minutes, all the major movements associated with the sky. These include the daily (*diurnal*) motion of the sky, the monthly motion of the Moon (including its phases), the annual motion of the Sun and planets against the background of the stars, and the precessional motion of the Earth's axis. There are separate projectors for the stellar background, the Sun, the Moon and the planets.

One of the simplest ways of obtaining the stellar background is by means of a sphere with many small holes drilled into its surface. The sizes of the holes are related to the brightness of the stars, and they are positioned so as to represent the stars in their correct relative positions. At the centre of this sphere is a point source of light, giving sharp images without lenses, mounted in gimbals. A hemispherical cup cuts out light for stars which lie below the horizon, no matter which way the projector is pointing. Light from the point source passes through the holes in the sphere, and causes spots of light to fall on the inside of the dome. The holes for the bigger stars are rather large, so these stars would appear as discs instead of

The Zeiss projector at London Planetarium. Set here for the skies of the Equator, it moves about the central ring to give daily motion, and adjusts about the horizontal axis for different latitudes.

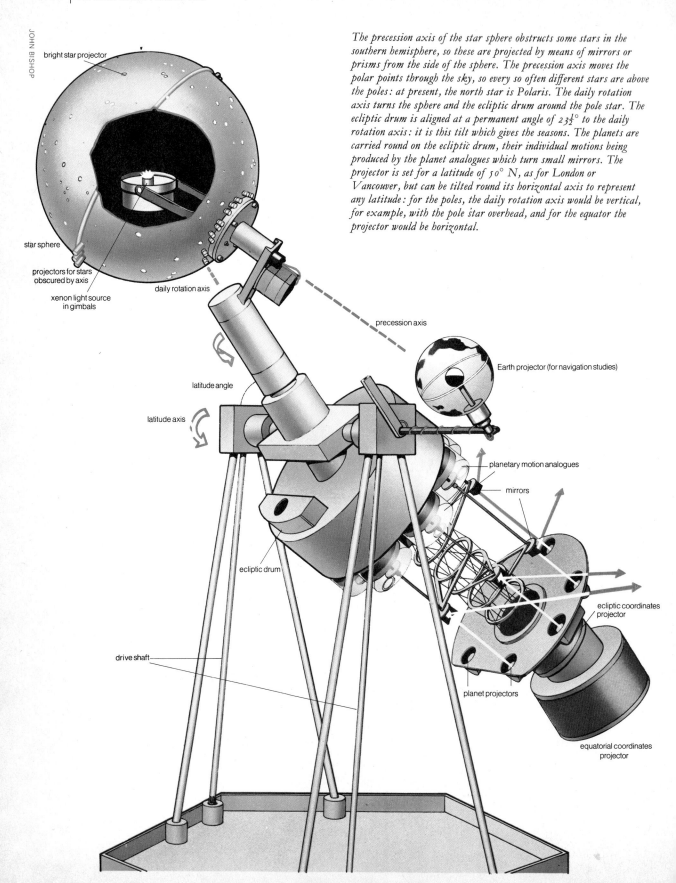

JOHN BISHOP

The precession axis of the star sphere obstructs some stars in the southern hemisphere, so these are projected by means of mirrors or prisms from the side of the sphere. The precession axis moves the polar points through the sky, so every so often different stars are above the poles: at present, the north star is Polaris. The daily rotation axis turns the sphere and the ecliptic drum around the pole star. The ecliptic drum is aligned at a permanent angle of $23\frac{1}{2}°$ to the daily rotation axis: it is this tilt which gives the seasons. The planets are carried round on the ecliptic drum, their individual motions being produced by the planet analogues which turn small mirrors. The projector is set for a latitude of 50° N, as for London or Vancouver, but can be tilted round its horizontal axis to represent any latitude: for the poles, the daily rotation axis would be vertical, for example, with the pole star overhead, and for the equator the projector would be horizontal.

bright star projector

star sphere

projectors for stars
obscured by axis

xenon light source
in gimbals

daily rotation axis

precession axis

Earth projector (for navigation studies)

latitude angle

latitude axis

planetary motion analogues

mirrors

ecliptic drum

ecliptic coordinates
projector

drive shaft

planet projectors

equatorial coordinates
projector

points of light. To overcome this difficulty the larger stars have small lenses which concentrate the light to form points. This type of system is used in the Spitz projector, which uses a mercury-xenon arc light source.

The Zeiss projector uses a different system. This projector has a dumbbell shape. Each end of the dumbbell has 16 small projectors, and each has its own optical system. These projectors are so grouped around a central 1000 watt bulb that together they can project a complete picture of the stellar background over the whole surface of the dome. Inside each projector there is a photo-engraved plate of part of the sky. Mechanical blinkers swing over the projection lenses like artificial eyelids, thus preventing star images which happen to be below the horizon from flashing across the eyes of the spectators.

Most projectors are able to move about three independent axes, to allow for the fact that the observer can be at any latitude, at any time of day, and at any era in time. The Earth's axis moves slowly like that of a top or GYROSCOPE, a movement called *precession*, and this has to be allowed for.

Left: the Spitz AP3 planetarium projector. The 17 inch (43 cm) globe projects pinhole star images on to the inside of a 24 foot (7.3 m) dome, which will seat 50 people in comfort. The motors for the latitude and daily motion drives are in the base, linked to the axes by drive shafts and controlled from a console at one side of the auditorium.

Below: within the central framework of the Zeiss are the planetary projectors. On the ruff below the main globe are projectors for bright or variable stars. The small globe projects grid lines.

Planets

Two different methods can be used to simulate the motions of the Sun, the Moon and the planets, which move along different paths in the sky at varying rates. In one system the projectors themselves do the movement, while in the other the light from the projectors reach the screen via a system of movable mirrors. The movements of the Sun and Moon present little difficulty. The inclination of their orbits to the celestial equator (the projection of the terrestrial equator on to the sky) is achieved by means of cylindrical wedges. The Moon projector has an automatic shutter which simulates the phases of the Moon.

The movements of the planets are simulated by means of *analogues*. These are mechanical versions of the Solar System which contain the Sun, the Earth and one of the planets. The Earth and the planet move around the Sun at the correct relative speeds, and at the appropriate distances. The planet and the Earth are connected to the same rod by means of sliding contacts. This rod represents the line-of-sight from the Earth to the planet in question. In the first system this rod carries the projector, and in the second system the rod controls the movement of a mirror.

There are auxiliary projectors for projecting on to the dome such things as coordinate systems, the meridian, the ecliptic (or the apparent pathway of the Sun against the background stars) and a view of the continents as seen from the centre of the transparent Earth, for navigation instruction. Some planetaria also have projection *orreries* which project on to the dome a view of the Solar System, including the Earth, as seen from deep in space.

PLASMA (see matter)

PLASTICS

The word 'plastic' comes from the Greek word *plastikos* meaning 'capable of being moulded', and it is the chief property of plastics that they are deformable and therefore easily made into almost any shape by processes such as moulding or EXTRUSION (see PLASTICS PRODUCTION). Plastics are composed of high molecular weight organic MOLECULES, or POLYMERS, made up of repeating units chemically linked together in the form of a chain or network. Plastics can conveniently be divided into two categories: *semi-synthetic*, in which the basic chain structure is derived from a natural product such as *cellulose*; and *fully synthetic*, in which the chain is built up chemically from small units, or *monomers*. The process of forming a polymer from its constituent monomers is called *polymerization*.

The first plastics to be manufactured commercially were semi-synthetic, and they were derived from the CARBOHYDRATE cellulose which was usually obtained from cotton waste. In 1862 the British chemist Alexander Parkes prepared a plastic material called 'Parkesine' which could be readily moulded and shaped. This was made by reacting cotton waste with a mixture of nitric and sulphuric acids to give a *nitrocellulose* compound which was then mixed with castor oil, a little camphor and a colouring material. Although Parkesine was easy to prepare on a small scale, it proved difficult to make in large quantities, and its industrial manufacture was not a success. In 1870 the American chemist John Wesley Hyatt prepared the first commercially successful plastic, *Celluloid*, which was similar to Parkesine but used camphor in place of the castor oil. The new material was used to make a wide variety of products including spectacle frames, combs,

billiard balls, knife handles and photographic film. The first synthetic fibre, introduced in 1889, was an artificial silk made of nitrocellulose.

The chief drawback of these early plastics was that they were extremely flammable, which is not surprising when one considers that the main ingredient, nitrocellulose, is very closely related to the explosive *guncotton*; both are forms of nitrated cellulose. For this reason another ester of cellulose, *cellulose acetate*, is normally used nowadays in preference to cellulose nitrate for preparing cellulose-based plastics. These plastics are mainly used for making textiles. Regenerated cellulose, or Rayon, is a fibrous material composed of cellulose whose molecules have been shortened by dissolving and reprecipitation (see FIBRE, SYNTHETIC).

Synthetic plastics The first fully synthetic plastics were made many years before they were manufactured on an industrial scale. In 1838 the Frenchman Regnault observed 'resinification' of vinyl chloride under the influence of sunlight but he did not appreciate the possibilities of the new material he had produced, now called *polyvinyl chloride* (PVC). The following year, the German chemist Simon reported the polymerization of the unsaturated HYDROCARBON styrene to give polystyrene, but it was not for another nine decades that this material was made industrially. In 1909 Leo H Baekeland patented a resinous

Above: an elevating plastic bucket in which linesmen stand to repair a 16,000 volt electricity transmission line during a thunderstorm. Plastics generally have very good insulating properties and are often used where high voltages are encountered.

Right: wash basins are heat formed from a sheet of Perspex.

product he had obtained by reacting phenol with formaldehyde (see ALDEHYDE), although the first phenol-formaldehyde resin had been discovered more than 30 years before by Adolf von Bayer in 1872. Baekeland's product, called Bakelite, was one of the first commercially successful synthetic plastics. Methyl methacrylate was first polymerized in 1877 by the German chemists Fittig and Paul, and the product they obtained, *polymethylmethacrylate*, was to form the basis of the plastic 'Perspex' ['Plexiglas'] which was introduced half a century later. The first experiments in polymerizing ethylene were conducted in 1879, but a lubricating oil and not a plastic was produced. Nowadays ethylene is polymerized industrially on an enormous scale to give the well known plastic *polyethylene*, or *polythene*.

Although celluloid was being manufactured commercially at the end of the 19th century, it was not until early this century that the first really significant advances were made in manufacturing techniques. Baekeland succeeded in developing a moulding technique for his phenol-formaldehyde resin Bakelite, and in 1919 Eichengrün was granted a patent for the injection moulding of cellulose acetate. Nowadays injection moulding is an extremely important technique for shaping plastics, and without it many utensils and implements could not be made.

Polystyrene In the 1920s much research work was done into the chemical structure of plastics, particularly by the German chemist Hermann Staudinger who was awarded the Nobel Prize for chemistry in 1953 in recognition of his work. Staudinger's research led to the development of new plastics on a more rational basis, and in 1930 commercial production of polystyrene, one of the most important of today's plastics, was launched by the German company IG Farbenindustrie. The raw materials for polystyrene production are ethylene and benzene, which are first reacted together to give *styrene*, $C_6H_5CH=CH_2$. The styrene is then polymerized to give polystyrene, whose molecules consist of chains of styrene units and can be represented as follows:

$-CH(C_6H_5)-CH_2-CH(C_6H_5)-CH_2-CH(C_6H_5)-CH_2-$

There are various other important plastics which are related to polystyrene, for example, impact resistant polystyrene (a mixture of polystyrene and RUBBER), ABS (a polymerized mixture of styrene, *acrylonitrile* and *nitrile rubber*), SAN (a polymerized mixture of styrene and acrylonitrile) and ASA (a polymere of styrene with a methacrylate ester). Polymers composed of more than one type of monomer, for example SAN, are usually called *copolymers*. Polystyrene plastics are used to make mouldings and in various electrical components. Expanded polystyrene foams, such as 'Styropor', are used as heat and sound insulation materials and in packaging to protect against mechanical shock.

PVC Another important modern plastic is polyvinylchloride (PVC) which was first produced commercially in Germany in 1931. The raw materials for PVC production are ethylene and CHLORINE which are reacted to give *vinyl chloride* $CH_2=CHCl$. This is polymerized to give PVC which can be represented as follows:

$-CHCl-CH_2-CHCl-CH_2-CHCl-CH_2-$

Above left: a field of potatoes is covered with polyethylene to promote an early crop by retaining heat and moisture.

Left: rope being manufactured from polypropylene, a plastic which is both strong and easily extruded.

PVC is used to make a wide variety of moulded products, and it is often mixed with a *plasticizer* which softens it and makes it more flexible. Plastic pipes and gutters, and flexible plastic sheets are frequently made of PVC. Copolymers of vinyl chloride with *vinyl acetate*, $CH_2=CHCOOCH_3$, or *vinylidene chloride*, $CH_2=CCl_2$, are also important commercial plastics.

Polyolefins

In 1936 the British company ICI succeeded in making the first ALIPHATIC *polyolefin* plastic, polyethylene. Olefins are hydrocarbons which have one or more double BONDS, and ethylene, $CH_2=CH_2$, is the simplest member of the group. It is polymerized at about 200°C (392°F) and a pressure of more than 1000 times atmospheric pressure to give molecules of polyethylene which are simply chains of $-CH_2-$ groups. The polyethylene produced in this way is called *low density polyethylene* which is a tough, flexible material. *High density* polyethylene is more rigid than the low density variety and is made by polymerizing ethylene at much lower pressure and in the presence of a CATALYST. The difference between the two types is that the molecules of high density polyethylene are straight whereas the molecules of low density polyethylene are branched. Another important polyolefin plastic is *polypropylene*, made by polymerizing propylene, $CH_2 = CHCH_3$. Polypropylene can be represented as follows:

$-CH(CH_3)-CH_2-CH(CH_3)-CH_2-CH(CH_3)-CH_2-$

Polyethylene and polypropylene are used to make plastic bottles and other containers, films for packaging, pipes for plumbing and many other applications.

Another plastic which is related to the polyolefin plastics is polytetrafluoroethylene (PTFE) made by polymerizing tetrafluoroethylene, $CF_2=CF_2$. It consists of chains of $-CF_2-$ groups linked together, and is used where heat resistance and low surface friction are important. Non-stick coatings on domestic cooking utensils are generally made of PTFE.

Polyamides

The first polyamide plastic was prepared in 1934 by the American chemist W H Carothers, although it was not until 1937 that production was started on a commercial

Above right: a bed of urea-formaldehyde foam successfully brought this airliner to rest from a speed of about 60 mph (90 km/h) without damage. Foam beds of this type can be used in the event of overshoot or an aborted take off.

Below: strands of nylon 6 being drawn from the cooling trough at the base of a polymerization reactor.

scale. The new plastic was called nylon. The chief raw materials used in the production of nylon are benzene and *butadiene*, $CH_2=CH-CH=CH_2$. Various intermediates, particularly *caprolactam*, are produced before the final product is obtained. Polyamide, or nylon, molecules have repeating units of the following structure: $-(CH_2)_nCONH(CH_2)_mHNOC-$

The subscript letters m and n represent numbers whose value will depend on the particular nylon; in nylon 66, for example, n is 4 and m is 6. Polyamides are chiefly used for making moulded articles and textiles.

Polyesters

These plastics are made by reacting an organic acid having at least two acid (-COOH) groups with an alcohol having at least two alcohol (-OH) groups. Polyester molecules have repeating units with the following general formula: $-R_1-CO-O-R_2-O-CO-$

R_1 and R_2 represent organic groups which will depend on the particular polyester. In 'Terylene' ['Dacron'] a common polyester used to make synthetic fibres, R_1 represents a benzene ring and R_2 represents a $-CH_2-CH_2-$ group. Polyesters are also used to make high quality plastic films.

Polyurethanes

Polyurethane plastics are widely used today, particularly in the form of flexible or rigid foams. Flexible polyurethane foam is used as an upholstery material, and the rigid foam is commonly used as a heat insulating material. Polyurethanes are also used in some paint compositions to impart surface hardness to the paint coating. They can be made by reacting an *isocyanate* having at least two isocyanate (-NCO) groups with an alcohol having at least two hydroxy (-OH) groups, and have the following repeating structure: $-R_1-NHCOO-R_2-OOCHN-$

Here again the groups R_1 and R_2 will depend on the particular polyurethane; for 'Perlon U' R_1 is $-(CH_2)_6-$ and R_2 is $-(CH_2)_4-$.

Most of the plastics discussed above are *thermoplastics,* which means that they will soften when heated and harden again when cooled. Some plastics, however, such as Bakelite, are *thermosetting*, in other words they cannot be softened by heating without destroying the chemical structure. Another example of a thermosetting resin is the melamine formaldehyde type such as Formica. Some ADHESIVE compositions, particularly *epoxy* adhesives such as 'Araldite', are also based on thermosetting plastics. Another common group of thermosetting plastics consists of the *alkyd resins* which are used in some paint compositions.

PLASTICS PRODUCTION

The manufacture of PLASTICS is normally based on one of three POLYMERIZATION processes: direct polymerization, *polycondensation* or *polyaddition*. Plastics are composed of *polymer* molecules consisting of chains or networks of chemically linked units or *monomers*. A reaction which involves the joining together of monomers into a polymer is called a *polymerization* reaction. If more than one type of monomer is used, the process is called *copolymerization* and the product is a *copolymer*.

In a direct polymerization reaction, a small number of monomers in the reaction medium are activitated by means of heat, pressure or an added *initiator* (CATALYST). The activated monomers usually have reactive end groups which are either ionic (positively or negatively charged, see ION) or have a free electron (an outer electron not involved in a chemical BOND), and they will readily react with the non-activated monomers. The result of the reaction between an activated monomer and a non-activated one is an activated molecule consisting of two monomer units which can then react with another monomer molecule. Chains of monomers build up in this way until they are deactivated, for example by reaction with a further activated monomer. The resulting polymer molecules may contain many hundreds of monomer units; a polyethylene molecule, for example, will typically consist of a chain of more than 1000 ethylene units.

Polymerization

There are essentially five different industrial polymerization processes: *bulk polymerization, precipitation polymerization, solution polymerization, suspension polymerization* and *emulsion polymerization*. Bulk polymerization is carried out in the absence of a diluent, in other words the reaction mixture consists only of the monomer and a catalyst. If the polymer is insoluble in the monomer, or the monomer but not the polymer is soluble in the solvent added, the process is called precipitation polymerization because the polymer will be precipitated as soon as it is formed in the reaction medium, usually in the form of small particles. In solution polymerization both the monomer and the polymer are soluble in the reaction solvent, so that polymer solutions are obtained. If polymerization takes place in an aqueous (water) phase, the process is termed suspension polymerization. In this case the monomers are present as small spherical droplets at the beginning of the polymerization, and the activated species are formed within them. If the activated species are formed in the aqueous phase rather than the monomer droplets, and *emulsifiers* are added to the reaction medium, the process is called emulsion polymerization. The emulsifier causes the monomers to become very finely dispersed in the

reaction medium, so that the monomer and polymer particles formed are much smaller than in suspension polymerization.

The most important plastics obtained by direct polymerization are also those which are the most important in terms of production volume, namely the *polyolefins*, the *vinyl chloride* polymers and the *styrene* polymers. These three polymers account for about 67% (polyolefins 33%, vinyl chloride polymers 20% and styrene polymers 14%) of the total annual plastics production in the West. The most important polyolefins are the polyethylenes and polypropylene.

The monomeric building block for polyethylene is ethylene, $CH_2=CH_2$, a gas having a boiling point of about $-100°C$ $(-148°F)$ which is one of the most important HYDROCARBON products of the petrochemicals industry. If polymerization is carried out under high pressure (from 100 to 300 times atmospheric pressure) *low density polyethylene* (LDPE) is obtained. Polymerization at pressures close to atmospheric pressure (up to 40 atmospheres) gives *high density polyethylene* (HDPE). LDPE is prepared by bulk polymerization, while HDPE is produced by a precipitation polymerization process. The initiator is usually oxygen in the case of LDPE and a 'Ziegler-Natta' catalyst (named after the inventors) in the case of HDPE. In both methods the final step is granulation. Well-known brand names for polyethylene are Lupolen and Alkathene. The polymerization of propylene, $CH_2=CHCH_3$, proceeds under similar conditions to the method for HDPE.

The vinyl chloride polymers are prepared by polymerization of vinyl chloride, $CH_2=CHCl$, usually by a suspension or emulsion method. Monomeric vinyl chloride is gaseous and boils at $-14°C$ $(7°F)$. The process is carried out at a pressure of about ten times atmospheric pressure in large stainless steel or glass-lined reactors. The polyvinylchloride (PVC) product can be recovered from suspension or emulsion by any of a number of conventional drying methods. While suspension PVC is obtained as particles about 0.1 mm (0.004 inch) in diameter, the primary particles of emulsion PVC are much smaller but form larger particles by agglomeration.

Styrene polymers may be prepared by almost any of the conventional polymerization methods. In the bulk polymerization of styrene, the monomer is first introduced into small

Below: two micrographs taken with a scanning electron microscope showing emulsion PVC (left) and suspension PVC (right). In each photograph the average particle diameter is about 0.1 mm (0.004 inch) although, in the case of emulsion PVC, each particle is an agglomeration of much smaller particles.

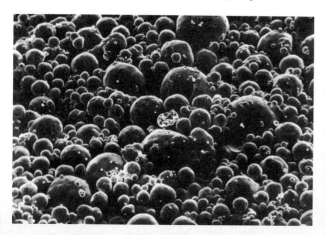
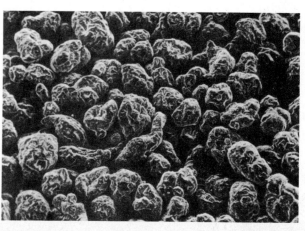

'kettles' in which the polymerization reaction begins. These kettles are water-cooled, since most heat is generated at the beginning of the reaction and it is important to prevent over-heating. When the polymerization is about 25% complete, the reaction mass is passed into the top end of a vertically mounted cylindrical reactor where the reaction is completed. As the reaction mixture passes through this reactor its temperature is

Below: diagrammatic representations of polystyrene production, blow moulding and injection moulding. In blow moulding, compressed air forces heated polyethylene, introduced in the form of a tube, against the cooled walls of the mould. The mould is then opened and the article removed. In injection moulding, heated plastic is forced rapidly through a narrow passage, or sprue, into a cooled mould where the plastic hardens in the required shape.

raised from about 110°C (230°F) to about 200°C (392°F). At this last temperature the product is fairly fluid and it is passed to an extruder which forms it into rods. Finally, the rods are broken into granules.

The starting materials for the acrylic plastics are esters of acrylic acid, $CH_2 = CHCOOH$, and *methacrylic acid*, $CH_2 = C(CH_3)COOH$, and *acrylonitrile*, $CH_2 = CHCN$. *Methyl methacrylate*, $CH_2 = C(CH_3)COOCH_3$, polymerized by bulk polymerization yields *acrylic glass* ('Perspex' or 'Plexiglas'). Pure or slightly modified polyacrylonitrile is a starting material for synthetic fibres such as Orlon and Courtelle. Acrylates can be combined with a variety of other monomers by emulsion polymerization to give latex-type products which are mainly used for finishing textiles, paper and leather.

Polycondensation and polyaddition In polycon-

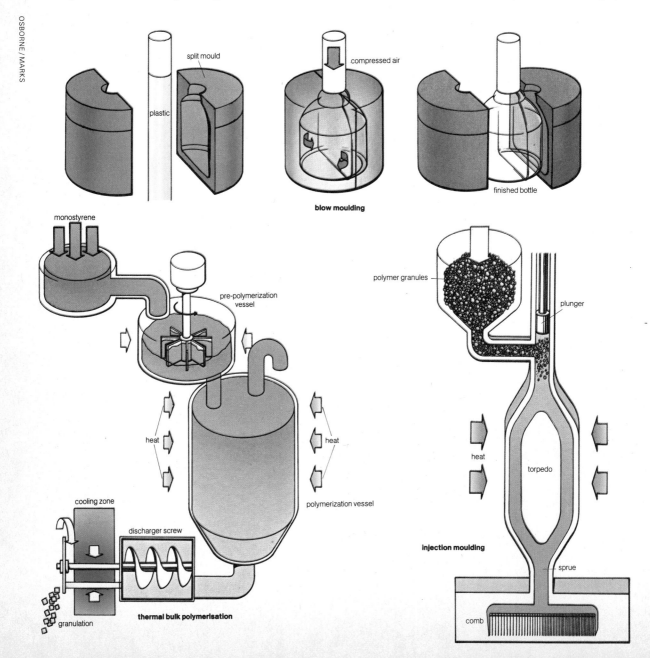

split mould

plastic

compressed air

finished bottle

blow moulding

monostyrene

pre-polymerization vessel

heat

heat

polymerization vessel

cooling zone

discharger screw

granulation

thermal bulk polymerisation

polymer granules

plunger

heat

torpedo

injection moulding

sprue

comb

densation, the polymer molecules are formed by reaction between monomers which each have two or more reactive groups. The process is best understood by considering first a simple condensation reaction between molecules each having only a single reactive group. Acetic acid, for example, will react with ethanol to give the ester *ethyl acetate*, and water is eliminated:

$$CH_3COOH + C_2H_5OH \rightarrow CH_3COOC_2H_5 + H_2O$$
acetic acid + ethanol → ethyl acetate + water

The reaction is between the acid group (—COOH) of the acetic acid molecule and the alcohol or hydroxy group (—OH) of the ethanol molecule. If the acid molecule were to have two acid groups and the alcohol were to have two alcohol groups it would be theoretically possible to built up long chain molecules, and this is what happens in polycondensation. The *polyester* Terylene [Dacron] is made by reacting *ethylene glycol*, HO—CH_2CH_2—OH, with *terephthalic acid*, HOOC—C_6H_4—COOH, and consists of a chain having the following structure:

—OOC—C_6H_4—COO—CH_2CH_2—OOC—C_6H_4—COO—

If the starting materials have only two reactive groups, linear polycondensates are obtained, but if they have more than two such groups, branched chain or crosslinked plastics are formed. The structure of a crosslinked plastic can be thought of as a three dimensional network. It is a characteristic of polycondensation reactions that low molecular weight compounds (water in the case of polyesters) are eliminated during polymerization.

Polyaddition is a stepwise process involving monomers having at least two reactive groups. In contrast to polycondensation, no low molecular weight compounds are eliminated during the reaction, which involves only the migration of a hydrogen atom. A good example of polyaddition is the formation of polyurethane plastics from a monomer having at least two *isocyanate* (—NCO) groups and a monomer having at least two alcohol groups (—OH). The isocyanate groups react with the alcohol groups by addition to form linkages having the structure —NH—CO—O—.

In industry, polycondensation and polyaddition reactions usually take place in a melt of the reactants themselves or in the presence of a solvent which is added. Acidic or basic catalysts may also be present in the reaction medium. Typical of polycondensation plastics are the *formaldehyde resins* (see ALDEHYDE). When formaldehyde is condensed with *urea* and *melamine*, amino resins such as Kaurit and Urecoll are obtained. If condensation is carried out with *phenols*, phenolic resins are formed, of which the best known are the Bakelite plastics. The condensation is usually carried out in an aqueous medium. By varying the reaction conditions, for example the temperature or the pH, a large range of branched or crosslinked polymers can be produced.

Various polyester plastics are also produced by polycondensation. As already explained, the building blocks are alcohols and organic acids, which are linked to each other during condensation by means of ester bonds. One of the most commercially important linear polyesters is *polyethylene terephthalate*, the starting material for synthetic *fibres* such as Terylene and Trevira. *Alkyd resins* such as 'Alkydal' and 'Glyptal', and unsaturated polyester resins such as 'Palatal' and 'Crystic' are branched or crosslinked polycondensates.

If *adipic acid*, HOOC—$(CH_2)_4$—COOH, and *hexamethylene diamine*, $H_2N(CH_2)_6NH_2$, are polycondensed, nylon 6,6 is obtained; if the starting material is caprolactam, nylon 6 is formed. Both of these are *polyamides*.

Above: newspapers being printed in Mexico City with plastic printing plates.

Right: a helicopter is sprayed with a white plastic coating compound to protect it against corrosion by salt water during shipping. Plastics are often used in applications where corrosion resistance is important since most are unaffected by water solutions of the common acids and alkalis.

PHOTOS: BASF

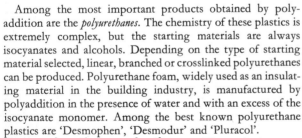

Above left: an automatic dispensing machine which accurately meters quantities of dye for dyeing polystyrene.

Left: in the thermal bulk polymerization of polystyrene, the polymerized mass is discharged from the reactor into an extruder which forces it through an apertured die to form strands. The strands are solidified by cooling (foreground).

Among the most important products obtained by poly-addition are the *polyurethanes*. The chemistry of these plastics is extremely complex, but the starting materials are always isocyanates and alcohols. Depending on the type of starting material selected, linear, branched or crosslinked polyurethanes can be produced. Polyurethane foam, widely used as an insulating material in the building industry, is manufactured by polyaddition in the presence of water and with an excess of the isocyanate monomer. Among the best known polyurethane plastics are 'Desmophen', 'Desmodur' and 'Pluracol'.

Processing thermoplastics

Thermoplastics are plastics which soften when heated but harden again when they are cooled, and this allows them to be shaped very easily. Softening and rehardening does not significantly alter the properties of a thermoplastic. As it is heated a thermoplastic first comes elastic, like rubber, and then completely plastic, like a very viscous liquid.

EXTRUSION moulding, carried out in an *extruder*, is a common method of shaping thermoplastics. An extruder consists of a heated, pressure-resistant barrel in which there is a helical screw, as in a domestic mincer [meat grinder]. The screw conveys granules of the plastic through a heated *die* at a temperature of about 200°C (392°F) and a pressure of from 100 to 300 bar (1450 to 4350 psi). A wide variety of differently shaped products can be made by this method, depending on the shape of the die aperture. If it is circular, rods or filaments are produced, if it is annular, pipes and tubes are formed and if it is a slit, plastic sheeting or film will be produced. The continuous products emerging from the extruder die are cooled by air, water, cooled rollers or by contact with cooled metal surfaces which give the final exact shape to the section. The finished product is then rolled up or cut into suitable lengths.

Injection moulding is one of the most important methods of producing shaped articles in large numbers. As in an extruder, the plastic is softened by being passed along a heated barrel by means of a screw. However, the screw has the additional function of a ram, which injects the softened plastic very rapidly into a cooled steel mould at temperatures of from about 180 to 300°C (356 to 572°F) and pressures of 1000 bar (14,500 psi) or more. After cooling, the mould opens and the article is removed.

Blow moulding is a process used to manufacture hollow articles with small openings such as bottles, cans, drums, tanks and toys. A piece of softened plastics (frequently polyethylene) tubing is extruded and introduced into a two-piece *blow mould*. As the mould closes it presses one end of the tubular section together to seal it. Compressed air is blown into the other end of the tube until it fits against the cooled mould and solidifies.

Above: an installation for the large scale production of styrene from ethylene and benzene. Huge quantities of styrene are produced annually for polymerization into polystyrene.

Right: moulds for making polyurethane shoe soles. When in use, the two halves of the moulds are pressed tightly together by means of rams which can be seen in the background.

The mould is then opened and the article removed.

Thermoforming is a process for making shaped articles such as bowls or beakers from plastics sheeting or film. The sheeting or film is heated with infra-red radiation to a temperature of between 120 and 180°C (248 to 356°F) until it is soft. It is then sucked against a single-section mould by applying a vacuum. After cooling (solidifying), the moulded article is separated from the remainder of the sheet.

In *rotational moulding*, plastics powder is placed in a heated, hollow metal mould, and the latter is rotated slowly about two axes which are perpendicular to each other. In this way the powder melts and is distributed evenly over the whole inner surface of the mould. After cooling, the mould is opened and the moulded hollow article removed.

Processing thermosetting resins   During their manufacture, *thermosetting* plastics undergo a chemical trans-formation which is called *curing*. This is brought about by the action of heat or by the addition of chemicals. Before curing, thermosets are liquid, doughy or solid but capable of being shaped under pressure and heat. After curing they are insoluble and can no longer be shaped even at high temperatures. The reaction time (the time required for curing) is usually several hours in the case of cold curing and a few minutes in the case of hot curing. The most common thermosetting plastics are

the formaldehyde resins such as Bakelite.

In *compression moulding* a quantity of granular, doughy or even liquid resin, often with a curing agent, a filler and a reinforcing material (such as GLASS FIBRES or a glass fibre mat), is introduced into a compression mould, generally made of steel. The mould is closed and the resin is pressed into the desired shape. The shaped article remains in the mould until curing is complete. If the resin is cured by the action of heat, the mould will incorporate heating equipment. The moulded articles can be removed from the mould while still hot.

Thermosetting resins can also be processed in injection moulding machines. They are heated in the barrel and injected at high pressure into a hot mould where curing takes place.

Thermosetting resins, particularly unsaturated polyester resins, are often reinforced with glass fibres to form large high-strength articles. The resin and the glass fibres are applied to one-piece moulds by hand, for example by spraying the resin and chopped glass fibre strands simultaneously on to the mould with a spray gun, or by brushing or pouring the resin on to the mould and then laying glass fibre mats on to the resin. These processes can be mechanized for the manu-facture of flat or corrugated sheets. Reinforced tubes and containers are formed by winding resin-impregnated glass fibre bands on to mould cores.

PLATINUM METALS

The platinum metals consist of a group of six rare closely related metals: *rhodium* (Rh), *ruthenium* (Ru), *palladium* (Pd), *osmium* (Os), *iridium* (Ir) and *platinum* (Pt), which is the most important member of the group. The first three occur at the end of the second series of TRANSITION ELEMENTS in the PERIODIC TABLE, before silver, while the second three, which occur at the end of the third transition series, precede GOLD and are among the densest known substances, having densities between 21.4 and 22.4.

Platinum and palladium are the most abundant of the six metals. Platinum was the earliest known, having been discovered by the Spaniards in the South American silver mines about 1550. The metal was referred to as 'platina del Pinto' (silver-like metal from the Pinto river) but was recognized as being different from true silver because it could not be melted (silver has a melting point of 960°C; platinum 1773.5°C). It also caused difficulties for the Spaniards, as its density was close to that of gold, and when gold plated it was virtually indistinguishable from the solid metal. The counterfeiting was only brought under control by dumping all stocks of platinum in the sea and forbidding its import into Spain. The properties of platinum were first seriously studied in the mid-18th century by Watson, Scheffer and Morggarf. In 1803 W H Wollaston showed that all platinum previously examined was in fact an alloy with similar metals. He managed to isolate two; one he named palladium after Pallas, a newly discovered minor planet, and the other rhodium from the Greek word *rhodon*, rose, because some of its compounds are rose-coloured. One year later Tennant discovered two more of the platinum metals, naming them osmium from the Greek *osme*, meaning a smell, as its oxide has an unpleasant odour, and iridium from *iris*, the Greek word for rainbow. In 1845 Claus completed the sextet with the discovery of ruthenium, which he named after a province of his native Russia.

Occurrence and extraction

Platinum metals are found in their native state in alluvial deposits in the Ural mountains and Colombia and in gold bearing rock at Witwatersrand in S Africa. Platinum occurs as its sulphide, PtS (cooperite), and a mixed sulphide containing palladium, platinum and nickel at Rustenburg in S Africa, and is found as *platinum diarsenide*, $PtAs_2$ (sperrylite), in the huge copper and nickel sulphide deposits in Ontario.

Where the metals are gathered in their native state they are concentrated by similar methods to those employed in the gold mines. Where, however, they are obtained as by-products in the large scale extraction of copper and nickel from their sulphides, the concentration is effected by adding slightly less than sufficient sulphur at the matte forming stage so as to preserve small regions of nickel or copper metal in which the platinum metals dissolve. These enriched alloys are removed by crushing and magnetic separation and further concentrated by heating with more sulphur and repeating the cycle. Electro-refining of the enriched concentrate leaves the platinum metals as insoluble anode slimes.

The separation and refining of the various members of the platinum family involves a series of complex chemical operations which may vary in detail but are basically similar. The first stage of the process is treatment with hot *aqua regia* (a mixture of nitric and hydrochloric acids) which dissolves only the platinum and palladium. These metals are precipitated separately from the solution as ammonium salts which are reduced to the metal at high temperature. The fraction which is

PHOTRI

insoluble in aqua regia is reacted with molten sodium chloride at 700°C in the presence of chlorine to form double chlorides which are water soluble. Osmium, which is not dissolved at any stage, is recovered from the final residue by forming its volatile oxide. Ruthenium and rhodium are precipitated from the double chloride solution as sulphides which are subsequently separated by redissolution, followed by individual precipitation. Iridium is finally removed from the double chloride solution as its oxide and reduced to pure metal by hydrogen.

In 1974 platinum was selling at £2.75 [$6.40] per gramme, almost the same price as gold, palladium at £2.20 [$5.10] and both rhodium and iridium at about £5.00 [$11.05].

Applications

Platinum is a useful catalyst for a wide range of chemical reactions, both organic and inorganic. For

ENGELHARD INDUSTRIIES LTD

example, it catalyzes the oxidation of ammonia in the production of nitric acid, its efficiency being increased by the addition of 10% rhodium. Both platinum and palladium catalysts are used extensively in the pharmaceutical industry where they enable highly specific chemical reactions to be carried out in the building of particular molecules. In the manufacture of MARGARINE, hydrogenation is brought about by a palladium catalyst. The metals are often most effective as catalysts when in the form of very finely divided powders known as 'blacks'.

The ability of platinum to initiate low temperature oxidation reactions was first exploited by Döbereiner to produce a lighter before the invention of friction matches. The principle is used today in ignition devices for domestic gas stoves. Platinum metals are also used to catalyze both the oxidation of unburnt

Above left: the radio aerial [antenna] of this spacecraft has 150 platinum wires in its reflector to focus the transmitted radio signals back towards Earth. The spacecraft, called 'Helios', was designed to travel close to the Sun, and so heat resistant materials such as platinum had to be used in its construction.

Above: pouring molten platinum into a mould. Platinum has a melting point of 1769°C (3216°F).

hydrocarbons and the reduction of nitrogen oxides in anti-pollution units incorporated in car exhaust systems, but their effectiveness is drastically reduced by lead derived from the tetraethyl lead component of high octane fuels. The high cost, however, of platinum metal limits its widespread use in catalysts, where cheaper alternatives may be substituted.

An important property of platinum metals is their outstanding resistance to chemical attack. Platinum itself is used for analytical apparatus such as crucibles, combustion boats, and grids for metal deposition in electrochemical techniques. Other industrial applications include spinnerets in the artificial fibre industry and crucibles for the manufacture of optical glass, where contamination from non-metallic refractories must be avoided. Often platinum is alloyed with up to 20% rhodium to improve its strength. Palladium has a unique affinity for hydrogen, absorbing up to 850 times its own volume of hydrogen, and is employed as a diffusion medium for the purification of the gas. In this application it is alloyed with silver to reduce the shape changes which would otherwise occur during thermal cycling.

The refractory properties of the platinum metals made them former candidates for electric light bulb filaments. Tungsten is now universally used, but the familiar trade mark 'Osram' is a reminder of the times when osmium was a contender. (The 'ram' part comes from 'wolfram', another name for tungsten). The thermal expansion coefficient of platinum is very similar to that of glass, which makes it an ideal material for glass to metal seals, although a copper coated nickel iron alloy has been developed which is also suitable and much cheaper. Thermocouples made from platinum and a platinum-10% rhodium alloy operate reliably up to 1700°C and are widely used in the steel industry. For very accurate temperature measurement, the platinum resistance thermometer is the accepted standard measuring instrument. The platinum metals are suitable materials for relay contacts which are required to switch reliably for many years without attention, and for electrodes in SPARK PLUGS for high performance internal combustion engines.

Platinum and palladium are used extensively in the jewellery industry for setting diamonds and other precious stones, palladium having the additional advantages that it is not under such heavy demand from the chemical industry and is about half the density. Like gold, both metals are seldom used pure as they are too soft in this state. A thin layer of rhodium, the easiest of the group to electrodeposit, electroplated on to silver prevents tarnishing through sulphide formation. The tips of fountain pen nibs are usually made from alloys of platinum, osmium and iridium, where the combination of hardness and resistance to corrosion by ink is especially valuable.

Below: welding the edge of a gauze pad made of a platinum-rhodium alloy. Gauzes like this one are used as catalysts in the oxidation of ammonia to nitric oxide, which is the first step in the industrial preparation of nitric acid.

PLAYER PIANO

The first mechanical piano player was a device which was placed in front of an ordinary PIANO, playing it by means of hammers which struck the keys. Later the mechanism was installed inside an enlarged piano cabinet, and the instrument became known as a player piano.

The earliest players were operated mechanically by *planchettes*, small wooden boards studded with projecting pins which played the notes by means of a system of levers. Some instruments were operated by means of slotted and folded cards, as used today in fairground organs.

The modern player piano, which reached its peak of popularity in the 1920s, is a pneumatic device which uses a roll of paper with perforations. The roll is 11¾ inches (28.5 cm) wide and the perforations are spaced nine to an inch (2.5 cm). The *spool box*, with a *tracker bar*, is placed in front of the operator, behind the keyboard; the drive mechanism is placed on the right-hand side. Directly underneath these is the *valve chest*, and underneath the keyboard are the *suction bellows* or *exhausters*, operated

Below: on the premises of the Perforated Music Company, City Road, London, in 1909, a pianist records a piano roll. The paper is 11¾ inches wide, with the perforations spaced nine to the inch; this leaves room in the margins for holes to operate the pedals.

Above: a Keyless Red Welte, so called because it had no keyboard and played a roll of red paper. The mechanical-pneumatic action was advanced for its time and beautifully made. Few of these models were made, between 1900–1910, and fewer still survive.

by pedals. The expression controlling devices are also located here: the sustaining (loud) pedal and the *half-blow* (soft) pedal, together with any accentuating mechanisms. The pedals of the piano are operated by two large pneumatics actuated by perforations in the margin of, the roll.

Operation The 'performer', having placed the roll in the spool box and hitched the leader to the take-up spool, starts pedalling. This exhausts the main pneumatic chest, and the drive motor moves the roll forward. The speed is controlled by the tempo lever on the front of the keyboard. Usually the tempo is printed on the paper: 40 means 4 feet (122 cm) per minute, and so on, but sometimes a red line is printed on the roll, and speed changes are accomplished by following this line with a pointer attached to the tempo lever. Underneath the right-hand end of the keyboard, a *suction governor* is connected in a tube from the motor to the exhausters. Moving the tempo lever also moves a slide valve which, in conjunction with a spring loaded pneumatic coupled to another slide valve in the governor, regulates the suction on the motor, controlling the speed independently of the pedalling.

As the first perforation opens a hole in the tracker bar, air passes in. This lifts a soft leather diaphragm, which in turn lifts a poppet valve which opens a port to the small note pneumatic connecting it to the suction chest. This pneumatic closes quickly and operates the piano hammer in the same manner as if the key were struck. When the perforation has gone past, air is cut off from the diaphragm, which returns to its original position. The poppet valve drops, cutting off suction from the pneumatic, which opens, allowing the hammer to fall back and the note to be damped. Equalization of air pressure takes place through a tiny hole by-passing the diaphragm.

The degree of suction determines the loudness of the music. Expression is achieved mainly by pedalling lightly or heavily but many player pianos have alternative means, making it possible to accentuate chords or single notes; it is in these devices that the various makes of player pianos differ. In the case of the *Pianola* (trade name of the Aeolian Company), the pneumatics are divided—44 notes in each half. The loudness of each can be subdued with respect to the other by means of levers operating sliding valves connected to suction governors, in an arrangement similar to that controlling the speed of the driving motor. This makes possible, for example, the melody (right-hand piano part) 'singing out' above the accompaniment (left-hand or bass part).

Development In 1904 in Southern Germany, Edwin Welte invented a device for reproducing the performances of famous pianists with a more life-like rendering than was possible with the acoustic recording method of the day. He called it the *Mignon* (French for 'dainty') to distinguish it from the much larger organs and orchestrations previously made by the Welte Company. By 1913, several other firms had built *reproducing* pianos with varying degrees of success and much competition. Two other versions of the Welte-Mignon were built, one by Welte's brother-in-law Karl Bokisch in Germany and the other under license in the USA. The American Piano Company brought out the Re-enacting piano which they called the *Ampico*, and the Aeolian Company of London and New York introduced their *Duo-Art Pianola Piano*.

Reproducing pianos work in principle pneumatically, the same way as ordinary player pianos, but they differ in three important respects. The motive power is supplied by an electric motor, and re-rolling is automatic. All expression devices, for

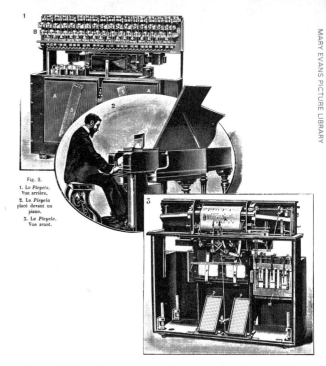

Fig. 2.
1. Le *Pleyela*. Vue arrière.
2. Le *Pleyela* placé devant un piano.
3. Le *Pleyela*. Vue avant.

Above: the 'Pleyela' player piano. The top view is the rear of the works, with the cabinet removed, and below is the front view.

subduing and accentuating as well as the pedals, are operated by marginal perforations on the roll; and the paper speed is set at the start and kept constant. Tempo changes and musical phrasing are obtained by differences in the length of the note perforations.

The Duo-Art machine will play any 88 note roll as well as the Duo-Art rolls; some models are fitted with both pedals and electric motors. When changing between types of rolls a switching arrangement is operated which cuts out the extreme four bass and treble notes. The eight positions in the tracker bar thus vacated are used to control expression. Those on the left control the accompaniment and those on the right control melody line. Using a series of graded pneumatics (ratios 1:2:4:8) singly or in combination it is possible to obtain sixteen degrees of 'touch'. The accompaniment regulator controls the whole piano all the time while the melody regulator accentuates any bass or treble notes as required; thus the 'touch' of the concert pianist is reproduced more accurately than on the ordinary player piano.

The popularity of the player piano began to die out in the late 1920s because of competition from broadcasting and from the new electrical methods of recording and playing gramophone records, which provided better sound from the record players than the acoustic method. In the meantime, however, such popular piano players as Fats Waller and George Gershwin made piano rolls which are still sought after by collectors and re-issued on records; such famous pianists as Josef Hofmann, Anton Rubinstein and Jan Paderewsky, as well as the composers Gustav Mahler and Claude Debussy, recorded their piano styles on the reproducing pianos. In addition, composers such as Paul Hindemith and Igor Stravinsky experimented with writing music for the player piano, taking advantage of its mechanical superiority over human fingers.

'PLEXIGLASS' manufacture (see plastics manufacture)

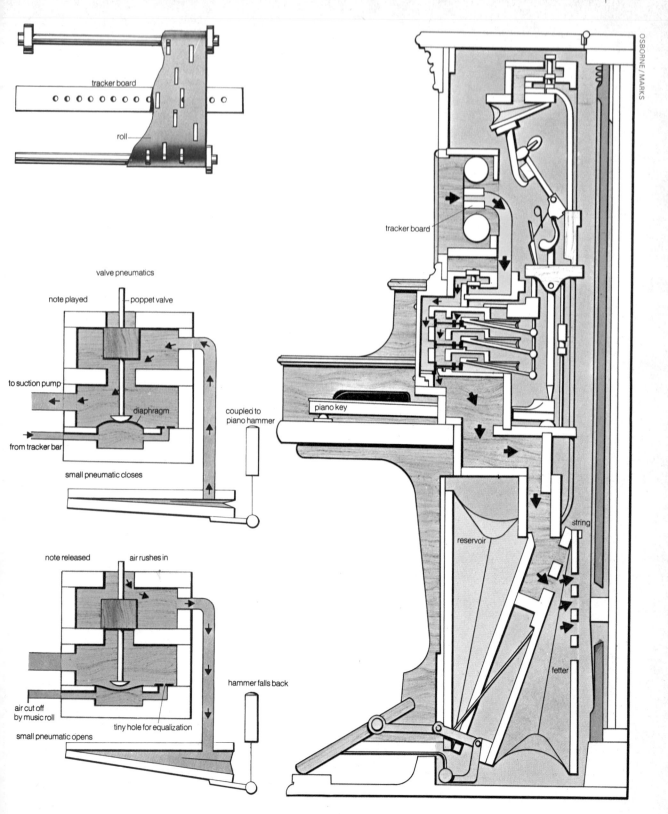

tracker board

roll

valve pneumatics

note played — poppet valve

to suction pump

diaphragm

coupled to piano hammer

from tracker bar

small pneumatic closes

note released — air rushes in

air cut off by music roll

tiny hole for equalization

hammer falls back

small pneumatic opens

tracker board

piano key

reservoir

string

fetter

OSBORNE/MARKS

Above: a player piano. Air is drawn into the piano through holes in the tracker board which are 'opened' as the perforations of the piano roll pass over them. The increased air pressure opens the internal poppet valves, and air from the small pneumatics is drawn out to the main fetter by the action of the pedals. The contraction of the small bellows activates the piano hammer linkage and a note is played.

Above: steam ploughing in the mid 19th century with a steam engine, windlass and rope system anchored at the corners of the field.
Below left: a primitive wooden plough is still used in Pakistan.
Below centre: on this modern 4-furrow fixed plough, the action of the mouldboards can be clearly seen. The plough also has a land wheel to help control correct ploughing depth.
Below right: a 2-furrow reversible plough. The disc coulters, shares, mouldboards, and skimmers can be seen on the right hand set.

PLOUGH

The most important implement of tillage is the plough, which performs a similar job to the spade in that it loosens the oversoil so as to break it up and expose new surfaces to the atmosphere. At the same time it turns the soil over, burying any trash. A modern plough in a few minutes can turn more soil than a man working with a spade can in one whole day. A great deal of energy is expended in ploughing and a large 7 furrow plough will need to be attached to a tractor of 100 hp or more.

History The development of the plough can be traced back to the Neolithic times. Then it was a very simple tool, being little more than a suitably forked branch with a sharp point. By Roman times there were three designs: the *aratum* or 'worker of soil', which was similar to a Neolithic plough; the *ard* which was a beam and spike tool; and the *carruca* which had a *mouldboard* to push the soil to one side. The carruca, however, did not gain widespread favour, as the mouldboard made the plough heavier to handle, and most soils in the Mediterranean were light and easily workable with a simpler plough. There were several forms of ard: the *beam* ard had a curved beam with a hole in it to hold the forward pointing stock, which might be shod with a metal share; the *body* ard had a straight beam and an L-shaped stock; while the *bow* ard, which was also used by the Scandinavians, had a bow-shaped beam with holes for the handles and the stock, which were wedged into the holes.

It was the Romans who also introduced the *coulter* or knife, which cuts a vertical slit ahead of the share which slices through the soil. In Norman times the plough was still essentially an ard type but with the addition of a wheel, coulter and a wedge type mouldboard which pushed the soil to one side without turning it.

It was not until the 16th and 17th centuries that the plough underwent any major changes; these were made by the Flemish and Dutch. The move was towards lighter ploughs and whereas the older ploughs had been based on a quadrilateral frame, the new types were triangular. The Dutch plough was brought to England, improved and patented in 1730 as the Rotherham plough. It still had a wooden frame, beam and handles, but the draught irons, coulter, and share were of iron, and the mould-board and sole were covered with iron plates. The coulter and share were shaped and set so as to cut a furrow slice without tearing it and the mouldboard was so shaped that it first raised and then gradually turned over the furrow slice. It was a great improvement which enabled one man with a team of two horses drawing the plough through a stiff soil to achieve as much as two men and a team of six horses working a moderately light soil with a wheel type plough. On the other hand, wheelless or *swing* ploughs required more skill to handle.

Another development in the 17th century had been the *turnwrest* plough. The normal mouldboard turned the furrow to one side only so the plough either had to be taken back to the beginning for the next furrow or it had to plough a different strip on its return journey. In two-way ploughing on slopes where the soil is always turned uphill, the ability to change the side of the furrow slice, whichever way the plough is facing, is essential. With a turnwrest plough, the ploughman removed the mouldboard and refitted it to the other side of the plough and adjusted the angle of the coulter.

More iron began to be used as a result of the Industrial Revolution, and in the 1760s James Small, a Berwickshire farmer, made the first plough with a cast iron mouldboard, giving it a mathematically deduced curve for better operation. Then in 1785, Robert Ransome took out a patent for cast iron shares, followed in 1803 by a patent for a hardening process which made the iron self-sharpening. He had found this idea accidentally when a hot share had fallen on to some icy water on the floor. The casting of components for ploughs now meant that spare parts would be available for standard ploughs and was the beginning of the mass production to come. In the USA in the 1830s John Deere introduced the first steel plough which helped in opening up the prairies.

In the latter half of the 19th century steam ploughing was enthusiastically tried. A stationary engine pulled the plough across the field with cables. Several ploughs could be used at once and the system designed so ploughs could work in pairs, one set for turning the furrow to the left and the other to the right, the sets being used alternately. Forty or fifty acres a day could be ploughed by an eight furrow plough powered by two steam engines.

In 1936 Harry Ferguson developed a farm tractor equipped with a hydraulically controlled 3-point linkage which enabled the plough to be directly coupled to the tractor, providing better and easier control of the plough.

Modern ploughs The two main types are the *mould-board* plough, which is widespread in temperate climates, and the *disc* plough, which is more suitable for tropical conditions. In disc ploughing 3 or 4 sets of discs are mounted vertically on an axle at a fixed angle of 45° to the soil surface. They do not completely bury the top growth and this makes them suitable for dry conditions; they are also resistant to damage from obstacles or misuse. There are also *chisel* ploughs which loosen the soil without inverting it, and are suitable for ploughing cereal stubble. Various shaped tines are available depending on the application. The chisel has the advantage over the mouldboard of a high rate of work, and of ensuring that fertile top soil remains on the surface.

The average mouldboard plough is a 3-furrow implement but models as large as 10 furrows are available. Furrow width may vary from 10 to 16 inches (25 to 40 cm), and in light and medium soils furrow depth is usually about half the width, but in heavy soils it is traditional to plough deeper. The depth of cut is controlled from the tractor via a tractor hydraulic linkage, often assisted by a depth wheel which may be preset mechanically. The plough itself may be tractor trailed, semi-mounted or fully mounted depending on its weight, as there is a limit to the amount that the tractor hydraulics can lift, so units larger than 4-furrow are normally tractor trailed. Ploughing is normally done by two-wheel drive tractors, one wheel running in the furrow and the other on unploughed land.

There are two types of ploughing, *fixed* and *reversible*, for both disc and mouldboard ploughs. Fixed mouldboard ploughs have one set of right hand mouldboards, coulters and skimmers. To use this type of plough involves setting out the field in such a way that 'lands' (sections) can be ploughed and eventually joined up. Reversible, commonly known as one-way ploughs have two sets of mouldboards, coulters and skimmers, one left hand and one right hand set. These are mounted one set above and one set below a central beam, which pivots. At the end of each pass the plough is rotated mechanically or hydraulically and the tractor runs back alongside the newly ploughed furrow. This leaves flat fields without any large ridges as when 'lands' are joined. In reversible disc ploughs it is slightly different in that the mechanism swings the discs so that they are offset to the right or left of the tractor.

For surmounting obstacles without damaging the plough, each base may be connected to a mechanical spring-trip (release) or a pneumatic-hydraulic mechanism which allow it to spring back. However, some designs, particularly chisel ploughs, have shear bolts; these break under impact and can be quickly replaced.

The *diamond* plough, so named because the inverted furrow slice is diamond-shaped rather than rectangular, is a recent innovation in mouldboard ploughs and has a number of particularly interesting features: it has no coulters; the furrow wall is cut by the leading edge of the mouldboard and instead of being vertical is curved; while the *skimmers*, which could be described as small ploughs fitted in front of the mouldboard to take the trash off the top of the slice and push it into the furrow ahead of the mouldboard, are fitted to the side of the mould-board. It is easier to pull than conventional designs.

PLUMBICON (see television camera)

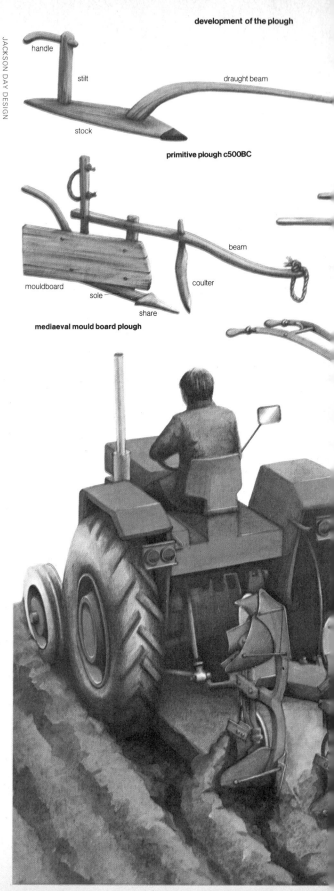

development of the plough

handle

stilt

draught beam

stock

primitive plough c500BC

mouldboard

sole

share

beam

coulter

mediaeval mould board plough

JACKSON DAY DESIGN

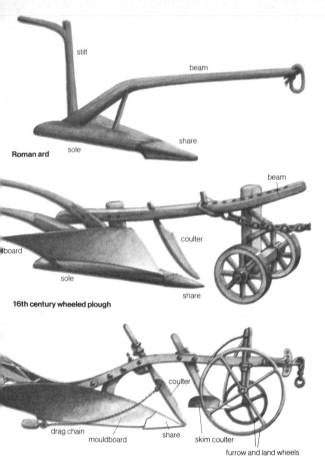

Roman ard — stilt, beam, share, sole

16th century wheeled plough — beam, coulter, board, sole, share

19th century metal plough — coulter, drag chain, mouldboard, share, skim coulter, furrow and land wheels

modern 4-furrow reversible plough

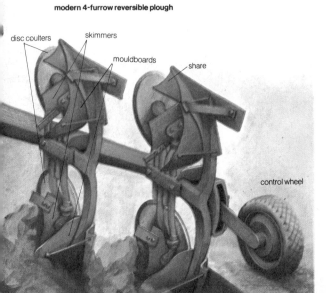

disc coulters, skimmers, mouldboards, share, control wheel

PLUMBING

The craft of plumbing originated in mediaeval times when the roofs of the great cathedrals throughout Europe were being covered in sheet lead which had been cast on a bed of sand. Later, when the water supply industry was developing, *pipes* and cisterns were made from similar cast lead sheet, although hundreds of years before that the Romans had made water pipes of lead to feed their fountains and baths.

Today the modern plumber embraces many skills and materials: cold and hot water supply, sanitation, roof covering and rainwater disposal, and the installation of pipelines in all types of buildings for the conveyance of all liquids and gases. He works in lead, copper, aluminium, cast iron, steel and plastics.

Cold water supply It is the task of the water industry to supply a pure potable water in sufficient quantity wherever it is needed; it is then the job of the plumber to ensure that the water is conveyed to all parts of the building where it is needed and to preserve its purity up to the point of use. Careful design and choice of materials are necessary to prevent the water becoming polluted, so there are regulations and byelaws which must be adhered to.

Because of geographical and physical differences, cold water installations vary from country to country, but in Britain there are two main designs. The first is where the cold water is fed from the main to all cold water taps; the second is where the cold water is taken to a feed cistern at high level from which all cold taps are fed, with the exception of the tap at the kitchen sink which is fed from the water main to be absolutely sure that the water is pure for drinking and culinary purposes.

From the point of connection to the nearest water main, usually in the road in front of the building, a service pipe, a pipe serving the building with water, is taken. At the boundary of the property there is fixed a stop tap, the service pipe and stop tap being buried in the ground at a depth of about two feet (60 cm) to avoid the possibility of the water in the service pipe becoming frozen during winter. Access to the stop tap is by means of a pipe with a cover from ground level so that the water can be shut off for repairs to the installation. The pipe continues into the building and there is usually a further stop tap for use by the occupier in emergency, together with a drain tap so that when the water is shut off either for repairs or to avoid frost damage when the building is unoccupied, the whole installation can be drained. The water is then distributed through the 'distribution system' to all cold water draw-off points.

Hot water supply One of the cold water draw-off points will be the ball valve in the feed cistern to the hot water supply system. In the United Kingdom, regulations demand that the cold water entering a hot water system should be by means of a cistern fixed at the highest possible point. In other parts of Europe cold water is fed directly into the hot water storage vessel but precautions are necessary first to prevent excessive pressure from bursting the hot water storage vessel and, second, to prevent hot water from passing back into the cold water main.

A simple hot water supply system consists of, first, the heat generator (see HEATER). This is usually a boiler, although it may be an electric immersion heater fixed in the hot water storage vessel. The boiler, which can be heated by solid fuel, gas or oil, is placed at the lowest point of the system so that the water can circulate between the boiler and hot water storage vessel by gravity through the differences in density between hot and

WILLIAM MACQUITTY

Above: a Roman lavatory (2nd and 3rd centuries AD) in an ancient Roman settlement at Dougga, 129 km west of Tunis. It was adjacent to a large bathing area and was serviced with running water.

Below: a domestic water system. To prevent contamination of the main water supply, air-breaks are provided—the feed cistern and water closet cistern are two examples. In Britain, the hot water system is fed via the feed cistern to prevent hot water contamination. Generally, all the cold taps are fed from the cistern except the kitchen sink tap, which is connected direct to the rising main. But often all the cold water supply is direct.

cooler water. Pumps are sometimes used to circulate the water when design considerations demand them and when space heating is also required. The hot water from the boiler ascends to a storage vessel into the top of which is connected a pipe which is taken to a point above the feed cistern, so that air can escape without water also escaping. Into this vent pipe other pipes are connected to convey hot water to the various draw-off points—bath, sink, wash basin.

Pressure is necessary to force the water out of the storage vessel to the draw-off taps, and this is determined by the height of the cold feed cistern. The higher the cistern the greater the pressure, as the cold feed cistern is connected to a feed pipe to the bottom of the hot water storage vessel. When a hot tap is opened, the pressure of cold water in the feed cistern forces the hot water upwards to the top of the hot water storage vessel and through the distribution pipes to the draw-off taps. The amount of cold water entering the hot water system depends entirely on the amount of hot water drawn off. This is controlled by means of a ball valve in the cold feed cistern, which opens as the water level falls and closes when draw-off of hot water stops and the level of cold water in the feed cistern rises.

There are several ways of providing hot water apart from the use of a boiler. An electric immersion heater has already been mentioned. This is fixed into the hot water storage vessel and can be used in conjunction with a boiler. There are instantaneous gas fired or electric water heaters ('geysers') which can be fixed to serve either one or several draw-off points. With these, the cold water is taken straight from a distribution pipe into the heater, where it passes through a HEAT EXCHANGER. When a hot water tap is opened, the change of pressure operates a valve which allows gas to pass to the

ALLARD GRAPHIC ARTS

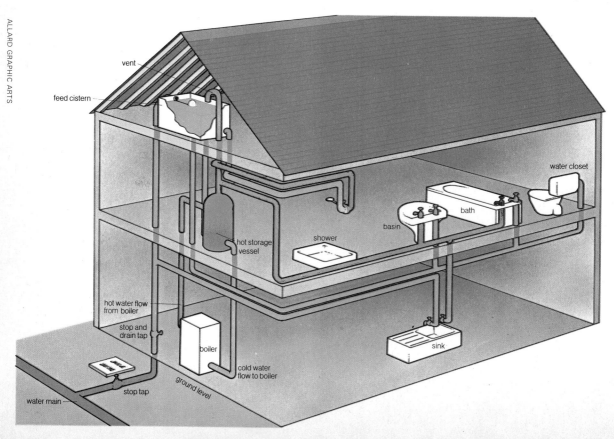

Left and above: this demonstration house has been cut away to show the arrangement of hot and cold water pipes to sink, wash basin and bath and waste pipe connections to the drain. Maybe the most important consideration is that the domestic cold water supply must remain pure—this is achieved by taking into account water pressure height of cisterns and air-breaks in the water circuit.

Below: the outlet pipe from the WC is kept separate from bath, basin and sink waste in small dwellings, but in most modern houses the single-stack system is used. In this, all outlets are fed via water seal traps which prevent drain gases from entering the building.

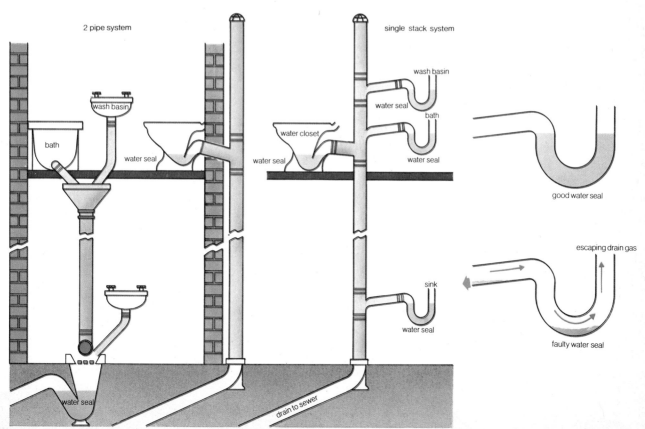

2 pipe system

wash basin

bath

water seal

single stack system

wash basin

water seal

bath

water closet

water seal

water seal

good water seal

sink

water seal

escaping drain gas

faulty water seal

water seal

drain to sewer

burners, where it is ignited by a pilot flame. As quickly as the water passes through the heat exchanger on its way to the draw-off tap it is warmed to the required temperature.

Sanitary fittings Hot and cold water distribution systems have to deliver water to the points where it is needed—to the fitments.

In domestic and residential buildings, as distinct from industrial requirements, these can be placed in two classes; ablutionary—baths, showers, sinks, wash basins; and those concerned with bodily functions such as water closets, bidets and urinals. With the former, direct connections to mains water are permissible but with the latter, where there is a possibility of contamination of the mains water, certain rules apply. There must be an air break between the ball valve supplying the appliance and the surface of the water in the appliance so that syphonage of contaminated water into the distribution system cannot occur.

Showers also present a problem in that some countries have a low pressure hot water system, that is, one in which the water pressure at the shower outlet depends on the height of the feed cistern above the shower outlet; others have high pressure hot water systems where both hot and cold water must be fed from a cistern at high level so that the pressures are approximately equal. If the cisterns cannot be placed high enough to give sufficient pressure, a pump must be used.

Just as fitments are classified into ablutionary and soil, so the drainage from them must go into separate waste and drainpipes—unless special precautions are taken with the waste pipes to ensure that if both ablutionary and soil discharges are connected to the same drainpipe there is no possibility of foul air from the drain passing through the water traps placed on the outlet of each fitment. Foul air is prevented from entering the building from the drains and waste pipes by means of a trap, which should always contain water. If the trap is wrongly fitted, the water in the trap could leak away, thus allowing a free passage of drain gases into a room.

PLYWOOD MANUFACTURE (see manufactured board)

PNEUMATIC TOOLS

Pneumatic tools are driven by air motors, which are powered by compressed air and operate in the opposite way to COMPRESSORS. The air motor has many advantages: it is physically small and light for the high torque and power that it delivers and it does not generate heat—even when stalled for long periods. It cannot be damaged by over-loading and if held in the stalled condition it continues to give high torque for little air consumption. In addition, means can be provided to give instant reversal without causing any damage to the mechanism. Another advantage is that the motor starts almost instantaneously and there is no overrun when the air supply is cut, except in high speed motors where no gearing is used.

Most of these points add up to low maintenance costs, reliability, ease of use and saving in unnecessary fatigue to the operator. Another advantage of air motors is their inherent safety. Many pneumatic tools are basically similar to power tools driven by electric motors, the main difference being the use of air motors instead of electric ones (see DRILL, electric).

The main types of air motors are the vane, piston and turbine designs. Turbines find applications where high speed and little torque are required, for instance, in some of the small grinders or in the dentists' drill (see DRILL, dental). Heavier work, where massive power and good starting torque is required at fairly low speeds, needs piston air motors.

But the most common design are positive displacement motors of the vane type, used in power tools. With this type one can get the most power into a small space. It is a flexible power unit with a high speed rotor which, when coupled to suitable gearing, is capable of producing high torque at the final drive.

These motors have multiple longitudinal vanes fitted into radial slots in a rotor which is mounted eccentrically in a cylinder, similar to the rotor of a rotary vane compressor. The compressed air enters the side of the cylinder at one end, and leaves through an exhaust port half way along the cylinder and further round it, turning the rotor as it goes.

Because of the nature of their construction, involving a

Below: copper tubes are used for all types of domestic plumbing and heating systems. Small bore copper pipes are shown in an underfloor heating system, which will be covered with a concrete screed.

COPPER DEVELOPMENT ASSOCIATION

Below: a pneumatic wrench used for fitting the wheel nuts to cars on an assembly line. The pneumatic wrench is fast and easy to use, and tightens every nut to the correct torque.

BROOMWADE LTD

relatively small overall diameter on a straight axial line, standard pneumatic tools lend themselves readily to 'close grouping' in specialized tooling set-ups, both bench-mounted and those associated with jigs and fixtures used in ASSEMBLY LINE work.

Bench mounting

The application of pneumatic tools to multi-tool bench mounted set-ups, is a natural and inevitable development out of their use as portable tools. With fixed multi-tool arrangements, however, the horizons are almost boundless, particularly so with the high degree of interchangeability that can be achieved and the versatility of the power units themselves.

The labour saving advantages of bench mounted pneumatic tools is typified by the machine used for securing the cap to a bottled gas pressure regulator by eight cheesehead screws, which previously required two full time operators and was a purely manual operation. With eight pneumatic screwdrivers fed from a common air distributor headstock through a hand actuated air valve, it became a task suitable for one worker. With quantities running into thousands per week, the adoption of this technique effectively eliminated a serious bottleneck in production.

When a number of the heavier tools are accommodated and there is a possibility of operator fatigue, a system can be adopted in which the tool heads are lowered and retracted by double-acting pneumatic cylinders. Such an arrangement is used for driving the screw securing the cap of a pressure regulator, the body of which is located in a recessed bed plate. The screwdrivers are fitted with extension adaptors to prevent the driving ends of the tools from fouling the 'top hat' profile of the cap when the tool head is lowered.

The air supply to the motors is routed through an air valve, which distributes air through a channelled mounting plate to the air inlets of the tools. When the air control to the pneumatic cylinder is opened and the tools are lowered, their screwdriving bits engage in the slots in the screws and, as the pressure increases, the drive from the motors is taken up by the spring-loaded clutches. The whole operation is essentially an indi-vidual process. Each tool drives its associated screw independently of the other tools and ceases driving immediately the torque loading of its clutch is overcome. Thus, every screw is tightened to the same pressure or, if the clutch torque settings differ, to the various pressures at which the different clutches disengage.

Although these spring-loaded torque clutches are used in the majority of tools, units are also available in which the driving bit is stopped by the *stall torque* principle, the magnitude of the torque that stalls the motor being governed by the air pressure setting.

Torque control

To cover fully the multiple tooling requirements of industry, two systems of torque control are available. The first is the *minimum torque indication* system (MTI) where the normal stalled torque motors are used in the conventional manner, but with a visual indication to the operator that the minimum torque value required has been achieved.

The second is a torque controlled motor system with visual indication (ITC). This system utilizes standard motors, each fitted with a control top. The torque reaction through the motor body is used to initiate an air signal which passes to the control top and shuts off the air to the motor. The movement of the control top shuttle valve actuates a RELAY which switches on an indicator light.

Uses

Pneumatic power is used to drive a wide range of tools, both those requiring rotary motion (such as drills) and those requiring reciprocating motion (hammers and chisels, for example). The need for a compressed air source (usually at pressures about 90 psi, 6.21 bar) makes them somewhat less portable than electric tools, but air motors are spark-free and so can be used safely in potentially explosive areas such as mines. They can also operate underwater.

Pneumatic tools used for assembly line work, and in other locations such as shipyards, include drills, riveters, reamers, grinders, screwdrivers, and nutrunners (socket wrenches). In the construction industry, the uses include rock drills, concrete vibrators, trench diggers, and concrete breakers (often misnamed pneumatic drills, see DRILL, pneumatic).

Below: this bench-mounted multi-tool drilling machine is a good example of the application of pneumatic tools to assembly line work and needs only one worker to operate it.

Below: a pneumatic grinder used for grinding the rough edges and surfaces from large metal castings. Pneumatic tools are lighter than their electric equivalents, making them less tiring to use.

POLARIMETER

Many chemical compounds can exist in more than one *optically active* form (see ORGANIC CHEMISTRY). Each optically active form, or *isomer*, of a compound will be able to rotate the plane of polarized light (see POLARIZATION) by an amount characteristic of that isomer. *Polarimeters* are instruments for measuring this rotation, and they are widely used in research and in the purity control of food, pharmaceutical and biochemical products.

A polarizing material, for example a *calcite* crystal (a form of calcium carbonate) or *Polaroid* (used in many sunglasses), will preferentially transmit light in a particular plane, known as the *transmission axis*. If a light source is observed through two crystals of calcite whose transmission axes are at right angles to each other, the field of view will appear dark since the first crystal will allow light through in a plane which the second crystal will not be able to transmit. If, then, a glass tube containing a solution of an optically active compound is inserted in the light path between the two crystals, a certain amount of light will be transmitted by the second crystal because the optically active compound will rotate the plane

Below: a simple polarimeter having a polarizer (right) and a rotatable analyzer (left). A glass sample tube fits into the trough between the polarizer and analyzer. The analyzer scale is divided into divisions of 0.2° and can be read to an accuracy of 0.01° by means of a vernier scale.

Bottom: a modern, entirely automatic polarimeter.

of the light emerging from the first crystal. The angle through which the second crystal must be rotated to restore the dark field of view will be a measure of the optical activity of the compound in the tube.

Construction The simplest polarimeters consist of two polarizing elements in series; the first, called the *polarizer*, is used to produce a polarized beam of light, and the second, called the *analyzer*, is used to observe the polarized light thus produced. The analyzer is mounted at the centre of a rotatable metal disc whose perimeter is graduated in degrees so that its orientation can be determined. The earliest instruments used a BUNSEN BURNER as the light source, and the flame was made to appear bright yellow by the addition of common salt since it was important to know the wavelength (colour) at which the measurements were made. The light source in a modern visual polarimeter is usually a mercury or sodium DISCHARGE TUBE.

To use a polarimeter, the analyzer is rotated until the zero transmission condition is reached, in which the polarizer and analyzer transmission axes are at right angles to each other and no light passes through the instrument. The reading on the graduated scale is noted. A glass tube containing a solution of the optically active substance is then inserted between the polarizer and the analyzer, and, as already explained, some light will be observed to pass through the analyzer. The analyzer is then rotated until the original dark condition is restored, and the new reading on the graduated scale is taken. The difference between the two readings gives the amount in degrees by which the polarized light has been rotated by the optically active solution.

The chief problem with simple polarimeters is that it is extremely difficult to determine accurately the zero transmission condition, that is to say the condition of maximum darkness. The problem can be overcome by introducing a third polarizing element known as a *half lippich polarizer*, which is made of calcite and is set halfway into the field of view between the main polarizer and the sample tube. The transmission axis of the half lippich polarizer is inclined slightly (usually at about 8°) to that of the main polarizer. The result of this arrangement is that the field of view is divided into two halves, and as the analyzer is rotated one half gets brighter as the other gets darker. The balance position at which the measurements on the graduated scale are taken on this type of instrument is the position at which the two halves of the field of view are of equal intensity, and this can be determined with considerable accuracy.

Modern instruments Measuring samples with the instruments described so far is a highly skilled and time-consuming task, and in this field as in others automation has taken over. With modern automatic polarimeters it is only necessary to place the sample to be measured between the polarizer and the analyzer for the rotation (accurate to about 0.002°) to be determined electronically and presented in digital form a few seconds later.

Sugars are among the compounds which rotate polarized light, and polarimeters are frequently used in the quality control laboratories of sugar refineries; in this application they are usually called *saccharimeters*. Some types of polarimeter automatically record optical rotations in graphical form throughout the visible and ultra-violet spectrum. This type of *spectropolarimetric* equipment has played an important part in determining the three dimensional molecular structures of many chemical compounds, and it was used in the research which led to the contraceptive pill.

POLARIZATION

In the seventeenth century Erasmus Bartholinus in Denmark discovered that crystals of Iceland spar, a form of calcite—natural crystalline calcium carbonate—would split light into two beams. This process was known as *double refraction*, and the differing properties of the two beams led Thomas Young to propose in 1817 that light is a *transverse* wave, in which the vibrations are perpendicular to the direction of motion of the wave. *Birefringent* crystals, like calcite, produce two beams whose directions of vibration are perpendicular to each other (and also both perpendicular to the direction of the beam); for example, light travelling horizontally straight ahead might be split into a beam of vertically vibrating waves, and one of waves vibrating in a left-right sense. These would be known respectively as vertically and horizontally *polarized* beams.

Light is now recognized as being only a small part of the total spectrum of ELECTROMAGNETIC RADIATION, which consists of transverse electric and magnetic waves, the magnetic field being perpendicular to the electrical. It is usual to call the direction of polarization that of the electric field, although it would be just as valid to use the direction of the magnetic field. Electromagnetic radiation is generated by the acceleration of charged particles, usually electrons, and the direction of polarization of the radiation is simply the direction of acceleration of the generating charge.

Ordinary light, from the Sun or a light bulb, for example, is produced by the random motions of the electrons in a hot body, and so the polarization of the waves is also random. On average, there is as much vertical as horizontal polarization and the light is usually referred to as *unpolarized*, even though each individual wave has a definite polarization.

Most methods of producing polarized light involve splitting unpolarized light into two polarized beams and then removing or absorbing one of the beams. Some LASERS, however, do produce polarized light directly, because the slanted ends of the laser tube reflect away one of the polarizations (as described below) and allow the other to dominate.

Dichroic polarizers

The most commonly used polarizers today are made of *dichroic* materials: substances which transmit only one polarization of light, absorbing the other. Some naturally occurring crystals, such as tourmaline, are dichroic, but plastic dichroic sheets can now be made much larger and more cheaply.

To illustrate the principle of dichroism, consider what happens when an unpolarized beam of radio waves meets a grid of fine vertical wires. The vertical component of the electric field causes EDDY CURRENTS in the wires, and these are damped by the RESISTANCE of the wire until their energy is dissipated as heat. All the energy of the vertical component is therefore absorbed. The horizontal component of the field, on the other hand, can only induce currents *across* the wires and since the wires are thin, there is little loss of energy. The emerging radiation is thus completely horizontally polarized, as long as the wires are thin, and as long as the spacing between them is less than about a wavelength (otherwise some of the vertical polarization will 'leak' through).

It is very difficult to make metal grids to polarize radiation of wavelengths as short as those of light (less than a thousandth of a millimetre) and in practice the very long thin molecules in plastics are used. A sheet of polyvinyl alcohol, for example, is softened by heating and then rapidly stretched to several times its original length, to pull the long molecules into line with each other. It is then fixed to a rigid backing, such as cellulose acetate, and dipped into a solution containing iodine, which reacts with the plastic molecules. The long parallel strings of iodine atoms so formed act as the fine conducting grid needed to polarize the light. Various grades of polarizer are made which leak different amounts of the unwanted polarization, although cutting down the leakage also reduces the amount of wanted polarization. This is reduced from the theoretical 50% to typically 40%, while the unwanted polarization might amount to 0·05%.

Other polarizers

Dichroic sheet polarizer, such as Polaroid, which can be produced up to 19 inches (48 cm) in width and in any length, is by far the most commonly used polarizer today. Until its invention in 1928, the most popular polarizer was the *Nicol prism*, a calcite crystal which had been cut in half and cemented together again with Canada balsam, a type of resin. The crystal is shaped so that one of the doubly refracted beams is totally internally reflected (see OPTICS) at the balsam, while the other passes straight through to be used in the polarization experiment. Another type of polarizer depends on the fact that light reflected obliquely from a surface, though not from a metal, is always polarized to some extent. (Metals,

This pair of photographs shows the way in which polarizing material can be used to cut out unwanted reflections. The upper photograph is taken with ordinary unpolarized light, while the lower one is taken through a polarizer transmitting vertical polarization only. The reflection from the water is greatly reduced, though that from the metal cutlery is unaffected. The effect is at a maximum when the camera is at an angle of 57° to the vertical.

BERNARD ALFIERI

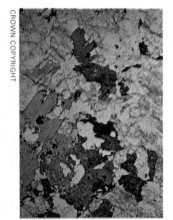

having good electrical CONDUCTION, will not work: for this reason, a reflection from a normal silvered mirror will not be polarized). The beam is completely polarized if the reflected light is at right angles to the beam refracted through the surface. The angle between the incident beam and the normal to the surface when this occurs is called the *Brewster angle*, and is about 57° for glass. A *pile-of-plates* polarizer is simply a number of glass plates set at this angle in a tube: as light passes through it, some of the unwanted polarization is reflected off each plate and absorbed in the blackened sides of the tube. The other polarization is not weakened by reflection losses and passes straight through the tube. Polarizers of this type can be made which pass less than 1% of the unwanted polarization.

Uses 'Polaroid' sunglasses are dichroic sheets which transmit only vertically polarized light. They cut down the general illumination because only 40% of the light falling on them is transmitted, but, more importantly, they reduce glare to an even greater extent. Sunlight reflected off horizontal surfaces, such as water, is partly horizontally polarized, and this glare is largely eliminated because of the vertical transmission direction of the sunglasses.

There are many industrial applications of polarized light, two of the most important being POLARIMETRY and *photoelastic stress analysis*. The former is used to measure the concentration of solutions of certain compounds, such as sugar, which consist of asymmetric molecules. These *optically active* substances rotate the direction of polarization of light, and the amount of rotation depends on the concentration of the solution. In its simplest form a polarimeter consists of two polarizers and a glass cell between them which can be filled with liquid. Initially the polarizers are 'crossed' so that no light comes through. The cell is then filled with solution and one of the polarizers is rotated until no light is transmitted again. The angle through which the polarizer is turned is equal to the angle through

Above left: polarization is of great importance in broadcasting. This house is in a hilly area, where some TV programmes come from a UHF transmitter 30 miles (50 km) away and others from a local repeater station. The main station has horizontal polarization (longer aerial) while the local station uses vertical polarization to avoid interference with other nearby repeater stations on the same frequency. This difference can be seen in the alignment of the rods on the aerials. The long horizontal bar on one of the aerials is an FM radio aerial, aligned on a different transmitter, again with horizontal polarization.

Middle left: polarized light can reveal differences in otherwise colourless minerals, as shown by this sample of diorite viewed through crossed polarizers. The coloured crystals are biotite and hornblende; the bands which appear are due to plagioclase.

Left: the same method on a larger scale shows stresses in an acrylic injection moulding.

which the direction of polarization has been rotated by the solution, and so its concentration can be calculated.

Photoelastic analysis is used to investigate the positions of maximum stress in mechanical parts. A model of the part is made in a plastic such as transparent Bakelite which is birefringent when stressed, and placed between crossed polarizers in a *polariscope*. Appropriate forces are applied to the specimen, and the regions under stress show up as light areas, because they rotate the polarization of the light from the first polarizer so that it is no longer perpendicular to the transmission direction of the second polarizer. The amount of rotation depends on the wavelength of light used, and so, by illuminating the specimen with white light, regions of differing stress will be brightest at different wavelengths and the result is a highly coloured 'contour map' showing the magnitudes and directions of the stresses in the part.

Circular and elliptical polarization
As well as the *linear* polarization discussed so far, light can also be *circularly* or *elliptically* polarized. In this case, the electric field of a light wave is not oscillating in a fixed direction in space, but moves around the direction of propagation. A circularly polarized wave has an electric field which is constant as it rotates, whereas an elliptically polarized wave is stronger in one particular direction than in the perpendicular direction. A linearly polarized wave can in fact be regarded as an extreme example of elliptical polarization, where its strength in the perpendicular direction is zero.

One form of polarization can be converted to another by an appropriately cut thin piece of birefringent crystal: for example, the easiest method of obtaining circularly polarized light is to direct a beam of linearly polarized light through such a crystal, known in this case as a *quarter-wave plate*. The circular and elliptical polarizations, however, are of considerably less importance than the linear in most branches of optics.

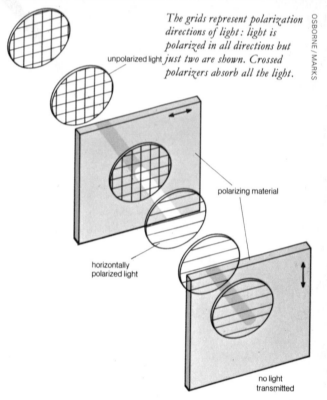

The grids represent polarization directions of light: light is polarized in all directions but just two are shown. Crossed polarizers absorb all the light.

unpolarized light

polarizing material

horizontally polarized light

no light transmitted

OSBORNE / MARKS

Below: the action of a Nicol prism. Unpolarized light enters from the left, and is split by the Iceland spar into two beams polarized at right angles to each other. The ordinary ray strikes the Canada balsam layer at a slightly greater angle, just over the critical angle for this material, and is totally internally reflected.

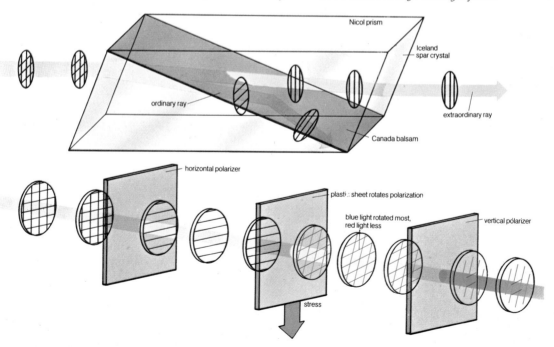

Nicol prism

Iceland spar crystal

ordinary ray

extraordinary ray

Canada balsam

horizontal polarizer

plastic sheet rotates polarization

blue light rotated most, red light less

vertical polarizer

stress

Above: how stress analysis is carried out using a plastic model. The plastic rotates the plane of polarization by different amounts for different colours. The eye cannot distinguish between the two polarizations, so still sees white light, but a vertical polarizer will transmit more of the colour which is nearest to vertical polarization. Thus more blue light than red gets through.

POLAROGRAPH

The *polarograph* is an instrument which uses changes in electrical current or voltage in order to make measurements of chemical changes. It consists of a device which applies a variable voltage to the system under examination, and then measures the changes in current which follow. It was invented by a Czech chemist, Jaroslav Heyrovsky, in 1925; he was later awarded a Nobel prize in recognition of its importance.

With the earliest instruments, the voltage setting was changed manually, the current read from a sensitive GALVANO-METER and the results were plotted as a graph. In later models the voltage was changed automatically by means of a motor, and the current changes were measured either photographically or by means of a PEN RECORDER. Modern electronic polarographs were introduced at the end of the 1940s, and nowadays a range of fully automatic electronic instruments is available.

Construction   A polarograph consists of a *cell* containing the *electrolyte* under test, often a solution of one or more SALTS in water. The cell is fitted with a large *reference electrode* and a *working electrode* which must be very small compared with the reference electrode so that the current density is high on its surface. This ensures that any reaction that occurs will take place close to the working electrode surface. If the reactions to be studied are OXIDATION reactions, the working electrode will be connected to the positive side of the electricity supply and will thus form the *anode*. If, on the other hand, *reduction* reactions are being studied, the working electrode will be connected to the negative side of the supply and will form the *cathode*.

The working electrode is usually a small drop of liquid mercury, about 0·5 mm in diameter, which is formed by allowing mercury to flow through a very thin tube, and to hang as a drop before falling off. Electrical connection is made through the mercury thread, and as each drop forms and is used for a measurement it falls away and a new, clean surface is provided by the next drop. The substance to be examined, say a copper salt, is dissolved in an electrolyte which acts to prevent movement of the electrically charged copper atoms or copper IONS in the field between anode and cathode. As the voltage between the electrode is increased, no change in current occurs until a voltage is reached where copper ions react. Then a reaction takes place, resulting in the reduction of the copper ions, and the current through the cell increases. As the voltage rises further, the reaction becomes faster, and the current increases, until the reaction rate becomes as high as it can be with this amount of copper present. The current then remains steady in spite of increasing voltage, until eventually some other reaction begins and a new current change commences. The voltages applied are less than 2 to 3 volts, and the currents measured are very small, as low as one *nanoampere*, one thousand millionth of an ampere.

This means that the method allows very sensitive and delicate measurements to be made, and the polarograph is used in environmental pollution analysis, both of the air and of the rivers and seas, in analysis of foods for traces of poisonous or dangerous substances, in industrial analysis, metallurgical work, and so on. Recent uses have been the analysis of Moon rock samples and the testing of archaeological specimens such as Bronze Age spearheads.

Right: a polarograph with two test cells (left) each with a dropping mercury electrode. On the right is the equipment for applying test voltages and measuring the resulting current changes.

POLAROID CAMERA

For the first hundred years or so of photography, producing a final print was a fairly time consuming process. The conventional procedure of processing and drying the negative, exposing through this on to a piece of light-sensitive paper, and processing and drying this print, requires darkroom facilities and time. Although this is still the most important and widespread type of photography, the introduction of the Polaroid process in 1947 made it possible to produce a print in one stage only, without a darkroom and within 60 seconds.

The invention of Polaroid photography was due to Dr Edwin H Land, then head of a research group concerned with military optics and the anti-dazzle Polaroid material, used for the POLARIZATION of light. After a holiday, his daughter had asked impatiently how long it would be before they could see the pictures they had taken, and Land decided to find a way of producing photographs almost instantly. His research culminated in the production of a monochrome (single colour— orginally sepia) print within 60 seconds, but there were additional benefits, since the prints had greatly improved sharpness and freedom from graininess, compared with other films of their sensitivity. Land's association with the Polaroid Corporation resulted in the name 'Polaroid' being used for both the camera and the polarizers, though there is no other connection.

The secret of the Polaroid process lies in the film used—it is quite possible to use Polaroid film with ordinary plate cameras, though in practice it is common to use the cameras designed for use with the film. The basis of the process is exactly the same as in conventional photography, but developer, fixer and print material are all combined in one film pack, thus doing away with the need for a darkroom.

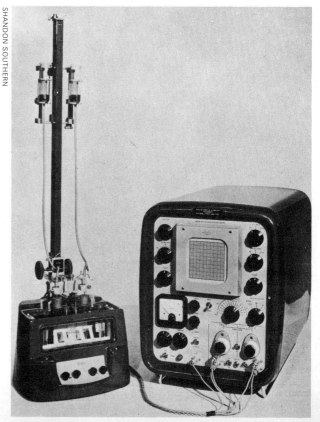

SHANDON SOUTHERN

All photography depends upon the light sensitive properties of grains of silver halide salts—silver bromide or iodide, for example—which form a *latent image* on exposure to light. In conventional photography, the latent image is developed to make the regions which have been exposed to most light black, that is, the reverse of the original image. The unexposed halide salts are dissolved away by the *fixer*, so that only the stable black image is left. In the Polaroid process, use is made of the unexposed halide salts. Because there are most unexposed grains where there was least light, by forming an image out of these and developing them to blackness, the result will be a black image where there was originally least light—just what is required in a positive print.

This is what happens in a reversal film, producing transparencies. The first negative image is bleached away after development, leaving only the unexposed areas, which are then developed themselves. In the Polaroid process, the unexposed areas are moved from the original material to the print material, which is in direct contact, by *diffusion transfer*, and are developed there. Because the result is to be viewed as a print, rather than as a transparency, less silver is needed. The light used to view a print passes once through the silver, and is then reflected from the white paper back through the silver again, being absorbed twice. This is the same effect as when looking at the colour of a piece of glass—the colour seems much denser when it is placed on a piece of paper, compared with when it is held up to the light.

This is one reason for the fine grain qualities of Polaroid film: less light is needed for a given effect. Alternatively, pictures can be taken in much darker conditions than before, for the same graininess.

Basic process In the simplest system, used for producing black and white prints within 15 seconds, there are three basic elements to the film pack: the negative, carrying the photosensitive emulsion; the pod, a small envelope lined with metal foil and plastic containing a viscous (jelly-like) processing solution comprising a developer, an alkali to activate this, and a fixing agent; and the receiving sheet or positive, which becomes the print after processing.

These components are brought together after the negative has been exposed. The pod is on the leading edge of the negative material, and after exposure the negative and receiving sheets are pulled together out of the camera between a pair of steel pressure rollers. These burst the pod, spreading the processing solution evenly between the negative and receiving sheets: both have opaque backing layers forming a sandwich which is virtually a small darkroom.

As in conventional photography, the developer converts exposed grains in the negative to metallic silver (see PHOTO-GRAPHIC PROCESSING). In this case, a monobath type solution is used, with an active developer and a weaker fixer combined. The developer quickly starts to develop the exposed grains, and the fixer dissolves the unexposed halides, forming *soluble silver complexes* in the process. These diffuse across to the receiving sheet, where they encounter nuclei which cause the silver to be developed. The small size of these nuclei is also responsible for the fine grain structure. The gap between the

Shown here are a Polaroid film pack, the holder which can be used on a plate camera (with film half out), a photograph with the negative sheet peeled back (with the mask for the white border still in place) and the swab used to preserve the image.

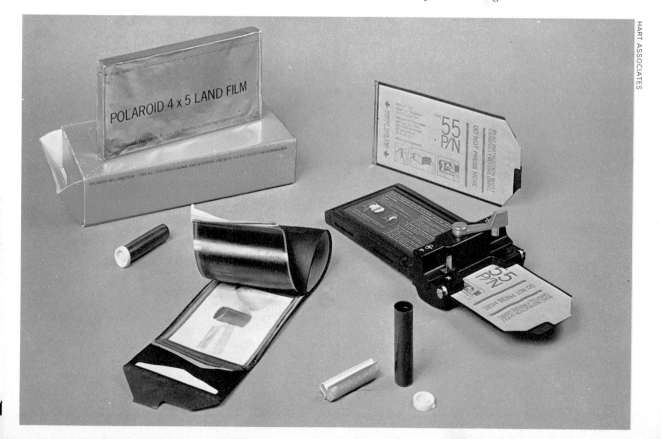

HART ASSOCIATES

negative and receiving sheet is so small that there is almost negligible blurring through diffusion, and the process can take place very quickly—in some 10 to 15 seconds. A chemical swab rubbed over the print removes or neutralizes the remaining chemicals, though in a recent improved pack this is done automatically.

Colour film The principle of the Polacolor process is diffusion transfer, as in the black and white one, with the addition of an ingenious method of linking the emulsions to the coloured dyes. All colour films these days have three layers, sensitive to red, green and blue light. In some cases the dyes are added after the development, but usually the dyes are coupled to the grains in the film, and steps are taken to make sure that they stay where they are. In a diffusion transfer process, the dyes have to move from the layer in which the initial image is formed, through other layers, and on to the receiver sheet. This is done by linking the dye to a developer compound which is in a layer close to its complementary emulsion layer.

The pod in this case contains not developer-fixer but an alkali which activates the developer, which is already in the film. Some of the developer-dye molecules meet up with exposed grains, and develop them, becoming immobilized in the process. Others, however, manage to diffuse as far as the receiving sheet—their chance of doing so is greater where there are fewer exposed grains. The receiving sheet contains a *mordant*, which has the same purpose as the mordant used in DYEING—it holds the dye fast and insoluble. Thus the image consists of a fast dye layer.

In the latest colour pack, the SX-70, a number of advances makes the whole process self-regulating. After the film has been exposed, a motor drives it out of the camera and the single sheet slowly develops itself, without the need to time the process before separating the negative and receiving layer, as in earlier systems. The film pack contains its own mercury cell type BATTERY in a thin layer which powers the 12,000 rpm motor, the EXPOSURE METER and the SHUTTER, and operates the flash if necessary.

An unusual feature of the film is that the positive sheet lies permanently on top of the negative, but is transparent during the exposure. An opaque material, which is spread between the two sheets on ejection from the camera, protects the emulsion layers from light and abrasion while allowing the dyes to diffuse through it. A quantity of titanium dioxide in this layer provides a brilliant white reflective backing for the colour image after processing. When development is complete, usually in less than five minutes, the alkali which initiated the development is automatically neutralized, the opaque layer, having served its purpose, becomes transparent, and the titanium dioxide covers the developed but unwanted negative image.

Left: a series showing the appearance of an SX-70 print 35 seconds, 1 minute and 4 minutes after it has been taken.

Right: in the cutaway representation of a Polaroid SX-70 print during development, the vertical scale is greatly exaggerated. The reagent is released between the layers and causes the dye-developer molecules to diffuse away from their layers. If they encounter an exposed region they are trapped, but otherwise they diffuse further. Because the layer is thin they will emerge at the surface rather than diffuse sideways. The reagent also permeates the timing layer: when it reaches the acid polymer, this stops the reaction.

At far right is the camera's viewing system. When the taking mirror moves up for photography, the rubber flap seals the gap.

The SX-70 Polaroid camera, just after taking a picture. The motor, powered by a battery which is an integral part of each film pack, drives the undeveloped print out of the camera where it develops automatically.

eye piece

taking mirror

12000 rpm motor

flash socket

L/D control

photocell

film pack

battery

shutter blades

lens

gear train

shutter button

printed circuit

developing film

processing rollers

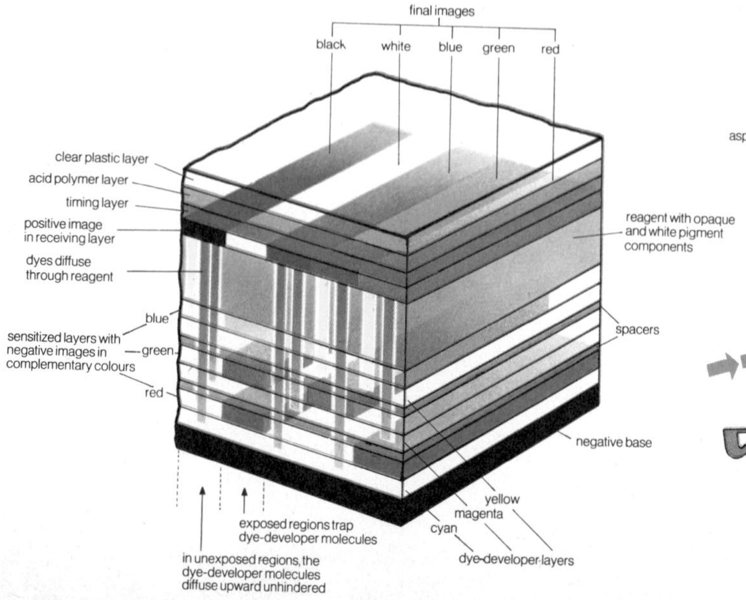

final images

black   white   blue   green   red

clear plastic layer

acid polymer layer

timing layer

positive image in receiving layer

dyes diffuse through reagent

reagent with opaque and white pigment components

blue

green

red

sensitized layers with negative images in complementary colours

spacers

negative base

yellow
magenta
cyan

dye-developer layers

exposed regions trap dye-developer molecules

in unexposed regions, the dye-developer molecules diffuse upward unhindered

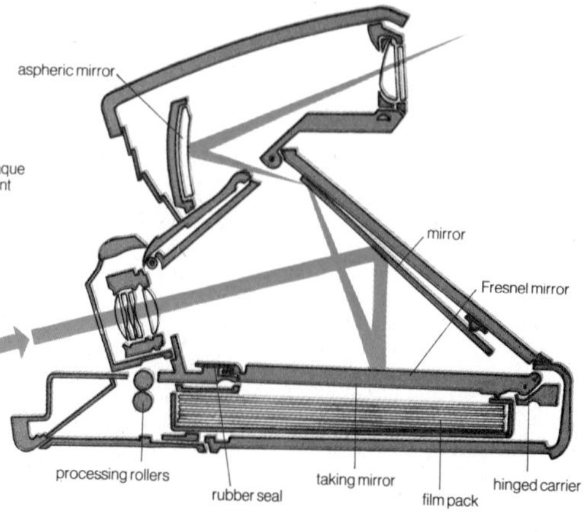

aspheric mirror

mirror

Fresnel mirror

processing rollers

rubber seal

taking mirror

film pack

hinged carrier

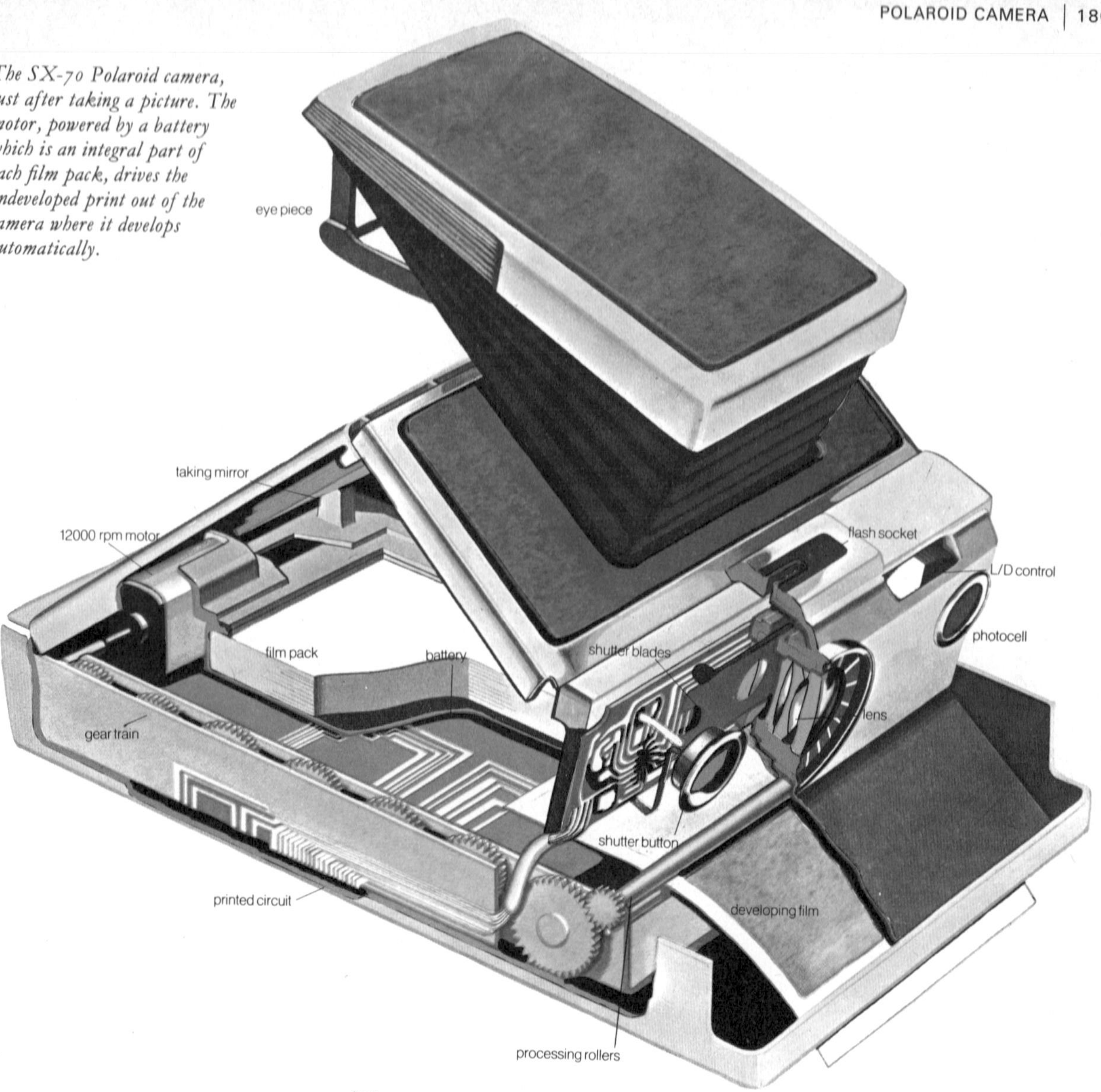

Cameras The high speed (sensitivity to light) of Polaroid black and white film makes possible several novel features. The lens, for example, need not be of fast focal ratio: on the Polaroid Swinger, for example, apertures of *f 95* are used, giving very wide depth of field—practically all objects, near or far, are in focus. Since the final print is the same size as the negative, the cameras must be rather larger than the usual 35 mm miniature camera, and if a large print is required, a large camera must be used. It is possible to fit a Polaroid back on to standard plate cameras, as used in studios. Film packs are available in various types and sizes, each size requiring its own particular camera. The cameras are generally automated to control the exposure.

Uses Polaroid photography does not appear likely to replace conventional photography because of its higher cost, larger size of camera (except the SX-70), the bulk of the film packs and the limited usefulness of prints compared with negatives (although a Polaroid pack which does produce a negative is available). It is particularly useful in a number of cases, however, where instant results are desired. These include dental photography, the recording of OSCILLOSCOPE traces, FORENSIC investigations, the production of identity cards and PHOTO-MICROGRAPHY.

Above: interior view of a Polaroid camera without film. In use, the bellows are pulled out and the lens is some distance from the film.

Below: because an SX-70 film is viewed as it was taken from the camera the image has to be reversed by a mirror before reaching the film. Here, coloured beams are set up to show the approximate light paths. When taking a picture, the lower mirror, covering the film, moves up.

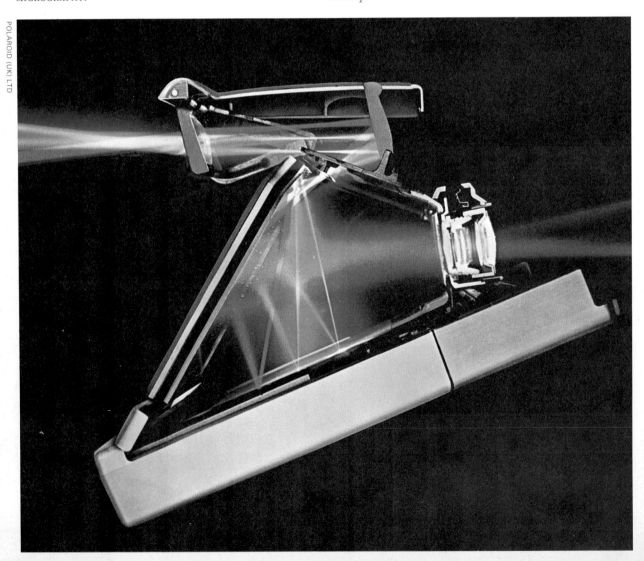